MARY QUEEN OF SCOTS

All History is necessarily Mythology.

COUNT KEYSERLING.

MARY QUEEN OF SCOTS
(Artist unknown. Nat. Port. Gallery, London)

MARY QUEEN OF SCOTS

★

MARGARETE KURLBAUM-
SIEBERT

Translated from the German by

MARY AGNES HAMILTON

NEW YORK

HARCOURT, BRACE AND COMPANY

195908

CONTENTS

1 SCOTLAND FIRST SEEN   11
2 DEGRADATION OF THE GORDONS   57
3 OUR GOOD SISTER, ELIZABETH   93
4 ADVENT OF THE LENNOXES   125
5 HENRY DARNLEY   155
6 BOTHWELL'S RETURN   184
7 THE MURDER OF RIZZIO   226
8 IN THE DEBATABLE LAND   261
9 THE CRAIGMILLAR PACT   305
10 "THE GOOD KING IS DEAD"   336
11 IN AINSLIE'S TAVERN   354
12 THE CASKET LETTERS   390
13 CARBERRY HILL   410
14 LOCHLEVEN AND LANGSIDE   462

ILLUSTRATIONS

MARY QUEEN OF SCOTS *Frontispiece*

FACING PAGE

LORD HENRY DARNLEY 156

DAVID RIZZIO 228

JAMES HEPBURN, EARL OF BOTHWELL 388

MARY QUEEN OF SCOTS

MARY QUEEN OF SCOTS

Chapter 1

SCOTLAND FIRST SEEN

QUEEN MARY STUART returned, at eighteen, to the kingdom she had left as a child of four, when she was taken by sea to France to escape the plots of England. Young as she was, she brought back with her more than a lifetime of experience. She was but seven days old when the death of her father, King James V of Scotland, made her a Queen. He lay, sick to death, in Falkland Castle, tortured in body and soul. A battle with the English had been lost: his nobles had shamefully deserted him. News of the birth of a daughter was brought to him. She would be his heir. "The Deil tak her! It cam wi' a lass, and it will gang wi' a lass," he muttered, with a groan. Turning his face to the wall he sank into heart-broken brooding, ended only by the pangs of death. The English, the French, and the fiercely contending parties of her own land struggled for possession of the little Queen. Her mother, Mary of Guise, of the house of Lorraine, finally transported her to the court of France, there to be betrothed to the heir apparent, and educated in her future kingdom. At fifteen, Mary was actually married to the Dauphin, who was a year or so younger than herself. At sixteen, the sudden death of her father-in-law, Henry II, brought her, with her boyish husband, to the throne of France. A year and a half later, she was a widow. Meantime, under the influence of the Reformation, civil war had broken out in her native land. The Queen Regent appealed for help to France; the Lords of the Congregation, meantime, looked for support to Protestant

England, where Queen Elizabeth had for some time been reigning. After a period of indecisive fighting hostilities were ostensibly ended by the Treaty of Edinburgh. The negotiations were not conducted by Mary of Guise: she had succumbed to a long and painful illness shortly before they began. Even after the conclusion of the Treaty the young Queen, Mary Stuart, and her husband refused to affix their signatures to the agreement entered into by the plenipotentiaries. Before anything could be done, however, about the main points at issue, King François II died. In her adopted country, Mary, as his widow, could play but a secondary part, since her relations to her mother-in-law, never good, although there had been no open breach, were growing steadily worse, the more so that Catherine de Medici was all powerful, as Regent for the twelve-year-old king. Mary, therefore, determined to return to her own kingdom. She came by sea, almost by stealth. On account of the non-ratification of the Treaty of Edinburgh, Queen Elizabeth refused her safe conduct through her kingdom for the journey overland, and even for the event of her being driven, by wind and weather, to take refuge with her suite on the English coast.

★

On Sunday, August 19th, in the year 1561, the morning preacher in the church of Leith, the fortified port of Edinburgh, was the great Scottish Reformer, John Knox. Stretching his arms over the pious throng crowded far below him in the dusky nave of the church, he cried across the silence, in a voice that rose to thunder, while sparks seemed to dart out of his black eyes and play over his swarthy face: "See, she draweth nigh, the daughter of Babylon, who was in her youth sold to the Godless that the potion might be instilled into her with which she comes to poison us! Be it so! No enemy will oppose her coming; the waves rock her ship gently. For in punishment of your sins God sends her to ye as a flail of vengeance, because of the bottomless ingratitude, the obstinate hardness of your hearts! Brands are now collecting on all

12

hands for the children of the Lord, who shall be sacrificed to
the maw of Baal! Such as were lit by that other Mary, the
Jezebel of England, whom God cut off in the fullness of her
sins! The clay idol of Antichrist, the Popish Mass, will rule
over us once more! She comes, from the realm of horror, to
prepare the abode of all adulterers, all perjurers, traitors,
murderers and evil-doers!"

Down in the hollow nave of the church, its walls still bleeding from the wounds of last year's image-breaking, the crowd
sat listening. All were clad in black, the women being closely
veiled over head, neck and chin. They sat quite still, though
their hearts shook within them.

The thunder of cannon from the harbour broke across the
silence.

John Knox started; the people were all ears. A second blast
followed; a pause; then the shots came continuously. "The
Queen is there!" a voice from without yelled into the ears of
the listeners within the church. Shouting, the noise of people
running, surged round the walls. John Knox raised his arms
to heaven: "So, she is there, the daughter of heathens, to bring
idolatry to the children of God! On the blessed Sabbath morning she comes, to disturb the festival of the Lord! And the
very skies give warning of what He intends with her coming.
Is not a fog, such as no eye here before beheld, a fog from the
pestilential cities of Sodom and Gomorrah, creeping in clouds
of fever over our land? But the signs from God are lost on this
sinful generation. There they go, the fools, the blind, the children of folly, and happy is the man or maid on whom the sun of
this most lofty, serene and royal countenance first shines!"

He spoke to empty benches. The church doors were wide,
the people storming out in a dense throng.

★

Down in the harbour, where the still water gleamed dark in
the fog like the windows of a house whose lamps are not yet
lit, a vast ship lay at anchor, looming up, its outlines indis-

tinct in the mist, like some fabulous monster that might, at any moment, swim up and shatter people and houses. The solid darkness of the formless gloom was shot with a dull, incessant red as the cannon poured out their rayless sparks: the detonating boom of their shots resounded from the mountainous ramparts of the fortress. Now, through the dull roar of the crowd, the magistrates of the town of Leith came pressing behind a handful of soldiers; raw-boned men, these, busy, as they came hurrying along, adjusting the hats and robes of office they had hastily cast on. The Provost, with trembling hands, was still attempting to get his officials into some sort of dignified order, as the first boats from the ship discharged along the gangplanks. A throng of tall, proud-looking men disembarked and ranged themselves along the landing stage. Hats and caps flew off, backs were bent almost to the ground, as, leaning on the arm of a tall man of princely and insolent aspect, a lady came slowly down the gangway. There was a gasp of tense excitement from the waiting crowd—"The Queen!" Mary halted on the edge of the quay, as the Provost approached, trembling with embarrassment, his knees knocking together. There she stood, tall and slender, in a black dress and beret, her face very pale. The glance of her light brown, wide apart eyes was lifted, for a moment, to the ramparts, which, in the fog, seemed to reach up into the infinite: it sank again only to recoil from the blank wall of human beings standing there, motionless, with no cry of welcome, no sound of any kind. Grey brown the muffling veil of fog stretched from sky to earth, dissolving in clammy moisture on their clothes. For an instant Mary turned to the cavalier at her side, as though asking help or comfort of him. Nothing there, however, save a cold disdain of all around. She released her hand from his arm, and, advancing a few paces, bent to the Provost, who was fumbling for words on his knee before her. "We are too early, my dear Provost," she said kindly, signing to him to rise. "But we are ready to be pleased with everything as it comes." The Provost rose, greatly relieved: the Bailies approached.

14

Soon messages were flying in all directions. Until evening, the Queen intends to lie in the house of a burgess who had been a faithful servant to her mother: then, attended by the dignitaries of her Crown, she will enter her capital of Edinburgh and her palace of Holyrood.

Mary still stood in converse with the dark, heavily built men, her long dress held out of the mud of the quayside with an easy, graceful motion of her hand. She asked about many things, speaking quickly, every turn of the conversation reflected in her sensitive face and the bright smile of her lustrous eyes. No one could take his eyes off her. All at once every bell in the city began to clang out noisily. Mary looked right into the wall of faces in front of her, pressed close together, rank upon rank, pale with excitement, a solid, unbroken mass. Involuntarily, the Queen's face lit with a smile; at a stroke, the air was rent with shouts. "Hurrah! Hurrah! Hurrah for the Queen! Long live Queen Mary! Hurrah! Hurrah! Hurrah!"

★

At midday a troop of gentlemen, of earnest aspect and rich attire, dismounted before the dwelling where the Queen lay. These were those Scottish nobles who had awaited their Sovereign in Edinburgh. First among them was the man who had, hitherto, been acting as Regent, Lord James Stuart, former Prior of St. Andrews, the eldest of the Queen's natural brothers. He was a short, pale-faced man, with eyes like black velvet buttons, and a dead black beard. With him came William Maitland, a cadet of the house of Lethington, and Secretary of State, that is to say, Foreign Minister, for Scotland. Maitland of Lethington stepped carefully on his long legs, with his narrow shoulders poked forward: from his pallid countenance, a ruddy beard streamed down over his chest: his eyes, of indistinguishable colour, seemed to slumber, under their heavy lids, until he suddenly glanced up into the face of his interlocutor with an omniscient irony. Both these gentlemen had already visited the Queen in France.

15

Towards evening Mary left the house with these two to ride into her capital. Her equerry and the main portion of her baggage had not yet arrived, for the English had attacked the convoy vessel. Such horses as there were in Leith had hastily to be collected for the Queen and her suite. The best of them was now led out, for her to mount: she started, and glanced at her companions. Such horses—undersized, thin, with drooping ears and rough coats, ill groomed and ill fed. Across her mind there flashed a picture of her own horse, Nymph, with his great tail sweeping the ground, and his lovely action, suggestive of some glorious bird. Mary looked about her, as if something had suddenly clutched at her heart. The fog still hung over everything: the crowded little houses were darkly oppressive. Her castle in Champagne rose out of the blossoming fields into the blue air; the wide windows were wreathed with Amoretti. Mary's lip trembled: although she strove to hold back the tears, they would rise. "A poor folk," smiled Lethington. Lord James Stuart's brow darkened. Mary laughed amid her tears, as though at herself. "In God's name, then!" She swung up into the saddle; her seat was proud and easy, she was a magnificent horsewoman.

Her suite joined her; first came her three French uncles of the house of Guise, the Duke Claude of Aumâle, François, Knight of Malta, and Réné, Marquis D'Elbœuf, all of whom had accompanied their niece from France to her new home. With them rode the French poet, Brantôme. The Queen brought her four Maries home with her to their native land, four young girls from high-born Scottish houses, Beaton, Seaton, Livingstone and Fleming, all, like the Queen, called Mary, all of the same age as herself and all taken with her to France as children.

As they rode slowly, Edinburgh rose before them, more and more clearly, out of the fog that fell from it, film by film, until, at last, it lay before them, a wondrous work of God and man. Following the line of a single ridge that rose out of the plain with a bold sureness of steady upward lift to its determined height, Edinburgh reared up to the sky its wealth of countless

16

gables and towers. A single street, High Street, known at its lower end as the Canongate, followed the ridge, right to its summit, on which it at last widened to a great open place, where Edinburgh Castle hung, with precipices yawning on three sides. On these steep sides, where there seemed hardly foothold for a cragsman, houses had been planted, on such a slope that the cellar of one would look out over the gable of its neighbour. A process of excavating, tearing away and filling up had created the most extraordinary confusion of houses, wynds and places, in and out of one another, with amazing corners and astonishing glimpses through and across them. At the lower end of the street, along the ridge, where it began its upward lift out of the plain, the royal palace of Holyrood, once an abbey, was comfortably placed with its buildings and out-houses. Beyond it rose another rocky mass, King Arthur's Seat, a natural feature of such mighty construction that it seemed inconceivable for the human mind, in face of such sub-limity, to entertain a petty thought.

Three quarters of the way to the town, a second body of horsemen met them, with waving flags, craftsmen's signs and emblems floating from long poles. The lords with the Queen stared. James Stuart's face darkened again: the Laird of Leth-ington smiled still. The troop advanced boldly towards the Queen, as if to stay her. She saw men of rough appearance, stoutly clad. Now they were quite near; Queen Mary reined in her horse. The leaders of the advancing troop, lads of ruddy-brown aspect, dismounted and knelt humbly in the mud of the street. "We come," so cried their spokesman, "Your Majesty's most faithful subjects, to welcome Your Majesty with all loyalty, and to express our obedience and faithfulness upon our knees. But let not Your Majesty's countenance darken if we venture in humble duty to appeal most earnestly to Your Majesty for justice and the exercise of Your Maj-esty's gracious kindness and goodness towards us, to free us from bearing a heavy punishment for a light offence. For our case is thus: we see traitors and knaves go unpunished, nay, highly honoured. And yet we are in truth Your Majesty's most faithful subjects, whom not the most calumnious heart can charge with the smallest failure in faithful duty to Your Majesty. And yet we are to be punished, and that most severely, to the bitterest injury of our lives, and of our trade and industry."

Mary looked at her brother. "What are these people? What have they done? What do they want me to do?"

"Rebellious craftsmen, the gilds of smiths, locksmiths and butchers," said James Stuart. "On Robin Hood's day, in defiance of the express prohibition of the Council, both national and municipal, and, above all, against the commands of the Church, they committed the most shocking excesses. To crown all, they actually laid hands on the Provost! Now they squeal because they have to take the punishment which they knew they were incurring!"

"Was any one killed or badly injured?" asked Mary.

"Your Majesty's dignity, the might of the State, the authority of the Church . . ."

"Was any one killed or badly injured?"

"No."

"It is the first petition made to me in my own country," said Mary, almost as gently as though she were the petitioner. She turned to the craftsmen, still prone before her in the dust. "Everything shall be inquired into, and, if possible, pardoned."

The men rose, beaming with delight. As the Queen's train proceeded, huzzas of satisfaction sounded all round it.

By evening, the town of Edinburgh was beside itself. In every street the windows were lit up. Bonfires flickered in great pans in the open spaces, on the towers, and all round the heights surrounding the city. Bells rang without intermission. Everybody living in Edinburgh or the vicinity seemed to be out in the streets. People who before spoke, if they spoke at all, only in terms of hatred and scorn, now clapped one another on arm or shoulder, crying: "What d'ye think? She speaks Scots! Faith, an angel she is! And kind, too. There is nobody in the world can match her. At the French court she was the fairest of them all. And only eighteen—just think of it! Oh, she is a daisy! Our Queen! Queen Mary! Long live our Queen!"

A great body of burghers gathered and went up to the palace to serenade her with drums and bagpipes. Mary appeared at a window, thanked them kindly, and asked to have the tune played again. They were intoxicated with delight. It was very late before the town settled to rest.

★

High days followed in Edinburgh. Armed men on foot and horseback clattered through the streets in companies; Highlanders in kilts, with bows and arrows on their shoulders, and men in leathern jerkins, with short swords on hip, from the marshes of the south or the mountains on the English border. Bagpipes skirled shrilly and drums rumbled incessantly. At the head of each company rode the chieftain of the clan with the young men of his family; these cavaliers looked carelessly down on the people on foot and rode, hand on hip, legs proudly stretched away from the stout girths of their steeds. The town houses of the burgesses and nobles, many of which had stood for long with shutters up, as though dead, were all opened, their double-winged gates cast wide to admit the endless stream of their lord's relatives, vassals, friends and dependants. And whether they came from the mountains of the Highlands or the plains and mountains of the south, they were bent, alike, on going to court, to present themselves before the Queen and discover the turn things were to take, in the State and in their personal affairs, now that their youthful Sovereign was among them. They all came full of hope. Hardly a year ago, rebellion had thrown the whole country into confusion; war had made every kind of property insecure and broken down every restraint. In flat opposition to their ruler, the Scottish Lords had established the Protestant Church. They had appropriated the rich lands of the Church, and ejected the monks and priests by force. For that reason the Queen had not signed peace with her rebellious subjects. But she had, both in speech and writing, promised to forgive and forget, if she found obedience when she landed. What could she do but promise mercy? It was said that she was herself Catholic through and through. Yet it was hardly conceivable that she would try to exact vengeance, or attempt to bring the country back to her own faith. Legally, the land was almost at her absolute disposal. It was, however, almost all divided among the vassal lords, on condition, of course, of inviolable obedience. If the knights observed their fealty, and came when their ruler summoned them, she had soldiers; if not, she had no army. Less than a third of the lords were Catholic. The Queen had therefore to be thankful that she was permitted by her subjects to hold Catholic service and celebrate Mass, for herself and her immediate suite, within the palace chapel, behind closed doors.

So the knights reflected, and therefore came cheerfully. And they were glad to come. For her French jointure made Queen Mary pass, in Scotland, as very rich.

★

In the second week after the Queen's arrival, John Knox was summoned to the palace, in consequence of a remarkable chain of events.

On the first Sunday morning after the Queen's arrival, Lord Lindsay, the most robustious of the young lords who came streaming to Edinburgh, took his way, with a body of lusty Scots, to the royal chapel, where they pushed into the yard, shouting: "Down with the Mass! Are we to stand Mass in the land? The priests of idolatry shall die!" Before the door of the chapel, however, Lord James Stuart was walking up and down. He stood in the youths' way, saying that he was on guard there to see that no good Scot, be he whom he may, might be troubled in his conscience by so much as hearing Mass through the door. As he spoke, the watch, standing in the courtyard on either side of the door, raised their long spears in cheery readiness. Young Lindsay, his knees knocking together, stuttered, with scarlet face, "Yes, yes. That was all very well. That—" he threw back his head, "had been in his mind too, so help him God!" Rage made his words stick in his throat. Let Satan seize him and Scotland too, before he would allow any French priest to so much as whisper here. Lord James nodded his agreement. That was all in hand, he said; the day before, a watch over the French priests had been undertaken by the other two natural brothers of the Queen, Lord John and Lord Robert Stuart.

Meantime, in the chapel, behind the closed doors, the blast of the organ sounded. Boys' voices rose high and clear: *Gloria! Gloria! Gloria in excelsis!*

Young Lindsay turned on his heel, and ran off as swiftly as though before the trumpet blasts of an archangel, without one look round to see what became of his troop, which melted away with all its staves, axes and beams.

★

Next day, a herald rode through the town, to proclaim a royal message from the town hall, before the Cathedral, and then affix it in the market-place. The people came streaming out of houses and lanes at the sound of the trumpet, with almost incredible speed, in almost incredible numbers, for where they all came from one could not imagine, and surged round the cross. Women had their skirts torn off them in the press: as soon as any one succeeded in scrambling up the steps of the cross he was pulled down by eager neighbours. There hung the young Queen's first decree. It ran:

"TO OUR CITIZENS AND SUBJECTS

"To her great distress, Her Majesty the Queen has been compelled to observe dreadful and shocking disorders and incidents which may cause harm through the recent changes in the kingdom. Since Her Majesty's mind knows no more urgent desire than to rule her Kingdom in peace and quiet, Her Majesty has, in agreement with her Crown Council, determined: It is forbidden on pain of death, in the interest of law and order, for any one to undertake innovations in the matter of religion; to injure or in any way molest any servant or other person who has come with Her Majesty into the Kingdom; or in any other way to stir up dissension or strife.

"At the same time Her Majesty is convinced that her good and loving subjects, in dutiful obedience, will never give cause for any severity."

Some among the crowd laughed; many cried "Oho!" Here and there some one said aloud: "That is quite all right. The chief thing is that she leaves us in peace." Others again murmured: "God help us! The accursed priests!" A stout woman folded her hands under her full breasts, and waggling her fat neck, said, "God bless the dear soul!"

As the crowd, soon tired, began to disperse, various young men in knightly garb moved through it up to the cross, in order to study the proclamation more at their leisure.

"It is a burning shame," said one, "that these idolatrous priests, with all their heathenish practices, should be back in the country again." Another, standing by him, answered, with a laugh, "One can see that you have but just come from outside, with the genuine serpent still in your bosom. Just wait till the court holy water has touched you! Every one is the same. I have been here five days now. At first all the talk was: Out with the priests! And now? . . ."

★

Next Sunday, however, John Knox thundered from the pulpit that the celebration of a single Mass in the land was more awful than if ten thousand men had landed for the express purpose of destroying the religion of God with fire and sword.

Whereupon the Queen sent for him to her presence.

★

John Knox obeyed the summons and was led through passages and up staircases, and across various moderate-sized rooms panelled in dark oak. Then the page opened a door, and showed him into a handsome room, with soft coloured tapestries gleaming on its walls. He crossed the threshold and stood before his sovereign. She was conversing with her brother, Lord James Stuart. With her right hand she was, absentmindedly, caressing a small white-haired dog, which was snuggling up into the folds of her dress, but, on the entry of the stranger, slunk off into the embrasure of the window, after snarling at him vainly several times, with every appearance of disfavour. Two young ladies, clad in dresses of light coloured silk, sat at their embroidery frames, the Queen's two maids of honour, Mary Beaton and Mary Fleming. The Queen herself wore a dress of black satin, out of whose high, tight collar, fitting right up to her ears and ending in a frill of finely gauffred lace, her face rose like a flower. A net of fine lilac silk braid covered her blond hair.

"Master John Knox," said Lord James Stuart, nodding to the minister to approach. He came calmly, with no sign of hurry, and met Mary's long look of appraisal with such a searching inspection of her face, her mien, her attire, that the colour sprang up in the Queen's cheeks. Seating herself, with the train of her gown widely extended over the ground, she said, her head held high:

"Master John Knox, I have sent for you that you might have the opportunity of answering for yourself to me personally."

She paused for a moment. He stood, tranquilly waiting.

"Grave reproaches against you are made to me. It is said that you stir up my subjects against me their ruler and Queen. You have written a book against my inherited, God-granted royal right. You have been a rebel against my mother, and also against me. And all your power, so it is said, comes to you through magic."

John Knox took but a moment to organize his opening sentence, and then replied: "Your Majesty, if to proclaim the truth of God, to fight idolatry, and to awaken a people to the true teaching and pure service of God is to be a rebel, then

23

am I guilty of that sin." He paused, to work out his thoughts. The Queen looked expectantly at him. It seemed to him, so he went on, that, hitherto, the Queen had found as much true obedience in her land as ever any of her forefathers had done. So far as concerned his book on the Regiment of Women, he must maintain his opinions at least until some one could refute him with sound arguments. Which hitherto had not occurred. Rather had his writing found agreement among the most noted men of learning in most lands. Indeed, he doubted whether there were ten men alive who could so much as think of venturing to attempt to refute it.

The Queen crimsoned right into the roots of her hair. The ladies in the window had ceased embroidering and gazed at the preacher: Mary Beaton, a round little body, with her mouth half open with astonishment: on Mary Fleming's handsome, intelligent face a smile of cold contempt. The Queen, in reply, obviously wished to speak proudly and convey the impression that she was dismissing an unsavoury topic once for all by simply mentioning it: but her youthful voice betrayed the beating of her heart, as she said:

"So you think that I have no rightful authority?"

John Knox, a little perturbed by so direct a frontal attack, raised his hand. "Ah, Your Majesty!" Then, he continued, "Have not Plato and many other sages written against the regiment of the time, and yet managed to take what came? Wherefore I say, if our land suffers no ill from the fact of a woman's rule, I shall in future disapprove such a rule in my heart only, and shall live even as quietly under Your Majesty as, for example, Paul managed to do under Nero." He went on to say that his book applied not so much to the ruler of his own land as to Queen Mary of England, the Jezebel, who at the time when the book was being written, was using her bloody sceptre as a scourge for the children of the Lord. Further, "Gracious lady, have not many things that before passed as unassailable, been taken in question in the last few years?" He defended himself against the reproach of having anything

24

to do with the Black art. "There are a thousand witnesses to the fact that I have at all times, and in all places, never ceased calling down the wrath of God, with all the testimony of Holy Writ to back me, on such hellish arts." He adduced the example of Christ. "The wickedness of the world accused Him, even Him, the Lord and Saviour, of being in league with Beelzebub!"

While he spoke, Mary never moved her gaze from his face. So soon as he had finished speaking, she at only replied, very stiffly, "But you have bidden my people choose another religion from that which their Princes could allow. That cannot be the precept of God, since God commands obedience to subjects."

At this John Knox smiled. "Your Majesty," he said, "the matter is plainly thus: Just as true religion derives neither its force nor its origin from worldly princes, but from God alone, so subjects can never be bound to conceive their religion as it may happen to please their princes. Are not princes the most ignorant of all men in the knowledge of God? What, for example, would have happened if the descendants of Abraham had accepted the creed of Pharaoh, to whom for long they were subjected? Or if the men of the time of the Apostles had sought after no other salvation than that imposed upon them by the Emperor, their suzerain?"

"Yes," answered Mary, speaking almost breathlessly fast, "but none of them raised the sword against their prince."

"God, Madam, had not given them the power and the means."

"You mean," cried the Queen, drawing herself up abruptly to her full slender height, "that whenever subjects have the might they are to proceed to rebellion?"

The flame in her glance did not so much as cause him to change colour. "Gracious Lady, whenever princes betray the right in virtue of which they are obeyed! Your Majesty, when a father is mad, and seeks to slay his own children, the children bind his hands, and they do right. They must do it, even if their hearts break. Does Your Majesty hold that the children then do wrong? Or that God will be wrath with such children? Or with the prince, who seeks to slay his own subjects?"

Leaning back in her chair, her brow in her hand, Mary seemed lost in thought. John Knox stood, modestly waiting, at her side. At last James Stuart approached his sister quietly, and bending over her, gently touched her hand. "What troubles Your Grace so?"

She let her hand fall, and her face was all wet with tears. She turned to John Knox. "I perceive now," she said, bitterly, "that my subjects ought to obey you, and not me, Master Knox. That they have to command me, and not I them!"

Horrified, he stepped back a pace. "God forfend! I give subjects freedom to do what they like? Never! I shall ever set life and limb, all I am and have, on their obeying God. And Kings, likewise. Why does Your Grace think," he continued, "that you are injured by the commandment to honour God? Who sets subjects under Princes? To be subject of God, and foster-father and foster-mother to His blessed Church, higher honour than this can fall to no flesh on this earth, since it leads to eternal bliss."

"Such is my belief also," she said; then shaking her head, with passionate earnestness; "But you are not the Church that I will nourish," she said, half rising from her seat, and stretching out her hand towards the preacher. "I will defend the Church of Rome, which I think the true Church of God."

John Knox remained calm, although his dark face blanched to an ashen pallor, as he replied, "Your will, Madam, is not reason; neither does your thought make the Roman harlot the true immaculate spouse of Jesus Christ."

Mary sprang up. Her eyes shone like dagger-blades. John Knox raised his hand as if to silence the Queen, then, placing his right palm on his heart as if to draw strength thence, said, "Wonder not, Madam, that I call Rome a harlot; for that Church is polluted with all kinds of spiritual fornication in doctrine and manners. Oh, Madam," he exclaimed, admonishingly, "before God, the Church of the Jews, who nailed Jesus

Christ to the Cross, was not so far alienated from God's ordinances and law, even those who publicly denied His law, as is the Church of Rome today."

The Queen sat back, motionless, very pale. "My conscience says not so," she replied, at last, with trembling lips, her slender white hands closing protectively about the golden crucifix which hung on a short chain on the front of her dress.

He shook his head. "Conscience comes from knowledge. I am afraid Your Majesty has not the right knowledge."

"Oh, I have listened and read!"

He bowed slightly. "So said the Jews who crucified Christ likewise. They read everything—the law and the prophets. But they interpreted it after their own fashion."

"So do you! You, yes, you!" said Mary. She rose to approach him, and stood so, in her long, rich robe, as tall as he. "Whom am I to believe?" she asked. "Who is to be judge?"

He raised his hands. "You are to believe God! Clear as heaven He declares it in His word! Take one example," he continued, in rising excitement. "Take the main issue, the point on which everything turns. Where does it stand in God's Word that the Mass was set up by Him, by Our Lord Jesus Christ? Never to all eternity! On the contrary, it is in truth an abomination in the sight of God; the invention of men and nowise a sacrifice commanded by Him who died for us upon the Cross,—once, and for all time. Bring the Book of God and show me, in clear words, that your position is there, and I will give in. Gladly, I long to do it. But, as it is, you are bolder in maintaining than in proving. And God has never commanded the Mass."

The Queen stood, her face averted, lost in thought, silent. John Knox, her brother, Mary Beaton, all looked at her. Only Mary Fleming's eyes wandered between her and the preacher. Mary let the crucifix slip through her fingers, though she still held the chain on which it hung.

"I cannot refute you," she said to Knox. "You are too hard for me. But—" her voice rose, as she spoke now more quickly, and the colour flamed in her cheeks again, for she saw John Knox smiling at her words—"If they were here that I have heard, they would answer you!"

He tossed his head. "I would the most learned Papists in the world were here, now!"

Mary's face changed; she smiled. "Well, Master Knox," she said, "if you wish that—the opportunity may come more swiftly than you expect!"

He looked at her in astonishment, as she continued to regard him smilingly.

"If so, my opportunity comes sooner than I thought. A Papist able to defend his theses, except by fresh assertions—such a man I would be glad to meet."

"So you say!" retorted the Queen, dryly.

A page came with the announcement that Her Majesty's dinner was served. The ladies in the window rose; the dog reappeared from his corner behind them. The Queen turned to go. As she bowed slightly, almost unconsciously, in leave-taking, John Knox said— "I pray God, Madam, that you may be as blessed within the Commonwealth of Scotland as Deborah was in the Commonwealth of Israel."

Mary smiled. Lord James drew near her to offer his arm; the ladies gathered round; the small procession left the room.

To his trusty friends, who had been awaiting him anxiously outside the Palace, John Knox declared, "If this woman have not a proud heart, a crafty wit, and a mind case-hardened against God and His truth, I have no judgment."

★

In Holyrood Palace, the servants had been at work all morning decorating the Audience Chamber. The director, a lean, middle-aged Frenchman, stood now on the threshold, his head thrown back, calmly giving a final order, now to this side, now to that, in a considering tone, while his eyes thoroughly surveyed the whole of the room; he was bent on presenting the dignity of his mistress, a one-time Queen of France, in a manner calculated adequately to impress both a people at once envious and barbarian, and the representatives of foreign Powers which, by comparison with France, were half barbarian too, and assuredly envious enough. The Frenchman might feel pleased with his work. The Queen's French tapestries smiled from the walls: the soft light of the hundred wax candles in candelabra on the walls, and more in the chandeliers pendent from the ceilings, where they swayed gently in the shape of ships of silver and women and angels in silver and gold, gave to the heroic figures of the tapestries a strange, almost overpowering, actuality and made their flower-wreaths shine with the deep radiance of some world of dream. With the sharp smell of the wax candles there mingled the sweet scent of perfumes, scattered about or collected in bowls.

The Queen was to receive the Ambassador of the Sovereign of England in high audience, when he was to convey his Queen's good wishes on her return home.

Mr. Thomas Randolph, the English Ambassador, thin lipped and parchment-pale of face, entered the hall, accompanied by pages. For a moment he stared, again overcome by the astonishment that had struck him on his arrival in Scotland the previous evening. He knew Scotland well, and had thought of it as a poverty-stricken land, closed in, overhead, by a dismal sky, with dark, close-set cities, where a silent and dour race of men (all but the nobles) dragged out a troublous existence, and a barbarous nobility shrank from no violence in the struggle for self-enrichment, conceived of no higher pleasure than the pursuit of deadly and sanguinary feuds. Yet Edinburgh, yesterday, and, today, this gorgeous hall, hummed with such gay life that Randolph felt like rubbing his eyes, and asking himself: Can it be real? Was it possible that hungry hawks could transform themselves into people capable of the joy of life? Above the press of lords and ladies, through which a way was made with considerable difficulty for the English Ambassador to pass, Randolph saw the lofty throne on which Queen Mary sat in all her magnificence, under a canopy, clad in her royal robes—a dress of velvet embroidered with pearls, with a huge white ruff and wide-flowing veil. Her whole person sparkled and shone. In her right hand, blazing with rare rings, and white as the pearls she wore as it rested on the velvet of her dress, was the ivory handle of a little fan, of gold embroidered silk. As she looked, with solemn gravity, at the Ambassador, she seemed, in all her finery, like a saint in some rich church, an image rendered only the more moving by the sheer grace of her physical loveliness. On either side of the throne stood the Scottish nobles, with those who had come from France with the Queen. All the gentlemen wore French attire.

Randolph dropped on his knee, to take the great, circumstantially-sealed missive from his Sovereign out of his ambassadorial wallet, and then verbally reiterate the good wishes of Queen Elizabeth. With a glance at the letter, handed to her by a kneeling page on a cushion of silk, Mary said that it made her happy even to see the handwriting of her good sister the Queen of England on the address of the despatch. Moreover, she rejoiced to gather from the Ambassador's speech that his exalted mistress was disposed to recognize the love and friendship felt so heartily by herself, and by her whole kingdom, for the neighbouring Queen. "In the immediate future," said Mary, "we shall send a special mission to England, in order that the greetings of our good sister may be reciprocated with the utmost warmth, and the bond of friendship between the two Governments, between your exalted mistress and ourselves, confirmed to a real union. As bearers of our will we have indeed selected the most trusty servants of our Crown, men whom we know to be hardly less devoted to our good sister of England than they are to ourselves and to our kingdom."

She motioned with her fan to the Ambassador to approach, that she might inquire of him, in a confidential tone, about the health of his Sovereign. He should hear more fully from herself as to her purposes, she assured him. Releasing the Englishman to mingle with the throng, she left the hall with a great suite.

Immediately upon her withdrawal, Randolph found himself surrounded by the Scottish lords. They all pressed up to him, eager to offer him every courtesy, and assure him of their devoted wish to serve him. Turning first this way, then that, in his dark silk dress, he seemed almost like a shadow among these lusty, magnificently attired men, and every movement of his suggested that, could he have consulted his own wishes, and forgotten his office, he would have obscured, or even, if possible, extinguished his personality altogether. Maitland of Lethington came up behind him so quietly that Randolph started in affright when, turning, he felt the hand of the Secretary of State laid, as softly as a falling leaf, on his shoulder. Lethington stroked his beard with his delicate, bloodless hands, smiling at the fright he had given him. He invited the Englishman to be his guest that evening; he would find Lord James Stuart with him. Randolph accepted. Amid incessant bowing, greetings to right and left, he worked his way back to the dais, where two lords, an old man and a young, had remained standing together awkwardly, as though they had been forgotten. The old man, with his bent legs, little red eyes deeply sunk in wrinkled face, and straggling beard, looked like a poor little bookbinder who, having borrowed fine clothes to come to a *bal masqué* at a rich house, feels wretched there. The youth, who, in comparison with the crumpled old man, appeared to be of gigantic stature, might have been a brewer: he had a paunch like a cask, and a fat face, a mere lump of flesh. And yet this father and son were the chieftains of the house of Hamilton, and therefore premier nobles of Scotland. The old man was also a Duke of France, de Châtelherault, and the first Scot after the Queen. According to himself and his house, and many others, the throne must fall to him if the Queen died without issue. On this account he had once been Regent for the little Queen, and he had, for several years, attempted to maintain himself in that position, handing it over finally to his ward's mother, Mary of Guise, in return for his French Dukedom with all the revenues appertaining thereto. His son, heir after

31

him to all these honours and claims, was the Earl of Arran.

The old Duke took up the English Ambassador's casual greeting with much *empressement*. He at once complained, in his screaming voice, "I am altogether neglected! You see how I am treated!" He nodded, with perturbed emphasis. His son raised his triple chin. "Yes, father, obviously," he said, laughing and puffing out his cheeks as if with pride. Randolph, flattered by the confidences of the great, tried to reassure them, although he felt as though he were standing on hot plates. Here, any word might be a danger. Since the two Hamiltons seemed inclined to stick to him, he could but take his leave and depart.

Next day he was summoned to the Queen, who talked in friendly fashion with him, and, in particular, renewed the assurances of her hearty good-will towards the Queen of England.

★

A large part of the French lords had gone, in the train of the two elder Guise princes. The youngest of her six Guise uncles, the Marquis D'Elbœuf, with a sufficient number of Frenchmen, remained to comfort and support the Queen in a strange land. The Queen, however, organized her Government so that its responsible head was Lord James Stuart, her brother, entirely trusted by the greatest party in the country, that of the Protestant Lords, and assuredly of a remarkable competence in affairs. He was further entrusted with the command over the palace guard and the management of the income of Crown and State. William Maitland looked after foreign affairs.

Both these gentlemen were on intimate terms with John Knox. They now endeavoured to employ this intimacy to induce their friend to deal gently with the Queen. She was a spoiled young woman, Maitland explained, of limited experience in spiritual matters. But, for John Knox, God did not speak in a still small voice. He prayed, after every service, before the full congregation, that the Lord might turn the

Queen's self-willed heart towards the truth, if such were His will. If not, let Him strengthen the hearts and hands of His chosen ones so that they might be able to oppose inflexible resistance to tyrants.

"She is more sensible than you are," said Maitland, grimly, to the preacher. "The patience with which she bears your raging shows a wisdom far beyond her age."

John Knox, however, turned a deaf ear. Here was a Queen who ought to be an example of moral life to her sex, and what was her behaviour? "They fiddle and sing and dance the whole night through, into the light of God's morning, and even the holy Sabbath sets no limits to their junketings. There is such a jingling and laughing, such a whispering and eyeing as has never before been so much as heard of in our Scottish land!"

It was rumoured that on a Sunday evening, the whole court, including all the Catholic and Protestant lords, had taken part in a masked ball, at which nixies and wood sprites had run hither and thither. Whereupon John Knox raised his staff and prophesied famine and pestilence to the whole land. But the Scottish nobles laughed at his curses.

★

On one occasion there was a discussion of religious matters at court. Lord James took the Protestant side; the Marquis D'Elbœuf the Catholic. Finally the Queen said she did not understand arguments and proofs. But she knew quite well what she believed.

In accordance with a practice established within the last decade, the Provost of Edinburgh caused proclamation to be made ordering all monks, members of religious Orders, priests, nuns, adulterers, coiners, and other such criminal persons, to leave the town of Edinburgh and the entire area of its jurisdiction, within twenty-four hours. Whereupon a Herald of the Queen appeared and summoned the Provost before the Crown Council where he was forthwith removed from his office.

★

What had winter in Scotland been like? A protracted, well-nigh unbroken burden, borne with bent head by every one. Now, it seemed, even in winter life could be attractive. Mary had seen that even in gloomy Scotland glances could pass between man and maid. She smiled, as she observed it, and went about unlocking closed-up hearts, so that they opened up their sorrows and their joys to her sympathy. She talked to obstinate parents, and held out to them prospects of her raising worthy suitors to rank and estate. Thus her three natural brothers were singled out to have loving companions in life found for them under the eyes of their Queen. First among them was, of course, Lord James Stuart. His father had originally designed him for dignity in the Catholic Church; he was nominated Prior of the Abbey of St. Andrews, but that was all. Now, he was called to the highest offices. His Sovereign made him Earl of Mar. And, thanks to the unwearying good offices of his sister, his long suit of Lady Anne Keith, the daughter of the proud Earl Marischal, was crowned with success. Lord John Stuart, whom his father had made Abbot of Coldingham, a very lively gentleman, enthusiastically devoted to the French new-comers, was betrothed to Lady Anne Hepburn, sister of the Earl of Bothwell. The Queen furnished the pair, poor as mice on either side, with an ample income, for no other reason than that she was very fond of Lord John.

★

Some time after her arrival, the Queen took a journey to the more important towns of her kingdom. In Aberdeen, she was presented with a golden beaker filled to the brim with ducats, and also with the Scottish Bible, which as a Catholic she might not read. She handed the book to a lord in her retinue, and spoke amiably with the burghers.

Riding through the streets of the town, however, the Queen suddenly fell insensible from her horse. It was a full quarter of an hour before she recovered consciousness. It was said that she had been subject to similar severe fainting attacks ever since she grew up.

★

In the late autumn, some of the Scottish nobles undertook a punitive expedition into the southern borders, into the "Debatable Land" which, in all the wars between England and Scotland in the past centuries—in which there was hardly a decade without war—had been so devastated by fire and sword that it was practically uninhabitable. Since, throughout long periods, no one knew to which kingdom any piece of this region really counted as belonging, it was the resort of fugitives from both the home of outlaws and exiles, the rag-tag and bob-tail of humanity. There they dwelt, in the secret places of the moss-hags, the woods and the valleys, breaking forth ever and anon, robbing and murdering, so that no one dared pass from one kingdom to the other unless armed to the teeth and protected by numbers.

From time to time both Governments were compelled to despatch armed forces, to assert authority, at least in punitive form, over these lost souls. The court that ultimately sat in judgment on such evildoers as were then taken, was not infrequently presided over by the King of Scotland. This time, however, Queen Mary sent Lord James Stuart to preside in her stead at the court, while the command over the expeditionary troop was assigned to the Earl of Bothwell. James Hepburn, Earl of Bothwell, the scion of a distinguished but impoverished family, was at this time in his six-and-twentieth year. The high responsibility of command over these perilous regions, in which his family estates were situated, had already been granted to the Earl by the Queen Regent, on the strength of the fearless attitude and unfaltering loyalty to the Crown shown by him as a mere youth, at the time of the Rebellion. Between him and Lord James Stuart a deadly enmity smouldered, barely concealed on the surface. Nevertheless, both did their duty, and more than thirty robbers were laid by the heels.

★

On a mild day in December, Mary was returning, with a small retinue, from a hunting expedition, in whose course she had enjoyed the hospitality of various nobles. The atmosphere was colourless, opaque; the light wan. The Queen rode, lost in thought. Suddenly they came to a deep ravine: she halted to look down the terraced sides of the gap. The view, however, was cut off abruptly by the cauldron of mist. She turned to inspect the ruins of a chapel, little more now than a heap of rubble, on the mountainous side. Here and there a fragmentary arch still rose; one windowless wall still stood. She asked her brother, who was at her side, which Abbey the chapel had belonged to. With some embarrassment, since the ruins bore witness to the spoliations of the past years, he replied that he did not know. Still she stayed; her companions puzzled as to what might be in her mind, every one awaiting the signal to go on. But instead of that she suddenly desired to dismount. By herself—no one else need trouble. Lord James leant over to her: "Your Majesty!" She looked down into his face: "Yes?" "Madam, it might be wrongly interpreted!" "By whom?" she asked. Without more ado, she swung out of the saddle, supported by a page. At the last moment she signed to one of the younger lords to come to her: "Sir John Gordon!" He was out of the saddle in a trice. She crossed over the withered grey grass to the ruin, went in and stepped among the rubbish, her long dress held up high. Young Gordon followed her, at a loss as to her mind, wondering, too, whether he ought not to warn the Queen of danger from the tottering, semi-charred beams, which might come down on top of them at a word or touch. Evidently, however, it pleased her to show disregard of peril. Between the walls of the choir, which still stood erect, she paused before a socle of grey stone. The delicate feet of a female statue were still visible there, and the billowing edge of a garment round them. The rest of the statue lay broken and overthrown among the

36

rubbish; the head by itself, close by the socle. Mary bent. "A piteous Mother of God!" she said, raising the face of stone. The knight, likewise a Catholic, stood by his Queen, strangely moved, at once by reverence and fear. "What have these savages done to the sweet Mother?" she wailed. "Every day I have to look at ruins, from my window, that once were sacred things, and every day it all stirs in me anew." She laid the stone head against her soft delicate cheek. "Holy Mother of God, forgive me that I let Thee be so contemned." Crouching on the earth, she endeavoured, with Gordon's help, to bury the head among the rubble, so that it was entirely covered up. They stepped out into the open, through a window of the choir which had been completely levelled with the ground, and came out at the back of the chapel. "Yesterday I was with the Laird of Lundy," she said to Gordon, who had only joined her suite a few hours previously. "And, in the evening, the old Laird came to me with his seven tall sons, all great strong men, and they all knelt down before me, and the old man said that he and his sons all belonged to me altogether, and that all that they possessed was mine likewise, and they would shed the last drop of their blood and spend the last penny they possessed for me with utter gladness. But one favour I must grant them—never to have the Holy Office celebrated in their house again! I asked, Why not? and old Lundy replied that a single Mass was worse than the Evil One."

"What did Your Majesty do?" asked Gordon.

"I gave it up—what else could I do?"

The Queen returned to her suite, which had stayed where she left it. She swung up to her saddle, and rode on, slowly, silent as she had been before. Lord James, at her side, looked as though a viper were gnawing in his bosom.

★

A few days later all was quiet in Holyrood; early in the evening the Queen, unusually fatigued by a long, brisk ride, dismissed her suite betimes. There were only a handful of French and Scottish gentlemen sitting over cards and wine in one or two of the rooms. Then, suddenly, without any one's knowing where or how it began, the palace was full of noise. There was a slamming of doors, and, in the distance, a sound like the clang of swords. Then, a rush along the corridors, with confused shouting; people running up; more people appearing, at half-opened doors; from other rooms, again, the loud jar of bolts being shot back. In a trice the passages were jostling with men and women, all asking questions at once. "What is up? What has happened? What is it all about?" No one could answer: everybody expected the others to be able to explain what it all meant. Then, from the inner courtyard, up came the Scots guard, rushing with a clatter of spears to the corridor before the Queen's apartments. They, too, could only stare. They knew nothing. All they could say was that the outer guard, on duty towards the streets and the town, might know something. They had come up, they said, because they had heard a voice from outside, out of the darkness, yelling, "Watch! They are abducting the Queen!" But, of course, there was not an enemy in the whole of the palace, and here, by the Royal apartments, everything was dead quiet, and not a soul had seen anything in the slightest suspicious! From without, two officers appeared, their spurs clanking. "They stood behind the bridge," said one, "and, Devil take them, it is all too true!" The other raised his hand, coolly. "Oh, come," he said, "the man is making up a scandal, that's all." "Who? What's that?" The first speaker was purple with rage. "As though you could jump to conclusions about squadrons and regiments right away, like that. Squadrons can't have vanished into thin air. Or do you think they did? Of course not. We shall hear about it yet! more people than you saw them." They continued to dispute, in angry terms; everybody streamed after them, as they made their way to the royal apartments, to make their report. A part of the watch, under Lord Robert Stuart, came up into the inner corridors. They had been outside. On the bridge, where the company of horse was said to have been seen, everything was perfectly peaceful. "Of course it is far too dark now, to discover anything," said another. Lord Robert agreed. Strong posts had been sent thither, nevertheless. Mary Seaton appeared in the doorway of the Queen's ante-chamber. Her Majesty, having been sufficiently informed, was now quite at ease, and completely confident in the fidelity of her subjects. Unwillingly, people separated. Mary Seaton returned to the Queen's bed-chamber, where the Queen, in a long night-robe, was sitting on a chair by her bed. Her fair hair hung down in plaits on either side of her face; with her wide eyes and scarlet lips, she looked like a little girl. Her brother, James Stuart, was with her. "I am not afraid," she said, looking bravely into his face. "It is quite an adventure. To-morrow we shall see." Lord James departed. The Queen wanted to send her maid of honour after him, but she begged to be allowed to stay. "Very well. I should have to worry about you otherwise, shouldn't I?" Tenderly, she took her friend's face between her two slender hands, and kissed her softly on cheek, chin, and brow. "My poor pet! My poor timid soft-heart! You are like a dear little frightened hare!" She hoped, if her wrathful enemies really did come to the door, to drag her away—that they would at least leave her her faithful Seaton. "For without you, my dear sweet thing, I should have lost my wretched plaits altogether!" She lay down in bed, covered herself close and curled up comfortably, and began to play with pictures of what these bird-catchers would really do with her, if they got her into their nets. "I think, they would shut me up in a kennel, on bread and water. Not a very comfy one, but not too bad, either. And I am to be converted to Protestantism. Or I must marry that fat stupid Arran. Every day he comes: 'Your Majesty, most devoted compliments, in utter obedience!'"—Mary mimicked his voice: "'Your Majesty, Your Majesty, yes, Your Majesty is really the loveliest woman in the whole world!' Then I say, 'But you do not know all the women in the world?'—'How does Your Majesty mean?'— 'Well, you really cannot know that somewhere in the world there is not a woman who is much more lovely than I am.'—'Ah, no: I do not believe it.'—'I do, however,'—'Oh, yes, I know every one says that—but I mean it.—And I am quite crazy with sheer love of Your Majesty.'—'That I do not believe, either.'—'It is true, though.'—'I believe you were already crazy, when my good sister of England turned you down; I, my Lord, have never seen you in any other condition.'—'Truly?'—'Certainly.'—'That is a great pity.'—'Yes, but there is nothing to be done about it.'—Or," the Queen smiled to herself, "Or, finally, Master John Knox comes to see me every day, and stands there, and wags his finger, and takes hold of his lovely long black prophet's beard, and glowers and cries, 'Already I behold the pit of Hell in which your bones shall rattle!' And he rolls his eyes, so that I have to say to him—'For the Saints' sake, my good man, take care, or they will fall right out!'"

Mary Seaton, who was still trembling inwardly, begged the Queen, at last, for her sake, to stop her contrary talk, for it did her no good, only made her feel as if she saw, there in the corner, what the Queen described: first this, and then that: so, so, and so.

Mary laughed. "So, so, so? What of it, then? Is it really so, so, so terrible? I do not find fat Arran so, so, so terrifying!"

"Madam!" stammered the other.

Mary sat up. "Children! What a world you live in! Afraid—today? That was only a silly trick!" Good-naturedly, however, she changed the conversation, and as she was in the humour for chat, spoke of clothes and of indifferent people at court. Finally, as her friend answered her only in monosyllables, she became quieter. Mary Seaton at last perceived that, her right cheek on her hand, the Queen was tranquilly asleep. She bent over her, to gaze lovingly at her face. Mary turned in her sleep, and raised her hand so as to push the quilt a little off from her breast. Mary Seaton looked into the delicate face, now lapped in a childlike peace, and sighed. She may well talk and scoff at fears, thought the girl. The crown and joy of her life is not, for her, in constant peril.

Next morning, orders were given for the doubling of the

watch about the palace. Lord James Stuart energetically set
an inquiry on foot, which, however, revealed nothing. There
were plenty of people who came and said: Yes, on the bridge,
there had really been a squadron of horse—no, a regiment, no,
an army. But just as many came and contradicted them. Did
they not live on the bridge? They had eyes and ears, even at
midnight—they talked as though seeing and hearing through
keyholes were a matter of course—but they had noticed nothing, nothing at all! It was further proved that, on the night in
question, there had been no one on the bridge, not even a tramp
sleeping out. All of which by no means prevented the report
from going through the town, and being everywhere believed,
that on the far side of the bridge, in the dead dark of a moon-
less December night, expressly selected for the enterprise, the
Earl of Arran had planted himself. So soon as midnight had
rung from the tower of Saint Giles, the palace was to be broken
into, with the aid of treachery within, the watch overwhelmed
and slaughtered, and the Queen abducted. There had been many
helpers and servers in the town, though these now found it best
to be completely blind and deaf. Some laughed and said, "What
folly! Even Arran could hardly be so mad!" "Because it is
crazy, it is all the more likely. The Earl has long lost his wits
over the Queen. He proposed to her; she refused; he swore to
get her, all the same!" "Oh, ho! The Queen of France! The
loveliest woman in the world!" "Queen of France! That's an
old story. Arran is the first man here. He tried to get the
Queen of England, before." "Did she take him?" "No, but he
courted her." "Yes, because he is quite cracked."

Others put up another defence. "He has no money for such
an escapade. His father gives him practically nothing." "Oh,
he had hundreds of friends who would help him, and are better
off than he is."

Every one knew that a Highlander regarded cattle-lifting
and abducting of women as knightly occupations.

The Queen was spoken to about these propensities, and
orders were finally issued for every knight dwelling in the

41

palace to be equipped with spear and armour for watch service. Moreover, if anything occurred, every one was to be liable to arrest. The exits of the palace were examined, and some secret ones blocked up. Iron gratings were fitted to all the windows on the first floor.

On the day after the adventure, the old Duke came to court, shaking in every limb with fury at the idea that such a base calumny on his house could be thought of. The Queen tried to reassure him; it was all gossip; she—and that, after all, was all that signified—had the most complete confidence in the entire Hamilton family. "I am well aware that Your Majesty cannot endure my son," said the old man, in a voice that, in his excitement, sounded as though it were cracked, "And he knows it, too. But for him to dream of an assault! . . . He would gladly sacrifice every hair of his head, to do Your Majesty pleasure!" The Queen smiled. Mary Fleming, who was standing near with Mary Livingstone, leant over to her companion: "Luckily, he has not got many!"

The Queen could not calm the old man. He departed in wrath, and retired from court to his estates. Arran had not put in an appearance at all: breathing vague threats, he chose to creep away to a ruinous old country house, allowed him by his miserly father.

★

This affair had hardly died down, when, again at night, a new alarm sounded, this time, however, in the town. Burghers, roused from quiet sleep, sat up in bed, asking whether this wild racket without had anything to do with them; then settled back contentedly into their pillows, when the noise died away in the distance.

Next morning, people were standing at all the doors, men and women, with a story: A few days ago, Cuthbert Ramsay, the clothier, had been knocked up, in the night, by men, who, although they wore black masks over their faces, were easily recognizable from their dress and bearing as knights, indeed as gentlemen from the court. They came to seek access to Cuthbert's ward, Alison Craik, a pretty and amenable young person, who had for some time been on intimate terms with the most distinguished of their number, although, as a matter of fact, she was in guard as the property of the Earl of Arran. Whether the gentlemen, whom Alison Craik knew as the Queen's uncle, the Marquis D'Elbœuf, her natural brother, Lord John Stuart, and the Earl of Bothwell, were, on this particular evening, not so agreeable as they might have been, or whether the lady suffered from retrospective pangs of conscience, or whether a hint had come to her from without—her protector was in the town and already suspicious—the gentlemen found the door barred when they tried to make a second entry, and no better cheer than an old woman cursing them out of a window on the upper floor. They threatened to break open the door, if it was not opened to them, forthwith. The old dame bawled back that they should betake themselves to the devil instead of spoiling decent folk of their good name and their hard-earned rest. Greatly incensed by this, the Lords broke in the door, while the woman shouted, more and more shrilly, first out of the window and then about the house. The Earl of Bothwell, who was ahead, succeeded in making his way into the room of the young woman and dragging her, three-quarters naked, out of the bed where she was cowering. He was about to throw the girl, screaming, beating, scratching, and spitting like a little cat, out of the window into his companions' arms, when they shouted up to him, out of the rampaging confusion and noise of a street brawl, to look first to how he was to get out of the rat's hole he was in. With swift decision, he thrust the girl, with a curse, into a corner of the room, and climbed through the window, by the outer wall of the house, down into the street, heedless of the imprecations breathed on him by Alison Craik from her corner; then, with his companions, he made off as quickly as he could out of the increasing crowd outside, which was gathering in greater and more hostile numbers every minute.

What next? At first, the burghers only laughed; to get excited about Alison Craik did not seem very remunerative. Cuthbert Ramsay, however, did not share this view. At the head of a body of members of his craft he pushed his way to the Queen herself, to raise his complaint aloud; shameful violence had been used to his innocent ward and niece by the most distinguished gentlemen of the court. The Queen made short shrift of his angry complaint, roundly telling him that if he had kept the girl properly, under good discipline and manners in his house, instead of positively driving her to the most vicious courses, there would never have been so shocking an affair. Later, however, she reproached the gentlemen of her court most bitterly—what was to come of it, if her immediate circle was diligently occupied in undermining the reputation of her court? The Marquis D'Elbœuf laughed grimly: had they not broken in to punish vice, and give a terrible and salutary example? Foaming with rage, he swore, later, that they would, and that right quickly, drag the creature from her hole, if the whole kingdom of Scotland stood at arms before her door. The news of this oath flew through the town, and at nightfall the very next evening there collected, in the streets and in the great open place, the Lawnmarket, friends and servants of the Earl of Arran, armed with swords and spears, in full armour and in such numbers as to prove that the Earl would not lack supporters, if there were any effort at a coup. Thereupon the three enemies of Alison Craik, or, now, rather of the protector of her honour and safety, the Earl of Arran, gathered their power in the town house of the Earl of Bothwell. About eleven o'clock—when the turmoil in the town had by no means yet subsided—a report ran that the troops were about to engage. It would be splendid, quite splendid, if there were to be battle; the old Duke, the Earl of Arran's father, was said to have come to town himself, to take command over his forces. It was no longer a question of the woman, of Alison Craik: the Earl of Bothwell was now to be done in, on account of the bitter hatred with which all Hamiltons hated him, far

worse than death or sin. At such an enterprise, Lord James
Stuart would wink, since on this one point he saw eye to eye
with the Hamiltons, bitter as the feud between them otherwise.

Now, thick darkness descended on the streets, though they
still throbbed with excited expectation; there was eager, furtive
spying out of the darkened windows. Any one who was bold
enough to go out openly after adventure, crowded into the
wynd where Cuthbert lived. There, with every bolt barred, and
every window black, the town watch was on guard, twenty men
strong. Since, for the moment, there seemed no more to be
seen here, the crowd streamed on to the town house of Earl
Bothwell. Its gates still stood open wide; great torches blazed
in the hall and in the guard-rooms off the courtyard, all the
windows were brilliantly lit with candles; before the threshold,
in the courtyard, at every window, soldiers could be seen going
to and fro, armed to the teeth and staring, taut with angry
passion, down at the gaping crowd. There was a glow of apprehension and pleasure about; a fight was certain. Suddenly,
the alarm bells started to swing out, all over Edinburgh; from
every steeple and tower, in Edinburgh and the whole region
round, their sharp sound came quick, anxious, penetrating.
"The court is in the street! The Queen herself is on horse!
Lord James, the Earl of Huntly, the Earl of Argyle, they are
all coming!" Actually, down from the palace, there was a
mighty rattle coming along the High Street. Calm, at the head
of a compact power, rode the two earls of Argyle and Huntly,
between them, Lord James, who, though he was small and they
of mighty proportions, seemed more important than either. A
herald on horseback came out of the troop, blew a loud blast
on the trumpet. In a stentorian voice he read his proclamation.
On pain of death, every one must go back into his house! The
herald fell silent; the royal troops stood like the stones at the
entry to the Lawnmarket; in a few minutes, the place was
swept bare of all save the royal guards; the last of the Earl of
Arran's people were disappearing round the corner. The Lords
left the half of their people here. The others were sent to the

Earl of Bothwell's house, where they found closed doors and
darkened windows.

Next morning, a new, larger body of burghers presented
themselves before the Queen. With them there came a deputation from the ministers of the land, then in session in Edinburgh for a Church Assembly, as well as certain nobles, who
had come to the town to attend the Assembly. A breach of the
peace of the land had been made by the lords of the court in
the passed night, they clamoured. How were such horrors to be
prevented in the future? The whole court was in a rage at the
mere intimation that such a deputation had been so much as
planned. Lords were standing in all the passages, in all the
yards. "What is this impertinent pack up to?" asked Lord
Robert Stuart, fuming. "My Lord, there are a thousand nobles
of the land among the pack," replied fierce young Lindsay,
striking on his sword till it danced.

The Queen received the deputation. She was distressed, she
declared. At the same time, she begged them to remember that
her uncle was a stranger in the land, and had young, hot-
blooded associates with him; further, that the blame was certainly not on his side. At the same time, everything should be
done to make any repetition of such doings impossible in the
future. No definite undertaking as to punishment was to be
extracted from her.

Meantime, the parties, driven off the streets, were concentrating in their town strongholds. The old Duke had been
brought back to town by anxiety about the projects of his son,
whom every one, his father included, had long regarded as half
mad.

Certain fellow peers and burghers gathered round him, with
the view that this hour should not be allowed to pass without
advantage being taken of it to tear up the evil of indiscipline
by the very roots; God would be with them in so just a cause.
They gathered their people—those who, accompanying them
everywhere, had come to this particular Church Assembly:
who, like every good Scot, were in the habit of going armed and

knew how to use arms; who were as devoted to their lord as was his own hand or foot. Weapons were handed out from magazines in the various castles; leaders chose themselves. Information was conveyed privily to the Earl of Bothwell that the Hamiltons were arming, and determined to seize him, dead or alive. He swore, with his deep laugh, let them but come! A fine success they would have! "They shall carry their shame not only out of the town, but out of the country!" Lord John Stuart, who, by his marriage with Lady Anne Hepburn, had become the Earl's brother-in-law, came to him with his brother Robert. Unfortunately, the Marquis could not be of the party; he was confined to his own room, under guard. When, on the news of the plans the Hamiltons were hatching, he had snatched at a halberd and tried to go out to the street to join his friends, ten men of the watch had seized him. The other two had got out of the way before they could be taken.

Throughout the day, the town was like an armed camp; no citizen dared to venture out; the shutters were kept up; no merchant opened his door; only the drinking booths flourished. Reinforcements rushed to the Earl of Bothwell, messages, definite promises; if he needed more, they were there, whatever and however many he might want! Let him but finish the Hamiltons! Money, soldiers in thousands, were there for him, if only he could at last break the pride of this intolerably overweening family which thought to tyrannize over the whole Scottish nobility! Lord James in Holyrood, the Earl of Huntly outside, were in movement the whole day long, trying with all their might to maintain or restore order. After the Queen, they were the nearest to the throne. James Stuart had, indeed, for long been charged with really regarding himself, as eldest bastard of James the Fifth, as the only legal ruler of Scotland.

Whatever may have been the mixture of personal and State motive, the Government took so firm and wise an attitude that not a single incident developed out of all this turmoil. After a few days, the Hamiltons departed to their western estates; the Earl of Bothwell emerged from his lair; Lord Robert and

47

John Stuart rode with the Marquis in the Queen's retinue when she went north. When the court returned again, after a short time, to town, the Marquis D'Elbœuf set out for his home in France. The Queen took charge of his little illegitimate son by a Scottish maiden.

★

One evening in March, when John Knox was sitting late at his books, under the lamp light, there was a knock at his door, and James Baron, a burgher of Edinburgh, came in, saying, by way of apology for so late a disturbance, that he did not come on his own behalf but on that of a highly placed gentleman about the court—to cut it short, of the Earl of Bothwell, who begged Master Knox to grant him, at once, in secret, a conversation with him in his study; the Earl was waiting now in the burgher's house for an answer. On the instant reply that Knox was at the Earl's service whenever his service was wanted in a good cause, when he would rejoice to do whatever might be in his power, the burgher departed; soon after, the Earl entered. With a brief greeting to the preacher, he dropped into a chair that stood by the writing-table in readiness for such visitors. John Knox had turned the lamp, so that its light fell full on his guest, while he himself was in shadow. He silently regarded Bothwell, as he sat lost in dark ponderings over what he had to say. At last, with a sigh, he roused himself, and drew in his long, outstretched legs more respectfully. With a hasty movement, he pushed back the brownish-red hair that had fallen forward over his forehead, which, though not high, projected powerfully; turned a penetrating glance on his counsellor, out of eyes which seemed to hold a dark and burning tide of passionate will and, at the same time, a painful foreknowledge of universal disappointment; and said, without preamble, "Master Knox, I fancy that I do not need to tell you much, about myself. I assure you, I am through with the whole thing. As things are, it cannot go on. What is to become of me?" He became excited. "I stood by the Queen Regent. Yes. What did she not

48

promise me? What indeed? And, then? They have not even repaid me my expenses!" To make a long story short, he said, he regretted that he had ever let himself be misled by the arts of the Queen Regent into open hostility to the Protestant Lords, his co-religionists, a hostility which, as John Knox knew, was specially bitter in the case of the Earl of Arran and Lord Ormiston. Now, however, he was set upon reaching a good understanding with the lords and above all with the two last-named. And he wanted John Knox to advise him to that end. "For," he said, "if I am on good terms with the Earl of Arran, I can come to court with a page and a couple of servants, instead of having to support a great horde of useless, ill-conditioned fellows for my security—an effort which is simply ruining me."

During this narrative, John Knox had controlled considerable feeling. As soon as the Earl had finished, he said, "My Lord, if your lordship comes to me to demand my counsel and help, I may say that it is among my dearest wishes to have the judgment and wisdom granted to me by God which may allow me to serve you effectively. For though it has not, until this moment, pleased God to set me face to face with your lordship, the welfare of your house has ever been near to my heart, and my soul has been much disturbed when I have heard of all the confusions that have hemmed you round. For, indeed, my grandfather, my uncle, my father, and many of my relations have served under your lordship's forbears and some fallen under their banners. For a Scot, as you know well, that is the strongest bond of devotion. On that account, and for the sake of my God-given office, you may imagine how gladly I would serve you, and how deeply it has distressed me that you have given ground of offence to men and more to God. Your lordship may command me, as fully as any of your thanes."

Thereupon, it was agreed that John Knox should exert himself on the Earl's behalf with the lords of the other side. When, next morning, the preacher set himself to this task, he found an appearance of readiness to accommodate—due perhaps, in the main, to the fact that every one longed to see an end to these apparently endless feuds and brawls. The most difficult person proved to be Lord Ormiston, who thought himself especially entitled to harbour a grudge against Bothwell.

In the years when the Queen Regent was at war with the Protestants, Bothwell, then one-and-twenty, had undertaken the task of diverting the subsidy sent by the Queen of England to the Scottish rebels. In pursuance of this effort, he had lain in ambush, with some followers, for Lord Ormiston, who was carrying great sums, overpowered him, after wounding him rather dangerously in the hand, seized the gold from him, and then let him go. Without this money, however, the cause of the rebels seemed as good as lost. Therefore, a troop under Lord James Stuart and the Earl of Arran set out to invest Crichton Castle, whither Bothwell had fled, in the first instance, with the money. Double and treble ground for bitterness against their enemy existed for them in the fact that the Earl of Bothwell had, so they alleged, a short time previously sought an armistice with the Lords in order that he might treat with them. He had even held out to them the probability of his deserting the cause of the Regent. The ambush took place precisely when the preliminaries to an agreement were under way. The rage of the Lords was indescribable. It seemed to them as clear as day that nothing but positively devilish treachery could account for the plight to which they had been reduced. The Earl of Arran swore that, if he ever got Bothwell alive into his hands, nothing should stop him from putting this traitor to the infamous death of a common soldier on the gallows. But when they reached Crichton, they learned that the Earl, given timely warning by faithful friends, had made off with the money to the Queen Regent. They sent messengers after the fugitive to ask him either to give up the stolen money or replace it. He repelled all advances with mocking scorn. In this case, so he declared, he had not been acting on his own behalf, but on that of the Queen Regent. Until he openly crossed over to the other side, he owed her obedience. In what sense, however, did the Lords talk of his armistice negotiation as a trap? Had Lord Ormiston been induced to go anywhere by false representations, designed to lead him to his death? or had the royal troops surprised him, as a matter of fact, upon a road chosen by himself? This answer incensed the Lords to such a pitch that they first plundered and then set fire to Crichton. Only the bare walls were left standing. Thereupon Bothwell challenged Arran, as leader in this raid, to duel on horse or foot, before Scots or Frenchmen. The answer came back that, so long as he was unworthy of the name of an honourable knight, forfeit through his breach of the armistice, there could be no question of a duel. Further, the Earl of Arran would never recognize Frenchmen as judges in matters of chivalry.

Ever since, ill-concealed through the conclusion of peace, the establishment of a new order, and the arrival of the Queen, a mortal feud had persisted between the two parties. Bothwell profited by the fact that the mightiest of his foes, Lord James Stuart and the Hamiltons, were likewise divided by a deadly hatred. A short time previously, moreover, he had taken prisoner Lord Ormiston's son, Alexander Cockburn, whom he held in Borthwick, a little fortress under his control.

Of this last stroke John Knox knew nothing, nor had the Earl uttered a syllable about it. When the preacher, who was much devoted to the lad, who had for long been his pupil, did learn it, he almost despaired of his task. News, however, came to him that the boy had been voluntarily handed back to his father, and, moreover, had been so extraordinarily well treated while in the fortress that he adored his captor. He declared that his imprisonment was the happiest time of his life: his talk was all of the future, in which he might devote himself, heart and soul, to the service of Earl Bothwell, his great friend.

With this change in circumstances, it seemed as though efforts at reconciliation were likely to come quickly to a happy issue. James Stuart, whom his sister had recently elevated to the rank of Earl of Mar, must, as head of the Government, desire a peaceful settlement. The Queen, further, was eager for a reconciliation bound to be advantageous to the Earl of Bothwell. She felt under obligation to him, on account both of his services to her mother and to herself. James Stuart, therefore, stated in writing that he was satisfied as to the attitude of the Earl of Bothwell. The Earl of Arran came with one or two companions, including John Knox, to a little abbey, the so-called Kirk-o'-the-Field, which had, ever since the Reformation, been used as a dwelling-house, and was both near to the Castle and yet, built as it was almost into the town wall, quite isolated. Here they awaited the arrival of the Earl of Bothwell, for an interview that should settle all points of dispute. He stepped up, quickly, with only a few friends with him, into the single apartment of the little building, on the first floor, where he met the others. After a courteous greeting, he moved to the Earl of Arran and was beginning the apologies which had been agreed upon, when the other turned to him with a friendly embrace—when hearts were at one, what need of formalities!

John Knox held the hands of the two lords clasped in one of his, and pronounced the blessings of Heaven and earth on their happy reconciliation. "So, I leave you now in peace," he said, "and wish with all my heart, that ye two, now friends, may act in such fashion only as to increase friendship and forget all former injuries." The companions of the two principals also embraced each other, while the two earls stepped, chatting together, into the embrasure of the window. On the next day, a Sunday, both attended the Cathedral with their followers, to hear the sermon. John Knox renewed, in the presence of the congregation, thanks and blessings for this new friendship, which had a lesson for every Christian and an importance for every Scot. A thousand painful experiences had taught every citizen of Scotland only too plainly what it cost the country to have its lords growling at each other like angry dogs, waiting for the opportunity to put their bared teeth into each other. On the Tuesday, the two dined together. After that, the Earl of Arran sent messengers to his father to acquaint him with the great and happy event.

Early on the following Friday morning, however, as John Knox was returning to his dwelling from early morning service, the Earl of Arran came to him, with two burghers, crying, with every sign of extraordinary agitation: "I have been traitorously betrayed! I have been traitorously betrayed!" Whereupon, trembling like a small child, he began to weep. John Knox, painfully disturbed by his whole bearing, asked gently, "Who has betrayed you, my Lord?" The other replied, with a harsh sob, "Some Judas or other! And they seek my life, and it must be quite indifferent to them!" "My Lord," said John Knox, "I cannot understand such dark hints. If I am to give you an answer, you must speak more plainly." "Well, I take these two here to witness, that I have said to you, and that I shall also write to the Queen: they want to charge me with high treason, and the Earl of Bothwell has said it to me, and he seeks to abduct the Queen, and she is to lie a prisoner in our castle of Dumbarton, because she cannot escape from there, and he seeks to kill Lord James Stuart and William Maitland and all of them, because she is at present entirely in their hands— and then he and I will rule together over everything. But," the Earl continued, still sobbing helplessly, "all that is invented simply and solely to get me accused of high treason. But I shall certainly tell the Queen. I take you, Master Knox, and these others, to witness, that I have told it to you, and I shall at once write to the Queen and likewise to Lord James Stuart."

John Knox reflected. "Have you in any way agreed to this plot, my Lord?" "No." "Well, then, in my opinion, these words, even if they have really been uttered, can never count as treason against you. Therefore, the best course will be to bury the whole thing in silence. Since you have resisted, the entire plan will collapse. It is not probable that any one will accuse you of a deed that he has himself devised and you, for your part, rejected." The Earl however went on weeping: "Treachery!

Treachery!" tumbling his vast frame on to a chair he whimpered, still blubbering, "Treachery! Treachery!" To all John Knox's remarks and admonitions, he merely replied that he was totally and forever lost; everything, everything, was for him at an end. There was only one thing for him to do—to write a letter to the Queen. And without any more delay. Accompanied by the two burghers, to whom John Knox, greatly perturbed, gave a sign that they should in no circumstances leave the Earl alone, he staggered, sobbing harshly, and pouring forth wild words, out into the street. The message to the Queen, which he could not deliver personally, as she was absent on a hunting expedition of several days' duration, was so firmly fixed in his head, that there was no moving him from it. After he had written it, and entrusted it to the hands of a trusty messenger, he betook himself to his father. But while the form of his anxiety changed, and first this apprehension and then that was entertained and abandoned, its pressure did not relax. From Hamilton Castle, where the Duke resided, Lord James received a second letter from the despairing man, which was a mere cry for help—he was lost, if he was not at once released. Even here, nay, especially here, his life was in hourly peril. Now, his father had joined with his son's enemies in the accursed plan of capturing the Queen, killing all her counsellors and friends, and handing over him, his own son, to the most atrocious doom.

The Earl succeeded in escaping from the room in which he was confined and fleeing to the town of Stirling, where he was again taken, wandering wildly up and down the streets. He was brought to Edinburgh and there held until the Queen's return enabled a thorough investigation to be made into the affair. Meantime, as a result of the Earl of Arran's charges, two arrests were made—that of the Earl of Bothwell, who, suspecting nothing, had attached himself to the Queen's suite, and of the Abbot of Kilwinning, a friend of the Earl of Arran. Immediately after the Earl's departure, John Knox had informed the court of all that had happened at his house, with the proviso that no weight could possibly be attached to the Earl's testimony, since he was quite obviously out of his mind. In prison he began to rave. Apparitions, celestial and infernal, appeared to him. He declared that he was bewitched; then, that he was the affianced groom of the Queen, to whom he furiously demanded access; only the hellish wickedness of accursed traitors was separating them. Nevertheless he was confronted with those whom he accused. Against the Earl of Bothwell, he maintained his charges, with a wealth of detail; the other, knowing that his existence was at stake, rebutted them with impassioned energy, declaring that every syllable of the charge was blackest calumny. Kilwinning he exculpated. When his father appeared, he became lunatic—there, as he looked at him, he wanted to kill him, kill, kill. He was taken back to prison in the fortress and later, as his disease became worse, to the Castle of St. Andrews.

Nevertheless, the Crown Council considered the case against the accused. It availed them nothing that they angrily asseverated their complete innocence, declaring that they had never conceived such plans, far less spoken of them to any living soul; that they dismissed the whole charge as the raving of a lunatic, now publicly recognized as such. The judges held to their personal conviction that the charges corresponded only too exactly to the characters of the persons charged to be entirely clear of truth. Moreover, here was a priceless opportunity for drawing the teeth of opponents. So, the Duke of Châtelherault was deprived of his command over Dumbarton, but the Earl of Bothwell held prisoner in Edinburgh Castle until further decision. Before that further decision could be taken, the Earl had escaped; breaking through the bars of his cell, he had clambered down the fearsome rock sides and got away. He reached his castle, the Hermitage, whence he appealed to the Queen, reminding her of his faithful service to her and her mother, which had found no sacrifice too great. So, now, he laid his vindication, his faithful loyalty at his Sovereign's feet. But the Queen was prevented from taking the attitude in this matter that her heart counselled. For the moment, the Earl's enemies had so decidedly the upper hand that nothing remained for him but to admit that his country had become impossible. He determined to go to France, where he thought of entering the Scots Guard of the French king. Here again, however, he was unlucky. His ship was wrecked off the English coast. As an old enemy and ravager of England, he was at once cast into prison. For a year and a day he lay there, with no better consolation than the fact that he managed to get on good terms with the commandants of the fortress, gentlemen of high standing. At last his Sovereign moved on his behalf with the English Government. The Earl, so Mary wrote to Elizabeth, was no rebel, but actually had rendered important services to her and to her mother. With these services the English were familiar enough—they had felt their edge. But they had no excuse for holding him prisoner save the fact that they did so out of neighbourliness to the sister kingdom, against which he had offended. At home, the banished man's mother was unwearying in her appeals and petitions for him. Mary asked for the release of this subject; that he should be allowed to go where he would. She had to ask a third time: then, the English gave way. The Earl went to France, where he was given a Captain's commission in the Scots Guard. His means, however, were so restricted that every day made him feel that he lived the life of a mere homeless exile. So he passed the time as best he could, for ever on the look-out for some change in events that might restore him his rights, his property, and his country.

Chapter 2

DEGRADATION OF THE GORDONS

MARY STUART returned, a stranger, to a country where the fires of rebellion, imperfectly quenched, were still smouldering. Means to enforce her will were altogether lacking. Her mother had been able to call on France, ruled by her son-in-law and her daughter, the Queen of Scotland, for funds and troops. Yet she had failed. Her daughter knew that France, torn by civil war arising out of religious strife, had its hands more than full. Catherine de Medici, regent for the eleven-year-old King, would look on at any troubles in Scotland with folded arms, since she chose to feel that her daughter-in-law dared to look down upon her as the scion of a Florentine merchant house. To the support of Elizabeth of England the Protestant Lords owed the victory they had wrung from defeat. There was no counting on any change of Elizabeth's heart towards her royal neighbour. Protestant policies were forced upon England's Queen, however fundamentally opposed she might be to the democratic principles of the reformed faith. Was she not the child of a union, consummated against the Pope's express veto, an act of defiance of him and the operative cause of England's separation from the Papacy? For the Catholic Powers, Elizabeth was illegitimate: since Katharine of Aragon, the only wife of her father whom Catholics recognized, was still living at the time of her birth.

★

Even before Mary left France, an event had occurred there momentous for Scotland.

Sir Nicholas Throgmorton, a skilful gentleman in the forties, had been sent as English Ambassador to Paris. One day, he was informed that the Queen of Scotland desired instantly to speak with him. With a beating heart and uneasy apprehensions, he made his way to the palace, where he was conducted straight to the young Queen, whom he found in a handsome room, surrounded by her suite. The elegant ladies and gentlemen at once rose, and with polite bows to the Englishman left by a side door. He was alone with Mary. She approached him, with a serious face and grave mien, and his mind misgave him since he knew that he would have to make excuses for faults on the part of his Government which he himself disapproved.

"Mr. Ambassador," the Queen at once began, "are you surprised at my dismissing my suite? I have important matters to discuss with you. It may be that I shall let myself go further than I might afterwards like. I hope, however, that may not be the case!"

Sir Nicholas bowed, in silence. She drew herself up to her full slender height.

"I do not care," she said, haughtily, "to have witnesses of my passion. The Queen of England appears to be of another mind. Or so I judge from the scene which she chose to make before our Ambassador and her whole court, when he sought an answer to my courteous request for a safe conduct."

The Ambassador stood still, waiting. The Queen continued, rapidly:

"Nothing in my life causes me so much regret, as that I ever so far demeaned myself as to ask for this safe conduct. I am under no more obligation to inform the Queen, your mistress, of my journeys, than she me of hers. I came hither, although the English Government was after me with all its ships. And I shall return unmolested to my own country."

With dignified liveliness she called the Englishman to witness whether she had not proved that nothing in all the world was further from her mind than to wish his Queen anything but good, good in all things. He knew perfectly well that she received, every day, the most attractive invitations to enter into alliance and friendship from the most powerful Princes of the earth, and yet was ready to turn them all down if only she might in future rely solely on his mistress, the Queen of England. She reminded him how he had always put it to her that the two Queens must of necessity be compelled to friendship. He had said so, and she had believed him and behaved accordingly. But what was the fact? The Queen of England was actually forcing her neighbour to seek other friends. For no State and no Prince could subsist entirely alone.

So far, Mary had, in speaking, adhered strictly to what she had intended to say. Now, however, Sir Nicholas, whose grave gaze never left the lovely face of the eighteen-year-old princess, saw how the recollection of an insult that had touched her to the quick made her blood flow faster. She blushed furiously. "Your Queen says I am young," she said, throwing her head back. "That means, of course, I am too young. She says also that I lack experience." She gave a little, scornful laugh. "I have, at any rate, enough experience, and am old enough, to know perfectly well at least how to treat my relations and my friends properly. And I hope that I may always have sufficient self-control never to speak otherwise than it beseems me, a Queen, to speak to a Queen who is my nearest kin!" She looked proudly at the Englishman, as though she were, in his person, casting the Queen and Cabinet of England, and all its lords and burghers, to the ground.

Sir Nicholas had already had to do with Queen Mary. He had learned that the best way to treat her was to tell her the truth. For that purpose he had come today. Therefore, when she at last made a pause, as though she had said what was on her mind, and, turning to one of the chairs set in endless rows along the walls, sat down upon it and looked questioningly into his face, with a "Well?"—he at once began:

"Your Majesty is indignant. And it would seem with the best possible grounds. But will Your Majesty not ask yourself whether there is not a cause for the behaviour of my Government though, at a first glance, it seems extraordinary?"

"Yes?" said Mary.

"Your Majesty, my Government was waiting for the signature of the Treaty of Edinburgh."

She replied, at once, with no sign of confusion, "The decision, at the time, was not in my hands. I had to obey my husband."

At these words there rose before the eyes of the Ambassador the miserable figure of the little dead King, a sixteen-year-old boy, with his stammering speech and face of greenish pallor. There, before him, sat a lovely young woman, glowing with health, will and spirit, like a tempered blade of finest steel, at once supple and strong, thirsting for great deeds. But he knew that it was the part of wisdom to make things easy for the future neighbour of his native land. And she seemed ready to meet him. "Am I not now hastening home, to settle all points of difference as speedily as possible?"

"Your Majesty is now entirely free to do what seems good to you."

"Mr. Ambassador, I am a Queen. Does the Treaty touch me only or my realm too? Must I consult my Estates, or no?"

"The Scottish Estates are parties to this Treaty. Is it to be assumed that they will now resist it?"

"My Estates!" replied Mary. "They seem to me rather my rebels." She rose to be nearer to the Ambassador, and bent her large, finely cut face more confidentially to him. "What has the Queen, your mistress, suddenly got against me?" she asked, smiling at him. "With the best will in the world, I go to meet her, and, then, all at once . . . ! Speak openly," she pressed him. He took the hint.

"Your Majesty, how can my Queen help being suspicious and irate? Your Grace knows the reason only too well. Immediately on the news of the death of Queen Mary of England—indeed almost before it had arrived—did not Your Majesty and your husband, as Dauphin of France, assume the arms of England everywhere, quarter them with your own on all your bearings and decorations, and even on the gold and silver of your table and on the coinage? How could any one regard this as anything but a declaration to all the world that France does not recognize my Queen as legitimate ruler of England? that, on the contrary, it accepts your claims to the English throne? Could a greater injury be done to a Queen, in this case to my Sovereign? The world expected to see France, as soon as it had the means, or merely imagined itself to have them, declaring war on us, and endeavouring to win for its Queen, who already wore the two crowns of Scotland and of France, a third, that of England. Your Majesty, we have suffered too much, in our wars of succession, and in wars with France,—it is all quite fresh, the traces are everywhere—how long ago is it since Calais was reft from us? . . ."

The Queen interrupted him. "Oh, Sir Nicholas! must you always go back to that?" Her face broke into a brilliant smile: graciousness radiated from her. "Are you still there?" Then, continuing, "I certainly did quarter the English arms with mine. But ever so long ago now, so soon indeed as I saw that there was a real storm about it, they were taken out again everywhere. And, when I assumed them, I was even less free than at the time of the Edinburgh Treaty. . . . For then, my father-in-law stood over me—how could I ever think of resisting him?" Her smile was yet more friendly. "True, I did not try, for to speak quite frankly, I saw nothing in the whole affair. Ever so many people, I know, who are by no means as near to the throne of England as I, always use the arms. I am entitled to do so, before every one of them, except your Queen. Or perhaps I am not next of kin to your Queen, Sir Nicholas?" Eagerly she proceeded to narrate, to herself as much as to him: "My grandmother was sister to King Henry, your Queen's father, and unless I have been wrongly informed, his eldest sister. So, if there be any one beside the Queen of England who is entitled to bear the English arms, who is it, if not I?" She paused; he must know that she had meant no wrong. "Please, do not imagine us so silly as to think of advertising such claims, if we had really harboured them, long before there was even

the shadow of a possibility of carrying them into effect!"
Finally, "No, no—let any one who has got excited about that,
calm himself. If we assumed the arms, it was only because they
looked well."

Throgmorton came back to his point—if so, why not now
sign the Treaty of Edinburgh?

"Your Majesty's envoys concluded it. England faithfully
fulfils all the conditions: withdraws its troops from Scotland,
urges peace upon the Scottish nobles—and then, when England
has loyally disarmed, the Treaty is not ratified!"

"Sir Nicholas," replied Mary, "I now appeal to your sense
of justice. What does the Treaty lay down? That I am to
renounce, on my own behalf and on that of my posterity, the
right to bear the English arms. Mr. Ambassador, that is mon-
strous; our plenipotentiaries ought not to have signed. If they
did so, they committed a grave error, that we must not repeat.
What if we were to be the only person in the world with the
right, nay, the sacred duty of bearing these arms? bearing
them high, before all the world? What then? We are, of our
own free will, to have abandoned that right—a right, clear as
daylight in the eyes of all men, in the eyes of God? And you
ask me here and now to settle this question? I am quite alone
here; all my relations are far away, as well you know. . . .
I know that the Queen, your sovereign, thinks more of the
friendship of my rebels than she does of mine. It has pleased
her to foster and encourage disorder in my country. Now"—
Mary raised her small head proudly—"she does this to us. I
know, and she knows, that if I wanted to, I could easily do
the same for her, in her country. If she relies on my Protestants, why should I not turn to her Catholics?"

Throgmorton endeavoured to assure her that his Queen really
had none but the most benevolent and cousinly feelings for the
Scottish ruler. Mary would find her by far her truest friend.

"So it appears," replied the Queen. "Well, we shall see."
At the close of the interview she remarked that she certainly
hoped that the wind would not cast her on the English coast.

"If it does, then your Queen will have it in her power to do what she pleases with me. Should she then be hard-hearted enough to desire my destruction, she can do what she will: she can sacrifice me to her temper. Monarchs must face such dangers. Peradventure that casualty might be better for me than to live!" Her lips trembled; tears sprang to her eyes. She still strove to present an appearance of proud assurance; then, giving way, she said, looking into his clever face with a childlike expression:

"My heart is very heavy, Mr. Ambassador." Then, with another effort after self-command, "In this matter, God's will be done."

★

A few days after this conversation, Mary was on the high seas. Queen Elizabeth was all friendliness; the Ambassador was sent to convey her wishes that her neighbour might escape all the perils of the journey home. Of what, if not of herself, was she thinking, in using such words?

Every week, after that, messengers passed between the Scottish and the English Queen, bearing presents, portraits of the one to the other, letters.

Yet one Queen would not sign the Treaty of Edinburgh, and the other would not drop it.

Finally, Mary wrote:

"If only, my good sister, you could bring yourself to believe that there is no one whom you could so well take to your great heart, and to a place by your side, as myself! But I have not, and cannot have, the right to renounce such precedence. For my own and my country's sake, for the sake of all for which I am responsible, I may not do it. Above all, not for your own sake."

Mary begged her:

"Will you appoint new plenipotentiaries to reconsider this unfortunate Treaty? Gladly will my heart submit in everything

63

to your insight and wisdom. The most careful scrutiny can but establish the fact that my submission seeks nothing but your rights."

Whereupon Queen Elizabeth temporarily remitted the question.

★

Maitland of Lethington came to London as ambassador from the Scottish Queen, and there went about among great and small, informing every one who was willing to listen to the following effect:

"Hitherto, England has always had to fight on two fronts. France was always a source of alarm, and Scotland hung over it like a cloud. Scotland owes its powerful position as a Kingdom exclusively to the fact that it is the gate to England." A note of pathos crept into Maitland's voice, as he went on, "Could the two peoples realize the blessing conferred upon them by the fact that they and they alone dwell on this isolated island, they would become, once and for all, so long as man can move only over earth or water, completely unassailable. There would be an end to fear of the power of France, no matter how strong. Spain could do nothing. It could only look helplessly on, while England and Scotland, united in Britain, sent their ships wherever they chose."

Queen Elizabeth knew all about these speeches. She made a wry face, drew herself up as though thereby to add an ell to her stature, and said, scornfully, "Must these people be for ever ringing the death's knell in my ears?" How old was she at this time? Not yet thirty. She said to Lethington, "Why should I not marry and produce maybe a dozen children?" He bowed profoundly. Obviously, such a decision and such a contingency would settle every question, and that in the happiest possible fashions. His mistress, in such an event, would only have her heartiest felicitations to offer. But Her Majesty had, hitherto, felt the independence of complete isolation as the only condition that suited her. Were she to continue in that mind,—then, in such event, his mistress permitted herself to recall to her her love, her loyalty, and her rights.

James Stuart also put in his word. He knew Queen Elizabeth of old, since he had carried through the negotiations between her and the rebel Lords before the return of his ruler. He wrote to London:

"Here are Your Majesty and the Queen, my mistress, closely related one to the other, both in the bloom of your years, of close resemblance in many admirable qualities poured out richly on both by God as gifts of fortune and of blood, both belonging to a sex that forbids you to gain fame through war and bloodshed but rather reminds you constantly that the fame of a Government consists mainly in the welfare of its people."

He went on to declare how deeply he regretted that his mistress should ever have given the Queen of England any grounds for mistrust:

"But for this alienation, I am convinced that you might have been as good friends as you are close relations. But since things have fallen out as they did at a time when both kingdoms were involved in war against each other, I fear lest there may be no real mutual confidence unless the evil be plucked up by the roots. Your Majesty cannot yield. To my sovereign it may well seem hard that she should be shut out of England as a stranger, when the kinship in blood is so close. Could a middle way of dealing with points of difference be discovered, we might all be at perfect peace. This has long been in my mind, but hitherto I have not ventured to put my plan before my sovereign, or any of my countrymen. Nor shall I pursue it further than may please Your Majesty. The problem is certainly too great for my understanding to grasp. And yet, perhaps Your Majesty's wisdom could build my modest proposal to authentic greatness! I venture, therefore, to lay it before you, and to ask whether there are insuperable obstacles in the way of Your Majesty's claims remaining altogether intact, for yourself and the heirs of your body, while it was provided that the Queen, my ruler, was assured of her legitimate place in the succession to the throne of England? Your Majesty will permit me to point out that by the law of every country my sovereign is the next descendant after yourself of King Henry Seventh, your grandfather. Supposing that, in the interim, this island were to be united by an eternal bond of friendship. The succession to its throne is regulated by God's appointment, and no human resolves can alter His purposes. It seems, however, as though, without any disadvantage of any kind, such an understanding would produce great tranquillity. Everything in the world must have its beginning. So soon as I hear from Your Majesty, that you could admit the idea of such an understanding, I shall begin to discuss the matter with the Queen, my sovereign, in the endeavour to move her to make all feasible concessions. If, however, Your Majesty cannot approve my plan, I shall drop it at once."

Meantime, Mr. Randolph, Queen Elizabeth's Ambassador, was passing his time pleasantly in Edinburgh. Every one at Court fed him with roses and lollipops. The Queen, a gracious and lovely apparition, was all friendliness. Confidentially she said: "It does not concern me whether or no you write to your mistress, but, if and when you write, you must be sure to put right in the front the warmth of my feeling for her. Outside of her I have no one belonging to me, and I simply long to be able to let myself feel the nearness of our kinship. Be sure, I beg you, to write to her in this sense. I write so; but she should hear it from every one. Soon I must see and speak with her, or else I shall never feel myself at home." Mary's burning eyes expressed her impatience. At court she spoke of the Queen's marriage as an event that must certainly take place, saying, with a little sigh, "If I could, Mr. Randolph, I should choose the Queen of England for my spouse, her and no one else." Mr. Randolph bowed to the ground; when he rose again, his eyes were burning in his earth-coloured countenance like little black glass buttons. Since marriage in the full sense was out of the question, neighbourliness in the full sense there should be, he assured her, his hand on his heart. A smile hovered over the Queen's lips.

James Stuart and Lord Lethington sought the Englishman out. Lord Lethington said: "For the country's sake it is of the last importance that she soon see and speak with the Queen of England: indeed, for that of the entire island, in so far as religion is an important question for England too. Unfortunately it is but too true that she will never come to God unless the Queen of England, through conversation with her, can convince her of the truth. She alone can do it," he added, "since she as Queen alone understands fully the nature of such a conviction. She ought to do it, since to do so is in her own interest."

★

There was great excitement at the Scottish court, for Queen Elizabeth had agreed to meet her sister sovereign face to face. The Queen of Scotland was to come to England, so it was reported, with a great suite.

At the end of August, a little more than a year after Queen Mary had returned to her own country, the Scottish court was ready to set out.

Mary came, with her ladies, to inspect the garments that, at her own expense, she had had made by her French tailors for herself and the whole of her immediate entourage. She walked about, in and out of the trestles and tables, stopping here and there, examining, feeling, surveying, giving instructions for an alteration here and there. She seemed to be in a sort of trance of happiness. Already, she saw herself in these lovely, costly dresses, draperies, veils, and could not imagine anything in the world more perfect than she would then be in form, in colour, in bearing, in movement. Her own garments she had ordered in black, grey, lilac and white. Her friends, however, were to shine in the loveliest colours. Every lady was to have five new dresses for each day. Gravely, the Queen remarked, "All this of course costs a great deal of money. But what of that? We must all look very beautiful and elegant."

Such talk was interrupted by the announcement of a fresh envoy from the Queen of England. What could he be bringing but the last formal details? Mary sent him to her ministers, Maitland or James Stuart. How glad she was that she need no longer hasten to deal with this message! She strolled, at ease, back to her sitting-room, accompanied by her suite. There she found Maitland and James Stuart. At the sight of their grim faces, her merry greeting died on her lips. "What is it?" James Stuart looked uncomfortably at his sister. He could not speak, and motioned to Lethington to do so. He reported that the Queen of England had sent to say that the religious war, stirred up by the Guises and again raging with fearsome intensity in France, made it impossible for the Queen of England to contemplate leaving her capital even for the shortest time, still less moving northwards with her Cabinet, and leaving her country defenceless against an attack from the south.

Mary heard the one thing she had set her heart upon, had looked forward to, expected miracles from, refused. On top of refusal came the blank insult—"Look at your relations!" Hidden in its terms was the further suggestion: "You are like them! A pretty plan of yours, to entice me away from my capital and leave the south open to treacherous attack."

Mary burst into tears. She fell sobbing on her brother's neck, seeking comfort and affection there.

By noon, she had so far collected herself as to receive the English envoy. Tears, however, compelled her to turn aside her head when she took the Queen of England's letter from his hands. There was, so he assured her, no question of abandoning the plan. The Queen of Scotland would find it set out in his mistress's detailed letter, that only the most extreme necessity could compel her to put off a visit on which her mind was so much set. Confidently, the Queen of England looked forward to next year.

Mary bent her head; unable, at the moment, to find an answer that might give the Queen of England pride for pride, she merely murmured, "Next year!"

On the following day it was announced that the Queen was going to her northern provinces in order to preside at the great Days of Law there, as had been the custom of her mother.

★

On a lovely still summer evening, when the waters of Edinburgh were singing in their deep beds under flowering elder trees, two young men, accompanied by a couple of servitors, strolled through the streets of the city towards the palace. The taller of the two was Sir John Gordon, younger son of the Earl of Huntly, the Chancellor of Scotland. He chatted with his friend and cousin, also a Gordon, telling him to have a dagger like his own made for him by an Italian merchant, recently come to Edinburgh in the retinue of the Ambassador of Savoy. Without stopping, he drew out the hilt of the weapon, hanging by his side, a little from its sheath, so that his friend might look at it; the latter, bending forward, was just in the act of feeling it when a door opened in a house they were just passing and a young man burst out so suddenly that his face was driven right into the chest of John Gordon, who was more than commonly tall. Both fell back a pace, reeling from the sudden collision. They stood, involuntarily breathing hard, staring at each other. Recognition followed: Gordon, with his superb height and carriage, drew himself up proudly, in his supple black silk jerkin. A smile of supreme arrogance crossed his pallid countenance, surmounted by its thick waves of bright, curling hair. He was turning to pass on without a word. The other, however, Sir James Ogilvy, a young man with brown hair and alert movements, was evidently beside himself with rage. His words tumbled over each other as he hissed, in Gordon's face, "You, you . . . son of a dog! Son of a traitor, and bigger traitor yourself! You . . . you . . . !" He cast about him for fresh insults. Gordon controlled himself, but every nerve was taut, his hand was on his dagger's hilt: there was a quiver of his proud nostrils, his expression said—Worm! I have but to raise my hand. . . . But I will spare you once again. But Ogilvy threw himself upon him, shouting, "You, you viper! You horse-thief! You pimp! What have you done with my inheritance, my estates?" A few minutes later he lay wounded, his blood splashed over the plaster, stretched to all appearance lifeless upon the ground. Gordon wiped his blade, before returning it carefully to its scabbard. "As you see, it is serviceable": he said to his companion. The other plucked at his arm. "Are you mad? Let us be off." Gordon raised his eyes to his friend's horrified face, and smiled. He glanced at the wounded man at his feet, over whom a squire was bending; shrugging his shoulders, he turned to go proudly on his way. Meantime, the squire's yells of "Murder!" had drawn a crowd out of the houses. It grew every minute. The young man attempted to raise his master's head, which drooped, white and deathly, as though it had been severed; then, letting it fall again, he tried to staunch the wounds, from which blood poured in a flood between his fingers. "My God, my God, he is dying." "No use troubling about him," observed one of the crowd, sadly. "Help! Help!" blubbered the lad. Several people knelt by him. Some one said, "A doctor lives over there." They carried off the wounded man.

Gordon pursued his way rapidly. "Shall you go away at once?" his friend ventured to ask, anxiously. "I must get horses," he replied. They went, quickly, silently, to Gordon's castle in the High Street; from outside almost windowless, as though barricaded. The knight crossed the courtyard, in order to tell the squires in the court to saddle: he intended to start in a quarter of an hour. He was going to see his father, he told his friend. He, like the other, thought only of how, before midnight, he could be safe in his father's territory, where the word or beck of a Gordon was the only law. Thence, if his opponent were really dead, he could go for a space to France; after a year, he could come back, and there would be no more unpleasantness. Soon, he had come out from the dark hall into the fortified court again. Overhead, in the pale summer sky, a few stars glistened, looking unnaturally large in the vague twilight. The squires were mounted in readiness. Gordon's cousin, who took it for granted that he should accompany him, led out his steed. Gordon remarked, "I am sorry for Jean. She was with my father above. She said nothing, but she was as pale as the moon." He shrugged his shoulders, "Anyhow, hers was a hopeless case." His hand on the horse's crupper, his foot already in the stirrup, he was in the act of mounting, when a detachment of soldiers marched firmly into the yard. Gordon gave a start; he came down from his horse, and met the leader of the troop with perfect courtesy. Standing, in order to lay his hand on him, the latter said, "In the Queen's name." Gordon turned, half-laughing, to his friend. "Unprecedented punctuality for Scotland!" Calmly he let the soldiers surround him. He was made prisoner in the castle.

A few weeks later, when Ogilvy, at first given up by the surgeons, had recovered save for a trifling lameness of his right arm, William Gordon, friend and cousin of Sir John, received a message, from the prisoner, transmitted to him by a secret messenger. Therein stood written—After gaining great benefits from the strict diet and perfect quiet of his present place of abode, he now thought it desirable to change it, since it would be a mistake to spoil such priceless advantages by excessive use. He was entirely at his friend's disposition, and would await his trusty cousin and companion at five o'clock of the afternoon of the same day, at a certain spot on the northward route.

★

Queen Mary held court with brilliant state in her city of Aberdeen. Some three thousand soldiers lay in the houses, in readiness to accompany the Queen on her journeys to the Highlands. The Scottish nobles gathered, in numbers increasing daily, from the valleys and the Lowlands. Thomas Randolph was in her suite and John Knox accompanied her.

To Aberdeen came Elizabeth, Countess of Huntly, to invite the Queen to Strathbogie, the seat of the Gordons. The Countess was a powerfully built, dark-complexioned woman, with a blackish shadow along her upper lip; she looked like a ruler who had never experienced anything but obedience to every command. She was accustomed to travel with a retinue almost equal to the Queen's, and, if she went out at night into the town, forty torch-bearers lighted her way.

Now she came almost like a Princess welcoming a young neighbour-sister to her territory, with a zeal motived rather by the youth of the visitor than anything in the nature of fear or a sense of dutiful respect. But in Aberdeen, hitherto regarded by her, as by every one else, and, above all, by its inhabitants, as the capital of her own realm, she met the insult of her life. She approached the Queen, ready to give her greeting and homage; Mary turned away, as though nothing but air occupied the space where the Countess was in the act of bowing to the ground. Astounded, hardly mistress of her thoughts, as though the voices of angels had thundered in her ears the collapse of all things in earth and heaven, blind to the averted eyes of the courtiers, who turned away, as if the proud dame had just been smitten by the plague, the Countess moved heavily to one side. Then, taking the hand of the Countess of Argyle, the Queen's illegitimate sister, who risked doing what Maitland of Lethington, Lord Arthur Erskine, and other former friends of the Gordons, refused with confused smiles to attempt, the Countess of Huntly once more endeavoured to approach the Queen. Mary was standing in friendly conversation with Mr. Randolph. Her cheerful expression was transformed to a freezing chill as the two ladies drew near. She was about to turn away again, ignoring the Countess; when her sister boldly addressed her: "Your Majesty, the Countess of Huntly would fain have you graciously turn your eyes upon her!" Elizabeth Huntly almost prostrated herself before the young Queen. "If Your Majesty would do us the honour . . . if . . . Your Grace . . . on Your Majesty's way . . . our castle of Strath-

72

bogie . . . all that our modest house can offer, all, all that we possess . . . for Your Majesty . . . Your Majesty will not pass us by. . . ." The expression of her dark eyes, anxiously seeking some trace of amiable softness in Mary's face, suddenly gathered firmness; she remembered her dignity. "Your Majesty will not so far insult your most faithful servants as to scorn the simple hospitality of our house!" she said, in a voice whose tones shook and rumbled with desperate injury. But Mary's gentle face showed only an immovable resolution. "Countess Huntly," she said, coldly, "it cannot be. Your son, Sir John, after depriving poor Sir James Ogilvy of his patrimony and then nigh killing him, has broken out of his imprisonment and scornfully derides all demands on him to submit to our pleasure. It is impossible for us to enter a house which is under our royal ban." Turning, she took James Stuart's arm and passed on, paying no heed to the Countess, who stood biting her lips with shame and pain.

Next morning, Queen Mary was sitting in her chamber, occupied with fine embroidery, seated in the niche of the window with the Countess of Argyle. In the background, the four Maries were amusing themselves by playing draughts. Mary Fleming left them and came over to the Queen in order to hear what she and Jean of Argyle were saying. Mary's brows were bent; she said, as if unwillingly, to her sister, "So, you will not stop worrying me? You know it cannot be, and yet leave me no peace. I can do nothing. Even if I wanted to, a thousand times! Sir John must go back to prison. That is as clear as day to everybody. What do they think? Am I to be made mock of?" She sat lost in thought.

"It is too gross a sin, to deprive a son of his patrimony!"

"Old Ogilvy hates James," the Countess retorted.

Mary started back, as if to imply that she could not have rightly understood.

"A father hates his own son? But that is too much. That cannot be. He has no right to do that. All the saints in heaven will cry out against him." She spoke eagerly. "And why does

he hate him? Has he any rational reason? Has the poor young
man committed a sin? Even if he had, his father ought not to
deprive him of his inheritance; the father, after all, did not
acquire, he only inherited it, and should keep it in the family.
But, really, no one knows anything against Sir James. The
fact is, his father took a Gordon for his second wife. That is his
crime. For now, of course, all that he has and is go to them."
Crimson with excitement, Mary sat up very erect on her chair
and gazed with serious reproof at her much older sister: she
herself looked extraordinarily young in the eager zeal that red-
dened her cheeks and lips and made her eyes shine with twice
their normal brightness. "Have not these Gordons got enough
already? Take this town—luckily I brought three thousand
soldiers with me! otherwise I should not get a single plate of
soup, except by favour of his grace the Earl of Huntly and his
mighty lady, the Countess!" She drew a deep breath. "Sir
John must absolutely give back all he has seized contrary to
right human and divine. Then we shall see. Not till then."

She ceased, full of confident pride.

Mary Fleming came to the Countess of Argyle's aid. "Poor
Jean Gordon is worn to a shadow. Jean Gordon and James
Ogilvy were on the point of being betrothed!"

Mary turned sharply. "Did Jean Gordon ask you to speak
for her?"

"Oh, no; she would bite her tongue out first. But her looks—
she looks as though she had passed through the seven years of
hunger and misery—she can't help them, poor girl!"

The Queen sat thinking. The others watched her, tense.

"You are all very unreasonable," she said, reddening with
anger. "It seems that I am to hear naught but this wretched
story: it is dinned into my ears, by one set of you on the left
and by the other on the right. One set say: Oh, obviously you
must have pity—such faithful servants, all being destroyed!
You cannot be inhuman to them! Then come the others: By
the Blood of Christ! This accursed race! These Gordons! Who
is Sovereign in this land? You? It seems more like Earl Huntly!

You don't see how they mock at you! How much heed did Sir John pay to your commands? . . . I can do nothing," she repeated, excitedly. "If John Gordon appears—then I will see."

"That he will never do," replied Mary Fleming, coolly.

"Let the devil take him, then!" Mary burst out. She rose and stood up, strongly moved, before her women. "I am to ask his pardon, because I was so presumptuous as to have him arrested? For such a trifle, too, as his half killing young Ogilvy, after taking his entire patrimony from him? Let Jean Gordon be grateful to her brother!" She strode up and down, and then stopped, in front of the others. "Of course," she said, "I have but to do what they tell me to, and then they will praise me, and say, What a gracious Queen! But there are five, six, ten, a dozen, no, a hundred, all standing there shrieking, Give! Give to me! Only to me! I am your loyal servant! I alone! All the others are traitors! Horrible people! Ruffians! Rogues! Give! Give all you have, all, all! Even so, it is not enough. You are a Queen! Give your robes, your throne, your garments! Still, you have your honour! Give that. Give! They laugh, and say: Look, she is unfit to wear the crown, is not she? Let us kill her." Mary's chin trembled with anger. "That is what they have always done: Who has found loyalty in them? Whom have they not destroyed?"

The ladies were silent. They all knew the fearsome history of the Stuart house, treachery on every page.

Even better, however, did they know John Gordon, first of the young knights of Scotland, who had danced with the Queen the whole winter through, while she smiled into his handsome face. His father was the most powerful man in Scotland. He owned almost a third of the kingdom. His people belonged to him; he had but to say, "I would know that man dead" and the enemy lay bleeding at his feet. He was the head of the Catholic party. And her women thought: What she has been saying does not all come from her. She must love the Gordons, because they too are Catholics. But she has been taught her lesson, and so well taught that, for the moment, she believes it herself.

And bitter wrath rose in the women's hearts against the man whom they saw as the creator of this evil anger of Mary's; in all their hearts, although Lord James Stuart and the Countess of Argyle were brother and sister of the same father and mother.

Mary, standing at the window, gazing out with unseeing eyes, suddenly turned, her face blanched, her brows drawn together, her lips tightly compressed, and moved towards her bedchamber without another word. The door closed behind her.

"There is nothing to be done, I know," said Mary Fleming, into the dim silence. A bell rang in the Queen's room; Mary Seaton, who was on duty, answered it. She returned within a brief space. The Queen wished to ride forth. The English Ambassador and Lord James were to be informed she wished their company.

Jean Argyle could only tell Countess Huntly, who was waiting in her own house to hear, that she would do well to leave the town of Aberdeen to the Queen, and make with all speed for her mountains.

★

Silently, in the mists of a heavy October afternoon, the Queen's forces marched, with her at their head, through the Northern Highlands, following the deep mountain glens. Throughout the march, they did not meet a single soul, not a shepherd boy on the hills, not a fisherman by the shores of the lochs among them. Loneliness lay behind the Queen's army: loneliness ahead: a loneliness hardly broken by the cry of a bird. Nothing but the sturdy little mountain sheep, with black legs and little black faces, cropping silently among the heather. The army went by Strathbogie, the seat of the Gordons, and left it dark and rejected on one side. The scouts in the van knew that danger might lurk in every bush, and behind every hillside. The savages dwelling in these glens hardly knew the Queen's name. They spoke a language Mary did not understand, which hardly sounded to her like human speech; they had no conception of civilization, and their notions of law were bounded by what had been taught them by their chieftain, the Earl of Huntly, whom they called by another name. Their code was primitive; for them there was the clan to which a man belonged: it was courageous to allow oneself to be cut to pieces for a fellow-clansman: his death must, at any cost, be avenged: if one avenger perished, three, five or ten would step forward in his place: to do so was the highest duty. They owned no King or Queen, only the chieftain of the clan. He now was threatened by a hostile power. Mary was informed that, in these regions, the word of Earl Huntly alone stood for peace and security. She shrugged her shoulders. "Three thousand! We have three thousand soldiers. Surely they can deal with a handful of half-starving Highlanders!"

One of the lords who happened to be at her side said, "Except that, here, Huntly's people know every inch of ground. What do we know of these mountains, which, anyhow, we dare not penetrate? The very fact that there are so many of us may be a danger in so narrow a space."

"Forward!" said the Queen, "I am not afraid."

The troops went on, thinking that the Queen was afraid of nothing because she did not know what she was about and that all one could do was to pray that Huntly might be either so stupid or so friendly-disposed as to believe in the Queen's favour and hold her good will as worth more to him than a *coup de main:* for, in these mountains, at the head of his clans, to attempt would be, for him, to succeed.

At night, the Queen slept in Kinloss Abbey, in the heart of the Highlands; next day, she held her Assize in the great hall of the castle of Tarnaway, the chief fortress of the region. She sat in the high seat at the table, with her ministers round her —all there, save only the Lord Chancellor, Lord Huntly. The hall where they sat was the largest in Scotland. From the far end, the table, with the Queen and the great ones seated at it, seemed a mere speck in the distance; a thousand armed men could gather in that hall.

Lord James Stuart once more presented the plaint of Lord Ogilvy against the clan Gordon. Elizabeth Gordon, a niece of the Earl of Huntly, had, as a young woman, become the second wife of Lord Ogilvy of Finlater and Deskford, and soon acquired such an ascendancy over the more or less imbecile old man that, without rhyme or reason, he disinherited his rightful heir, the sole offspring of his first marriage, a young man deserving well of God and man. In his place he set Sir John Gordon, and to make matters worse, he gave him the property in question at a rental in his own lifetime. Lord James declared that, despite all kinds of pressure from various quarters, he had, at first, definitely refused to raise the matter as a complainant because he might seem to be an interested party. Now, however, Sir John Gordon himself, by conduct of such unexampled insolence as set morals and every code human and divine at defiance, had made any further patience simply impossible. Documents were laid before the Queen to prove facts: a copy of old Ogilvy's will and of his son's protest against it, and depositions as to the fight between the two young men. The Queen signed an order of her Council commanding Sir John Gordon, on pain of being held guilty of high treason, to hand over unconditionally to the Queen's representatives the castle of Finlater and Deskford as well as all other properties belonging to the Ogilvy-Finlater estate which had been seized by him.

As much as could, at this stage, be effected in the matter was therewith done. It was now for the Gordons to choose between peace and war. The Queen rose; all those present stood up. They stood, expecting some ceremonial; something very important was to occur. The clerk at the other end of the high table took up a scroll, and read aloud from it, addressing James, Earl of Stuart and Mar. In view of his great loyalty and incomparable services both to the person of the Queen, and the state and realm of Scotland, Her Majesty was pleased to confer on her brother the Earldom of Murray, for long, without just claim or right, seized by the Earl of Huntly. Now, however, it was the Queen's will that the estate should enjoy a new lease of prosperity—under the wise rule of the Earl of Mar, who, from today on, was Earl of Murray. The Earl approached his sister, in order to kneel down before her. She invested him with his new dignities, said Mary, in order that he might take the oath of allegiance as Earl of Murray. "Swear to me on your knees to protect, defend and guard, with all your powers, with total abnegation of all thought of personal advantage, with all you are and have, even unto death, my sovereign rank, my realm and my person, chosen by the grace of God, from every danger from without and from within, remembering always that all the good enjoyed by you in this life comes to you solely by the grace of the Queen whom God has set to rule over you." The Earl repeated the oath, his folded palms enclosed between her warm ones, saying: "In the name of Almighty God, and the precious Blood of His Son, through which alone forgiveness can be extended to us sinners, may I be looked upon as the last of all detestable and ungrateful traitors to all times now and to come if I do not, so far as strength of body and soul is graciously granted unto me, devote the last drop of my blood and breath of my body not only to guard, protect and defend the Queen, my Sovereign, but rather seek out in advance any and every danger that may threaten her sacred head and ward it off from her." Thrice repeated Earl James: "So I swear, so may the Blessed Trinity be merciful to my soul." Thrice did Mary press his hands between her soft, delicate palms. Then she released him, to hand over to him the commission which, signed and sealed, lay there establishing the Earl as new Lord over the rich Earldom of Murray, which included the Castle of Tarnaway.

★

Three days later, the Queen, the royal troops and all the Scottish nobles had reached the far north of Scotland, where the mountains run down into wild forests, and stood before Inverness, one of the chief strongholds of the Earl of Huntly. Mary drew up her horse before the drawbridge of the castle.

Like all her companions, she was mired to the waist. They had a frightful ride, hours long across a completely trackless country, through morasses, over stony moors, through wild forests, by the side of precipices, along deserted lochs. Mary seemed beside herself. "Storm!" she cried, raising her hand against the barricaded door. "We are in superior strength. Within an hour, we must be in the castle. Is Earl Huntly King of Scotland? He refuses us entry to his castle? He has nothing of his own! But for our favour, he is a beggar!" Still on horseback, she stood aside while her troops prepared, by torchlight, to break through the neglected moat to the gate with axes and hatchets. The captain of the castle, another Gordon, Alexander by name, had refused the Queen admission, when, towards evening, she came out of the woods at the head of her troops. He had no orders from his master. Without his permission, no one might enter the castle. Mary rode restlessly to and fro, stimulating her men. In her excitement, she talked incessantly. "We cannot fail. My brave fellows! The gate is nothing: it is mere child's play. Far too easy for us; it is hardly worth while; how many have they got within? Not twenty men! Oh, ho, they had no idea that we should jump on them so swiftly!" She stretched and reared. "Oh, if only I were a man! Then I should put on harness and spend the night in the field!" Actually, the ineffective resistance from the castle was soon broken. Within an hour, the drawbridge went creaking down. The troops poured over it. By the light of the smoky flames of torches flaring against the darkness of the immemorially aged towers, the Queen rode into the courtyard, against whose walls the soldiers had ranged themselves, with raised lances, so thick that the stone of the walls were almost hidden by them. The captain was brought before her; she addressed him, in furious wrath: "Sir, you have dared to forbid my entry? This is rebellion, rebellion, Sir Captain! You must have known what you were doing?" At midnight, after a hastily summoned council of war, the man was hanged; his severed head stood on a pike over the gate when, on the following morning, Mary left the place, henceforth to serve as a royal fortress.

Mary returned to Aberdeen, unmolested, protected by her three thousand, although the reports of the judgment she had executed flew round her route like a swarm of ravens. In striking down Alexander Gordon she had struck at the whole of the eastern Highlands; therefore she was now in enemy territory. Who would conquer? The Queen was told that every rock on the way might hide an ambush of Sir John Gordon's, who had sworn that he would have her in his power, though it might cost him a year without sleep in bed. Mary established herself in Aberdeen, in order to prevent the Gordons from making the town an effective stronghold of their own. While the lengthening nights threatened to extinguish altogether the pale light of day, she held great festivities, prepared for her by the troubled people of the city, and attended by every one who wanted to display his fidelity in these threatening times. Meantime heralds were sent through all the land proclaiming that George Gordon, Earl of Huntly, must within eight days present himself before the Queen's Majesty, there to answer for his deeds. If he did not do so, his name would be affixed to the pillory, and he, in punishment of his defiance of the royal power, would be deprived of all his titles, properties and friends, and compelled by force of arms to obedience.

This summons was the reply to a fresh stroke of John Gordon's. Furiously disappointed that the Queen had escaped him, as every one in the land was well aware, he had stormed Finlater, the castle handed over to him by old Ogilvy, where the Queen's representative was just installed. There, the Gordons were this time in superior force, and their violence successful. There was an attempt at defence, and some dozen of the Queen's men fell. Gordon took the leaders prisoner, commandeered all the weapons of the troops and, taking the Queen's captain in his train, departed again before so much as the news of his assault had reached the camp of the enemy. The Queen was on fire: she would show this high handed fellow that there was nothing even for him but obedience to her will.

Old Huntly behaved as if he had not so much as heard the summons to appear. Thereupon the order of obedience was posted on the stocks in Edinburgh, Aberdeen, and every other town of importance in Scotland. The Queen issued the call to arms. Soldiers were called up; the man who enlisted under his Sovereign's colours was assured of every care for his dependents and tax exemption for several years. For him, however, who raised his sword against his Queen in accursed rebellion, there was to be no mercy for life or limb.

Earl Huntly gathered his power together; the Queen put her troops in the field. On October 22nd, 1562, the two sides were so near each other that they knew if they remained where they were battle must be joined on the morrow. Who would conquer?

In Scotland, rebel nobles had often ere this seen their King vanquished. On the other hand, their Sovereign had often before rushed down upon them like a volcano. The armies were drawn up on either bank of the Corrichie burn, with a wide valley still lying between them. Mary herself awaited the issue in Aberdeen. Her forces were commanded by the Earl of Murray. A main division of the army was commanded by Lords Forbes, Hay and Leslie who, so it was believed, loved Huntly dearer than they did Murray.

The old Earl, who had assigned command over the various detachments of his six to eight hundred men to his two elder sons, George and John, and other young Gordons, had entrenched himself on the hills on the far side of the burn. On the night before the morning fixed for the battle, the old man said that he would prefer to retire and submit, with all his people, to the Queen's mercy. Nothing so very terrible would be done to them. The younger men, whom he had summoned to a council of war in his tent, replied to this speech only by a bleak silence. Whereupon he asked them what their mind was. Even if they were victorious on the morrow, what then? "Father," said Lord George, the eldest son, "we all know that the question now is,

Shall Scotland be heretic or Catholic?" Another, Alexander by
name, added, "Tomorrow we shall hold the field. Fifty will
come over, with all their following. The Queen will rejoice: she
may then show us what is really in her heart. For the rest—we
are up against the preaching of heresy—yes. At bottom you
know well the Mother of God may well have found much to displease her. And hitherto she has always shown her influence,
when she wanted to. So it is." No one answered him. The men
sat brooding over their plans, wishes and chances, until old
Huntly rose from his seat. He was going to bed: they needed all
their strength for the morrow. He departed. Before his tent two
pipers had for some time been marching up and down, sending
the war chant of the Gordons out into the night in the shrill
tones of the pibroch.

The old Earl slept long. Morning was fully broken before
they could rouse him up out of the sleep that lay like an en-
chantment on him. On the news that some of his friends had
gone over to the other side, he replied confusedly. "Men often
think of their own advantage," he muttered. He would bear no
one ill will for that, no one, no one. No one could judge another.
He looked with vacant eyes at the face of the man busy putting
on his armour. "Otherwise, otherwise, otherwise," he whispered,
hardly moving his lips, as though talking to himself. The man
asked him, stammering, what it was he wished otherwise? Then
he realized the words were not addressed to him: his chieftain
was as though in another world.

When the Earl reached the crest of the hill to marshal his
men, he was in full possession of himself again. His three sons,
including the youngest, a pretty, sixteen-year-old lad, came to
him; all of them, even Sir John who, as a rule, wore none but
French attire, were in Highland garb, short kilts in the blue and
green tartan of their clan, plaids of the same over their shoulders, fastened with jewelled brooches set in silver. Many of the
soldiers were armed with bow and arrow: others carried
hatchets and axes.

The old Earl reviewed the enemy position. That great mass

of men, rapidly approaching from over there, was not to be feared, he said, as he raised his hand to point to it. Hay and Leslie were leading: so far, so good. But behind them, in that small dark cloud, there might lurk a thunderbolt. "There is James Stuart, hatching his serpent's eggs. But"—he turned, to measure his own host—"we are enough for him, and God will be with us." His mail, worn under his plaid, rattled as he knelt down and raised both hands to heaven. "Lord, I have, I know, been a bloodthirsty tyrant, and much innocent blood has flowed on my account. But if Thou wilt give me victory today, I will serve Thee henceforth, all the days of my life."

His infantry threw themselves down the hill, to meet the advancing foe. Dark waved the kilts; the bare knees shone white. Just before they came into collision with the enemy, the attackers swerved; the vanguard of their opponents followed them without a break, as though they were, in march, merely altering their position. The movement, however, left a clear space for the small, compact centre about the Earl of Murray, above which floated the scarlet lion, rampant on a white ground, the ensign of the House of Stuart. Earl Huntly, still on the crest of the hill, but now mounted on his horse, said, contentedly, as he watched the unresisting retreat of the vanguard, "Ah, ha! Our friends are honest men! Forward, now, at the rest!"

The enemy likewise had appealed to God, so he armed for the day. Maitland of Lethington rode beside the Earl of Murray along the front of the centre troops, who were, as every one in this camp equally well knew, the only reliable ones. Lethington exhorted each man to turn to God; each must do his duty; no one should feel afraid. Sitting on his horse, he raised his hands: "O Lord, look down on Thy servants, for whose blood unrighteousness is shrieking. Our refuge is in Thee alone, as is our hope. Speak today. O Lord, Thy judgment between us and our enemies. If ever we have unjustly sought to shed the blood of the just, let the cutting edge of the sword fall upon us. But, Lord, if Thou knowest our innocence, sustain and protect us for the sake of Thy great mercy." Thereupon the troops charged the enemy on the hill.

Huntly's troops did not stand, not even those about him and his sons. They could not cope with the better weapons and more skilful generalship of the other side: James Stuart counted as the best general in Scotland. Without deploying, he made for his goal, the old Earl himself, whom he sought to take dead or alive. The fighting became close; infantry and cavalry struggled in a dense confusion. No one could see more than an arm's length in front of him. Suddenly a shout went up in Gaelic—"The great head is dead!" Sir John fought like a lion against two horsemen, assisted later by others; he was a doughty fighter, and his fangs bit. While he was unweariedly delivering blows right and left in his defence, a horseman caught him, with catlike skill, from behind, and pinioned his arms, while the others smote his blade from his hand and threw him from his mount. Battered, wounded on the brow so that blood poured down over his eyes, they took his dirk from him, and the pistols from his belt; then led him over the battlefield, on which, after a bare quarter of an hour, the fight was now at an end. But few wounded lay there, only some two dozen, turning over groaning in the grass, or, more seriously injured, lying stark and stiff in awkward positions. Almost all the wounded were Gordons. The victor soon gathered his men together in good order. John Gordon realized that the victory of the others could hardly have been more complete, the defeat of his house hardly more pitiable. A troop of soldiers came by him, with his little brother, Adam, a prisoner. Sir John looked about him; away over the hill some of his men were still visible in flight; he recognized the blue-green of their kilts. His guards brought him past the spot where, huge, almost superhuman, the corpse of his father was lying on the short grey winter grass; at the very beginning of the fight, old Huntly, struck in the neck as though by the hand of God, had been thrown crashing from his horse. There was no visible wound. With eyes and mouth open, he lay there, his face turned to heaven. The people about

85

Sir John let him stand for a few minutes by his father's body, until he turned to them of his own accord. They led him to headquarters, and thence to Aberdeen.

The corpse of the old Earl was, in the first instance, brought thither likewise, and laid on the bare stones in a small chamber. His arms and outer garments had been taken from him, leaving only his short trews and shirt. As he lay so, covered with brine, even his enemies admitted that for power, will and sheer craftiness, Scotland had not seen his like in three hundred years. Encased in a coffin of lead, he was then brought to Edinburgh by sea, and there his coffin was set upright before the assembly that sat in judgment on him as a traitor, and proscribed his whole house and the entire clan, everything called by the name of Gordon, to outlawry. The story however passed round that his wife, who was on good terms with evil spirits, had been told by a witch on the day before the battle, that on the day after it her husband would be in the Council hall in Aberdeen without a wound in his body. When Lord James Stuart himself brought the Queen the news of the unexampled victory of her troops, which had hardly cost her six men, Mary turned very pale, and averting her eyes, at first spoke no word. On the same evening, however, she signed the order for the capture of Sir George Gordon, who was now to be regarded as the head of the clan, and who had succeeded in making his escape. This order attainted him, like all the other Gordons, of high treason. And Queen Mary did yet more. Something horrible.

★

Eight days after the encounter by the Corrichie burn, Sir John Gordon was beheaded as a high traitor in the Aberdeen marketplace. Every one in the entire region who was not afraid of being seized by the law so soon as he put his head out of his hidingplace, came for this grim hour. A detachment of soldiers stood six-deep about the place of blood, their lances held shoulder-high. A certain number of persons in authority waited by the scaffold. The executioner with his assistants stood by the black-covered block, in his hand the long, highly polished sword, which John Gordon, as a man of high birth, was entitled to have used as the instrument of death instead of axe or gallows. From the Courthouse, the Sinner's bell began to tinkle, faint and shrill, as a sign that the condemned man had started on his way to the place of judgment. The crowd, which had been swaying this way and that round the scaffold, like a heavy sea under a wind, fell quite still. They rose on tiptoe; there, from there the procession must come. Then, all at once, a great movement turned them all to the other side. All eyes were open wide. At a window in the house exactly opposite the place of blood, belonging to the Earl Marischal and, as every one knew, at present the abode of the Queen, there appeared, accompanied by her brother, her ladies, and by other ladies and gentlemen, the Queen herself.

Down below, some one remarked: "And he was her darling!" They asked one another: "What is she up to?" "Inhuman woman," said another, "she wallows in the blood of her lover!" "Poor Queen!" replied others, "she wants to see him once again! She had to have him condemned, but it was all against her wish. How ghastly pale she is!" But all these people loved the hideously shattered house of Gordon. Therefore they eagerly contradicted any one who had a good word to say for the Queen. "She alone is to blame for the whole thing. When her uncles from France were here, they told Sir John that he must free the Queen from her imprisonment by the heretics. And she promised him that if he would do it, and his happiness were in it, she would take him as her husband. Afterwards however she did not think him good enough for her. And now he has to die as a punishment for being a Catholic!"

John Gordon went in front of the guards who accompanied him up to the scaffold. He wore the elegant black silk in the French mode which he affected. He was not noticeably paler than his wont, and walked with slow, proud steps. In Scotland it was the legal right of a condemned man to speak to the crowd before his execution. John Gordon approached the railing of the scaffold. He stood with his back to the Queen's window. He looked down, over the serried rows of the forest of spears on the soldiers' shoulders, to the white faces lifted up towards him. It looked almost as though he were smiling, as if in scorn; he opened his lips to speak; and did not speak. For his gaze rose, above the crowd, above the houses of the town, so low that he could look right over their roofs from the sharp elevation of the scaffold. They lifted their many-coloured gables into the blue air, misted still as with the gold from the rains of the previous days; from many a chimney, a thin smoke was rising, that spoke of work, of life. Beyond the town was the sea, dark blue, with snowy, curling crests on its waves and a fresh tang in its air as of eternal gladness. Gordon's words died on his lips and his scornful smile faded. He turned; he saw the Queen at her window with all her suite, her brothers and all the other lords and ladies, packed in behind her like the crowded background of a picture, and took a step forward, as though he could not trust his eyes. "Your Majesty!" he stammered, his face flaming red. He raised his arm: "Oh, Queen!" he cried aloud. His gaze fastened itself on Mary's face, which was white as death, blank of expression, motionless, as though it were a painting or an apparition, that did not look down but only straight ahead, quite rigid. John Gordon drew himself up to his full proud height and found again his old arrogant smile. "What an honour is done me!" he said aloud. "There is Your Majesty yourself, so that my last glance may take the gleam of Your Highness with it! Certes, I may be thankful that no future can detract for me from this supreme moment." No expression was reflected in Mary's face; it was as though she had heard no word, and yet the place was not large, and the house, at whose first-floor window she stood, not high. Thousands of men stood below; thousands of faces stared up to her. Gordon's colour came and went swiftly. "Good people," he cried, "it is at me you must look, at me, me; look, this way!" Stepping right up to the rail of the scaffold, he spoke very loud and quick: "Yes, I have deserved to die, and die a just death.

For certainly I have been a thorough traitor. It is all quite true, what they say of me. I have, in truth, lain in ambush with the single thought how I might get Her Majesty the Queen into my power, wholly in my power, body and soul. Once she was so near to me that I could have held her garment with my hand. Only she had so many people with her that I could do nothing, and she escaped me. But she raised her white hand right above me, and did not know that we lay hidden there. True is it, too, that I have laid plots against the Earl of Murray, who then was but Lord James Stuart, and I will further admit: four times have I tried to compass his death. And I say now, on the block, that I regret nothing in my whole life save that this plan failed: that I do regret." He threw back his handsome head, and laughed contemptuously. "And now I utter my last wish," he cried, his face flaming a dusky red. "It is that nothing worse may wait in the future for the Queen's Majesty than to have fallen into our hands would have been for her. I am glad to die now, in youth, and glad that I shall not have to look on at what will be prepared for her by those into whose merciless hands she has now fallen. Pray with me, good people, for the Queen's Majesty, that she may live long, and in peace give glorious years to this blessed Scottish land of ours."

The crowd stared at him, as he knelt and bent his head in prayer, pressing to his lips the crucifix that hung on his breast on a golden rosary. The Chief Justiciar signed to the executioner, who laid a firm hold on his sword. The people pressed closer to the scaffold; women began to sob and shriek aloud. Gordon sprang to his feet. "Make a quick end," he bade the executioner.

Mary stood in her window, erect as a dart. She too looked out over the roofs, and saw the blue sea with its glancing white crests, and the free air above. She saw, too, the market-place, and the thousands of people down there, all staring up at her, with blank eyes, asking: "What are you? Are you a mermaid?" She saw the scaffold, hung with black, and the close ranks of the soldiers' spears around it; she saw the scarlet executioner and the officials in black gowns about the block. She saw John Gordon, pale, tall and young in his elegant garb, whom she had always heard called the handsomest man in Scotland, with whom she had danced. With whom? Was it not another, who would come again in the winter, and kneel, smiling, before her again? She could not have danced with a man for whom such horrors could be prepared—it was not from such a world that she chose her companions! She heard every word that Gordon spoke down there, the sound of his voice and the special melody of speech which belonged to him alone. Through the picture down there, which retained its clear outline, she saw another scene—the courtyard at Amboise, steeped, too, in scent and sunshine, where she, a young wife of sixteen, Dauphine of France, had come down on the arm of her child-husband to look at the men who had been hanged as rebels, there in rows, all round the court. Indifferently, she had gone along the rows, as she saw all her relations and friends doing, and thought: Rebels, what a good thing: how fortunate that the power of the King had been able to make so speedy an end of these sacrilegious persons. Now, there would be order and peace in the land once more. She felt her little husband, who she knew loved her dearly, press her arm hard; she turned her eyes to him and saw that his body was all shaken with horror; from him she looked to see what it was that filled him with such nameless fear, and found herself staring into the face of the corpse directly in front of her. Yellow teeth in the grey mouth grinned at her; glazed eyes gleamed pearl white. It was as though, from behind, a black hand passed over her eyes. Amboise vanished. She saw the gate of the castle at Inverness, through which she had passed hardly two weeks ago. There was the severed head of the captain on a pike above the gate, grinning horribly, and she suddenly realized now that, as she passed under the gate, blood had spattered all over her. A sigh broke from her. Her mind surged darkly. She wanted to cry out. A thought came. I am Queen! I do not have to bear this! In Amboise I could say nothing. But here, here! Here I can pardon! I, I can do it! Mercy is mine. Ah, that, only that, is what I came here for! Now I know it. I do not have to suffer so atrociously. She strove to rise; her brother's arm was round her shoulders like an iron girder. Opening her lips, she sighed, shaking her head, as if she were struggling for air, for consciousness. Below there was a crying; people pressed wildly up to the scaffold, as though to storm it; the soldiers lowered their spears with a rattle, moved, clanging, forward. Mary looked down; Gordon, unskilfully struck on the shoulder by the executioner's unfamiliar weapon, lay in a bath of blood by the block. Swaying, the Queen caught desperately at the window frame. The executioner struck again. When the crowd again had eyes for the window they saw the Queen being carried out fainting by her ladies.

For a very long time Mary lay unconscious. When she came to, she demanded to be brought straightway out of the town, back to Edinburgh. The court travelled slowly. Her ladies, the four Maries, and Jean Argyle, gave free vent to their indignation to the Queen. What an ordeal! To drag her to such a spectacle? Was it not enough that the whole race of Gordon lay broken in the lowest conceivable depths of human misery? Now, prone, as usual, to foresee the worst, they brooded over the way in which all hearts would be alienated from the Queen, if her mind and spirit were really to prove broken. Lord James took part in one such conversation. "You talk according to your judgment," he remarked in cold wrath to his sister Argyle, "but quite otherwise than you ought. It is not as if you did not perfectly well know the talk going on among the people. We were up against a hard necessity."

"Of which every one will now be inalterably convinced," she replied, darting sharp glances at him out of her black eyes. Her pointed chin trembled above her high white coif.

He merely shrugged his shoulders contemptuously.

"No quarrelling," begged the Queen, lying exhausted on her bed.

She reached Edinburgh, and there became seriously ill with fever and pains in her limbs.

She allowed the process declaring perpetual outlawry against the house of Gordon to run its course. But when it came to the death sentence on the two surviving sons of Huntly, George and Adam Gordon, on the ground that they had openly taken arms against their Sovereign, she refused to sign. Lord George's guilt was not clear, and as for Adam—was she to send a child to the scaffold? They were incarcerated separately in royal fortresses. Their clansmen fled abroad or took to the morasses and caves of their mountains. The women lived with relations, silent and sad.

Chapter 3

OUR GOOD SISTER, ELIZABETH

THE Queen soon recovered, and life went on as before in the palace; fiddles and flutes played every evening for dancing; in the daytime, the Queen rode to the chase with a great suite. Hardly a week passed without the Queen giving some resounding entertainment in honour of her knights, either in town or in the country. John Knox and his ministers poured out their old imprecations with renewed force: "This, however, I say unto you, that God, who, from the beginning, has chastened the despisal of His word and ever poured His vengeance on all proud mockers thereof, will not spare them now. Rather before the eyes of this evil generation will He this time exact His vengeance on the pride that treats every warning as the breath of the wind." And John Knox preached: "Hear, therefore, ye Kings, and mark well, ye that judge on this earth, that God has never yet let pass the case where ignorance, scorn and vanity pursue the children of virtue and love with unrighteous hate!" The ministers about him prayed openly, "Release us, O Lord, from rule by these alien bands! Turn the heart of our gracious Queen to Thee, or send her a speedy end."

Again did Mary send for John Knox, to call him again to account. Again, he stood erect and righteous before his Sovereign, and said, yes, he had spoken of the rights due to kings and of the duties that flowed out of and corresponded to them, and that there were few kings and princes on this earth who even tried to fulfil this task fully. "For see and hear," he went on, "where on this earth are not persecution and hideous murder, oppression and evil loosed against the poor saints of God? Where are they not beaten and burned? Where are they not

93

cast in dungeons, tortured, martyrized, driven, poor and naked, from their homes and lands? How can such violence be explained save through the fact that Evil in living form has taken its seat on the thrones of this earth? Yet," he continued, "against Your Majesty's rule I have not preached. Nay, more: although I find in the scriptures no praise for such worldly dancing as Your Majesty has now introduced amongst us, but rather see it characterized as a pleasure for madmen and not for rational beings, I will not altogether damn such worldly doings. On one condition: that the dancing be not that of the Philistines, without measure or modesty! Such dancers cry to Hell, where doubtless their refreshment awaits them."

Mary, who received John Knox in her small audience chamber, in the presence of her suite, sat very upright in her deep chair, her hands crossed in her lap, listening without any appearance of displeasure to what he had to say. She knew well enough to whom his words of thunder about the evil rulers of this earth applied—to her relations in France, the members of her mother's house, who, restored to the throne after a long period of impotence, were striving by every means, worldly and spiritual, to overthrow the hostile Huguenot party. When John Knox had finished, the Queen replied: Since her uncle and John Knox did not profess the same religion, there could be no talk of an understanding, so little, indeed, that it was best to waste no words on that. "But, Master Knox," continued Mary, "I want to say this: when you have any fault to find with my own behaviour, come and tell me of it yourself; I shall always listen to what you say." She looked almost confidentially at the preacher, whose face coloured for an instant at this unexpected request. He soon collected himself, however. "Madam," he said, "of the fact that your uncles, acting as enemies of God and of His Son Jesus Christ in shedding the blood of the innocent for their own glory and their own worldly pomp, can have no more success than so many others before them, I am so certain in my heart that I too can leave that for the moment. As for the case of Your Majesty yourself, I should surely be glad to meet Your Highness's suggestion. But, Madame, I must say this: the condition must be accepted that I pass not the limits set for me by my office. Your Majesty knows I am set in a public position in the Church of God, and am set there by God in order to erect a dam against sin and vice. I am, however, most assuredly not called upon to come to each individual and put before him wherein he has offended; such a task were endless. Therefore, if Your Majesty would attend the public preachments I have no doubt that you would fully comprehend what I approve and what I must oppose, in Your Majesty as in others. Or," he continued, undismayed, as though blind to the faces of the courtiers round the Queen, deaf to the rustle through the room telling him that he had said something quite impossible, "if Your Majesty would fix a special day and hour at which it would suit you to hear of the teachings of the Church of this land, I shall most gladly expect Your Grace. But to stand before your chamber door or elsewhere and to have no freedom but that of whispering my views into Your Majesty's ear, or communicating to you what is thought and said of Your Majesty outside—that neither my conscience nor my commission from God allows me to do."

Mary still sat erect and silent, her hands quietly crossed in her lap, looking at him with a calm which nothing he could say was able to disturb. She seemed neither to see nor hear the murmur of indignant astonishment that came from her entourage at such strange outspokenness. When he had finished, she merely smiled with perfect friendliness and forbearance. He flushed a deep crimson. "Madame," he said, hastily, "although I am here at Your Majesty's express command, I may not know what others think of the fact that at such an hour in the day, I am here at court, in waiting, instead of sitting at my books."

At this, all the ladies and gentlemen round imitated the smile of their Sovereign. The Queen rose from her chair. "Well, Master Knox," she said, in her clear, soft voice, "I think that you will not always sit over your books." With that she turned, and after a friendly greeting to him, went out of the room, followed by her train of ladies and gentlemen. John Knox suddenly was all alone in the great room, with the faces in the bright tapestries on the walls looking down, pale and solemn, upon him.

He strode through the corridors, past a group of courtiers. As they saw him, they put their heads together, and looked after him, as though at some fabulous beast. "Of a truth, he is not frightened." The preacher paused. "I do not see what should frighten me in the pretty face of a young noblewoman," he said, proudly.

★

One morning, a short time after this, in the Queen's smallest and most remote chamber, there stood before her and Mary Fleming another man, small, well-built, with a thin, clean-shaven face, and a small fleck of white at the back of his hair. "Say to His Holiness, I beg Your Eminence, that I am always his obedient daughter. But what can I do? Had our most Holy Father known how it is with me here, he would never have thought of sending you hither. I thank him on my knees for his love and his heavenly remembrance of me. My heart bleeds that I must never cease to think of the danger that hangs, reverend father, over your head. I can give you no passport. I think indeed you will journey more safely without one." The man bowed to kiss the Queen's hand. She sank on her knees before him. Tears poured over her face. The thought that she was torn like a withered leaf from the living tree of her religion, overpowered her; every other difficulty in the country seemed to rise up before her; at this moment there rose in her a sense that she was as powerless as a shadow; that, far from ruling, she did not rule—she was lying in an airless dungeon vault, bound hand and foot. She gave a hard sob, as she kissed the hand her visitor extended in blessing over her.

She bade Mary Fleming show the Catholic gentleman out. It was high time she did: the Protestant entourage of the

Queen, who had gone to a man to the morning service, might return at any moment.

Mary Fleming, followed by the stranger, stepped out briskly. She knew that it was already too late: every instant the people she was afraid of meeting might stand before her. She opened the last door: Baron Maitland of Lethington, Lord James, and Mr. Randolph were coming up the staircase, in lively conversation, prayer-books in hand. The maid-of-honour's eyes, as in a lightning flash, crossed those of the Secretary of State; for a second, as though he were astounded, the colour rose in his face: then, shrugging his shoulders, he dropped his eyes. Hastily returning the greetings of the gentlemen, the maid hurried by; she felt as though the little white fleck on the back of the man's head behind her were like a spotlight moving from step to step. The others had stopped on the landing, while she went down the winding staircase with her protégé. The men could hear the lady's silken dress rustling against the banisters. Now she had reached the floor below; they caught the click of her firm little feet. From her companion came practically no sound. Lethington stretched his neck, to see through the bars of the staircase.

Then he turned to answer the English Ambassador, whose remarks had been so suddenly interrupted by this surprising encounter that his words seemed still to be hanging in the air. Lethington, taking his long, silky beard in his right hand, said, "Of course you are only too right there, Mr. Randolph. The question how most effectively to repel a pretty, spoiled young woman from teachings in themselves unattractive to her is unexceptionably solved by our preachers!" His interlocutor, who had, just now, been speaking most energetically in this sense, said no word in reply. Lethington smiled. Still caressing his beard, he went on calmly: "At the same time we enjoy one good fortune, that has fallen into our laps as it were, of itself, while in other States streams of blood flow for its sake. With us, every one is free to live according to his own faith, whatever it may be. Perhaps, really, one should advise our Queen to be unpleas-

ant once, in her loving subjects' interest, that they may, afterwards, learn to prize her subsequent reversion to mildness.
They ought to be on their knees in thankfulness for their
mercies. Instead of which, they yell and shriek for what they
would like to have. That, then, is all that matters to them.
In that there is not a pin to choose among them: they are all
the same."

But Lord James Stuart and Mr. Randolph merely knit their
brows. A page appeared. Her Majesty awaited his lordship,
the Earl of Murray.

As the Secretary of State and Mr. Randolph descended the
staircase together, the Englishman began: "A by no means
commonplace countenance." Lord Lethington replied tranquilly: "You think so? Well, Miss Mary Fleming has a varied
assortment of friends."

In the evening, however, he came to Randolph, to apologize
and explain. "You see how it is. Her Majesty has merely
yielded to the extreme pressure put upon her by her Catholic
subjects, the letters of the Pope himself, and those of her
French relations. The unfortunate man arrived in disguise,
quite privily: he has hardly dared to show himself in the light
of day. The Queen knew nothing about him, until he landed.
Now he is well away."

Soon, however, rumours flew about among the people, that a
nuncio had been sent to Scotland from that fount of sin and
idolatry, Rome itself. A group of determined young men got
together, and bound themselves by solemn oaths to see that this
limb of Satan, this emissary of Antichrist, this lapdog from
the haunts of bloody tyranny, was traced to his hole, dragged
thence and hanged. In their headquarters in a wynd off the
Lawnmarket they collected pikes and cudgels. They were on
the point of setting forth to do execution when some sensible
men, older friends and relatives of the enthusiasts, intervened;
such a murder would be useless and might have unpredictable
consequences.

98

No one knew, meantime, where the fugitive was hid. Deprived of nourishment, the excitement died down.

★

What use, meantime, denying that no one would willingly have caused the young Queen sorrow? By now, she had been nearly two years in the land and her presence there had brought good with it.

There was peace on the borders, as there had not been for years. Mary had done much for the land. The Universities had collapsed beneath the storms of the Reformation; the Queen, of her own means, raised them out of the dust. Law in Scotland was harsh even for the well-to-do, unless they belonged to the governing nobles: for the poor man, absolutely inhuman. Mary provided that three days of the week were set aside for cases affecting the poor, and had a defender assigned to them at the State's expense in official prosecutions. She frequently attended the courts of justice, and would sit for a whole morning through the cases.

So, there was rejoicing whenever she appeared in the town, either on foot, accompanied by some ladies and pages, or high on horseback, with full court suite in attendance. On the news of her approach, men left their work; women lifted up their children so that they might see the lovely friendly face of the young Queen. Wild with delight, incessantly shouting "Hurrah!" the boys and girls would run after the royal train.

★

Mary appeared at the opening of Parliament, the first she had held. Assembling her retinue at the Castle, she came down with great pomp. First came soldiers in Highland dress, with bows and staves; then the palace watch, in complete mail. After them came the court, with a full complement of nobility, all the men wearing French attire. In the midst of them, the Queen walked beneath a canopy, clad in white and silver brocade, a veil waving round her and the crown sparkling on her head. Every inch a Queen she looked as she stood on the steps of the throne in the Parliament house, where the walls had been hung with tapestries from the royal household and great tubs of flowering and other shrubs stood about everywhere. On her right knelt the Earl of Murray with the sword and on the left Maitland of Lethington with the sceptre.

She opened Parliament in a speech in Latin, delivered extempore. Her hearers were wild with delight. "God save that sweet face! In truth, the voice of a goddess! Did ever mortal speak so charmingly and so wisely?"

Parliament had to ratify the abasement of the Gordons and establish the new dignities of Lord James Stuart, with all the other changes effected in the past two years. This decree would remain in force till the Queen's twenty-fifth birthday. Then, in accordance with the old Scottish law, maintained in the case of every ruler for the last two hundred years, the Sovereign would review and re-distribute all the dignities, titles and other gifts she had granted, this subsequent decree alone being permanent.

Contemporaneously with the meeting of Parliament, there was a Protestant Church Assembly in Edinburgh, to which came practically every minister in Scotland. They raised hands and voices in plaint of their poverty. Their parishes were often very poor, and they had nothing but what their parishes gave them of their own free will. Many a minister was too poor to give help to the starving. They cried, "The Government must help us. It has appropriated the goods of the Catholic Church. That money belongs of right to us. Parliament exists to give us our rights."

Nearly all the members of Parliament were Protestants; the few Catholics had been frightened into silence by the awful fate of the Gordons. Nevertheless, they soon came to the ministers and explained to them that this Parliament would have too much more important business to transact to find time for Church matters. But let no one despair on that account. For, so the members suggested, "the Queen will soon be marrying. Whomever she chooses, she must ask us, her Estates, to assure her consort adequate standing. Then she will have to make concessions on her own part, and then your case, that of the Church, and yours, that of the ministers, will come before anything else. And so you will be satisfied."

The ministers, however, thought differently, and held desperate meetings of protest. They described their incredible poverty, and declared with bitterness that they knew perfectly well why they were put off and played with. "Who holds the property of the Catholic Church? The great nobles who sit in Parliament." One old minister, his whole frame shaking with pain and wrath, and his voice choking with tears of indignation, rose and cried: "Do you know what impious and blasphemous words Earl Morton had the insolence to utter in Parliament? He said—I give his very words—'Are the parsons mad? Have we cleared out the Papists to throw all that money into the maws of these starvelings?' "

The nobles however did not pay much heed to the rage of the ministers. They knew that the people, at the moment, were interested in other matters than the sorrows of their spiritual guides. One question and only one occupied great and small, gentle and simple, man and woman, from early to late, in every wynd, court and hall, in town and country, in the plains and in the mountains, south and north, east and west—Whom is the Queen going to take as her second husband? It rejoiced them all that the proud and mighty ones of the earth came to their Queen as wooers, thick as flies in summer.

★

In the spring of 1563, Baron Maitland of Lethington journeyed to the English Court as envoy extraordinary of his mistress, who had no standing representative in London. During his sojourn he visited the Spanish Ambassador in London, Bishop Alvara della Quadra. Their meal over, the gentlemen were still chatting of this and that, when Lethington threw out: "If only your exalted Sovereign, the Most Catholic King, would seriously consider the wishes of the Scottish people, he would then have no difficulty in making himself ruler of the entire world." He reminded the Spaniard of the immense area of his Sovereign's possessions: already he ruled over Spain, America and Burgundy; without any effort he could add Scotland, Ireland and England. The Spaniard turned the reflective glance of his prominent dark eyes on the other, as Lethington went on, in a conversational tone, to say that he was charged expressly to convince della Quadra of a truth that he, in his turn, would fail in his duty if he did not sufficiently stress to his Sovereign, the Most Catholic King; this was the fact that Queen Mary of Scotland was possessed, day and night, by a single passion—the desire of adding to the immense possessions of the Spanish crown the three islands he had just mentioned, through her marriage with his son, the Infant Don Carlos. Della Quadra asked: "Do you forget the difference in religion between the two countries?"

Lethington did not so much as change colour. "What of it? True, a majority among us, the Scottish nobility, is Protestant. Such facts cannot be denied; who seeks to deny them? At the same time, Her Majesty is Catholic. My opinion is, moreover, that we, the nobility, in perfect loyalty to our Sovereign, have shown that we are not only full of heart-whole devotion to our Queen but completely penetrated and suffused by an entire fidelity, an enthusiastic obedience. Is it conceivable that we should not accept as her future husband the person on whom our sovereign lady has set her heart?" The Spaniard was silent. "The fact that I am sitting here," Lethington continued, "that I sought this interview with you, and pursue it now with such zeal, should be for you the most effective proof of the genuineness of our ideas. Am I not a Protestant myself?" He declared that the conclusion of such a marriage would bring the greatest possible advantages to the Catholic religion in Scotland and throughout the world. "It would be impossible, after it, not to permit Catholics with us at least to celebrate

the Holy Office in their own dwellings. More probably, their own
churches would be reopened." Della Quadra still said nothing.
Lethington then put before him the wealth of his Queen; she
possessed an income of two hundred thousand ducats and a
capital of eight hundred thousand in jewels and gold and
silver. At last the Spaniard opened his lips, although even now
all he said was that he had always heard that the Queen of
Scotland was to marry the son of the Holy Roman Emperor,
Archduke Charles of Austria. He was a fine man, of the right
age for the Scottish Queen, and acceptable to his master on
account of his close kinship with the Spanish royal house and
his being undoubtedly a good Catholic. Further, he had been
informed that the French relations of the Queen of Scotland
favoured his suit. Lethington became animated. "But the Archduke of Austria is of no use to my Sovereign. He may be a
handsome figure of a man, and is admittedly a knight *sans
reproche* and a man of good and friendly temper. But the
Emperor, his father, though he may give him a great position,
is poor. He can give his son practically nothing. Moreover, he
is remote, so remote that the idea of him, and of any power he
may have, cannot possibly exert the smallest effect on the imaginations of the people of this island." Lethington reflected.
"No, no, the Archduke is no use to us. There would be no getting him accepted, with us, by our nobles. A Catholic, but without the shadow of authority!" He went on to say: "Only in one
contingency could the Austrian be considered by us. If the
King of Spain decided to endow his cousin. Perhaps with money.
Or, still better for us, if His Majesty, the Catholic King, could
bring himself to conclude a firm alliance: pledged himself explicitly and at once to come to our assistance with men and
money and all he has, whenever we need it—in the event, I mean,
of difficulties arising, despite our wishes, and our good intentions, from some quarter or other, I do not say what. But—
without such a priceless endowment? No—the Austrian would
be of little use and possibly great harm to us." The Spaniard
smiled: he understood. Finally Lord Lethington gave him some-

thing more to ponder over. "If my Queen should not find in the King of Spain the true ally for whom she must long with all the passion of her heart, I fear lest she might finally be driven, much against her will, of course, but still, driven to a course of action that might not wholly please His Most Catholic Majesty."

The Spaniard realized that the Scotsman was threatening him with a Protestant husband for his Sovereign.

Lord Lethington had so far convinced him that he, next day, wrote to acquaint his Sovereign with the Scottish proposals.

"It is entirely clear that if these Scots can set their Queen on the throne of England, her religion is a matter of indifference to them. That heretics should think in such a manner is comprehensible when one considers the immense advantages for every individual as well as for the country as a whole that would be secured by the union of their small and poor state with its richer and more powerful neighbour."

He added that even in England the Scottish Queen had an extraordinarily large party.

"I am informed on good authority that five hundred cavalry or more could be counted on; there would be no great difficulty in the conquest of England by Spain once His Serene Highness the Infant is husband of the Queen of Scotland. France could then easily be held in check, nor would it be difficult then to break the back of the resistance in the Netherlands, which is certainly fed continually by England."

★

Lord Lethington returned home. His Sovereign received him with a letter in her hands, brought to her by Mr. Randolph. Queen Elizabeth wrote that if the Queen of Scotland had it in mind to choose as her husband either the Archduke of Austria

or any other foreign Prince, she was embarking on a course
that must swiftly, surely and permanently destroy the good
understanding between the two countries. In such an event, any
hopes of the English succession which the Queen of Scotland
might entertain had better be at once laid aside as the most idle
and empty of dreams. Loyalty and a real concern for the welfare of her young neighbour, a real desire to spare her bitter
disappointment, induce Queen Elizabeth to utter this warning,
and to say, quite frankly, that any husband other than a man
of English birth is impossible for the Queen of Scotland. No
other can lay the foundations of a secure peace between the two
countries and at the same time secure the succession of the
Queen of Scotland in England.

Queen Mary gave her minister the letter to read, saying:
"Whom can she have in mind? It would appear that she has
some one."

Certain experiences during his journeys rose before Lethington's mind's eye, as clear as if they had happened an hour
ago, and compelled him to smile.

"Your Majesty, the Queen of England said to me one morning—we were strolling together in the garden, where she had
graciously called me to her—'If only your Sovereign would
listen to me and be guided by me! Then she should assuredly
have all that her heart can desire. She should have a husband,
oh, such a husband! one on whom God has in truth showered
every gift of nature and of mind. There is no Prince in the
world to be compared to him for an instant.'"

"Whom did she mean?" asked Mary.

"Your Majesty," replied Lethington, "the Queen of England went on to say that, were she thinking of marrying, this
was the only man she would choose."

"Then . . . ?"

"Yes," he replied.

The Queen let her arms drop. "But it is impossible!"

"It must have been he," replied the Minister.

"Oh, no!" cried Mary, again.

"There was no misunderstanding her," he replied. "Lord Robert Dudley and several other gentlemen were in front of us on the path. The Queen looked at him constantly, while she was speaking to me."

"I am to wed her old cast-off lover!"

"Oh, not cast-off! No female heart could make a greater sacrifice."

Mary looked at him, nonplussed. "What is she after?"

Lethington raised his shoulders. "Perhaps my Lord's elevation to King of Scotland and father of the heir to the two crowns."

"Why then does she not marry him herself?"

In a low tone, Lethington replied, "The English people have never loved Lord Robert Dudley; he is detested by most of the nobility. Since his wife, Lady Amy, was found, with her neck broken, at the foot of her own staircase, such a marriage has become impossible."

"Why?" asked Mary; then, amplifying her own question, "Whom has she to consider?"

Lethington was silent for a moment; then he said, "It is said, as Your Majesty must know, that Queen Elizabeth is incapable of bearing a child. She herself knows best whether this is so. Who can tell where the truth lies in this?"

"And I am to be second wife to a creature who killed his first?" After a pause, she resumed, "What did you say to this?"

Lethington reported, "I said that I, of course, appreciated to the full the very notable proof of kindness Her Majesty had it in mind to give to my gracious Sovereign, in offering her an object so very near her own heart. I was however afraid that, in the event of my exalted mistress coming to feel for Lord Robert a love comparable to that felt for him by his royal mistress, on account, of course, of his own extraordinary merits, must not Her Majesty my Queen then, just because of the ardent devotion she felt for Lord Robert, hesitate to take him away from his Sovereign? Must not her own feelings then tell her what separation from such a treasure must cost?"

"And she?"

"She thought that my Queen might then establish her residence in London, where she would enjoy all royal honours and maintain them at England's cost, as the presumptive heir to the throne."

"*Mon dieu!*" said Mary, laughing so much that she had to hide her face in her hands.

Lethington also laughed. "Soon, she dropped this proposal. Finally, she said to me, with a sigh, 'If only God had made the Earl of Warwick, Lord Robert's brother, as charming as our favourite. Then we might each enjoy our heart's desire.'— I did not understand this hint, at first, but she stuck to it. After all, the Earl of Warwick was not a bad-looking man, except that he was decidedly clumsy. One must admit, however, that he was a rough fellow, altogether lacking in the delicate charm of Robert. Yet so brave and high-minded a knight was not unworthy of being a Queen's husband. Whereupon," Lethington continued, "I ventured to make the following proposal to Her Majesty—that she should make a start by marrying Lord Robert herself. If she has children, then everything is all right. If not, and if God in His mercy then takes her to Himself, it would still be possible for Your Majesty to inherit both throne and husband, and with one lady or the other Lord Robert ought to be able to produce a family. On that she let the subject fall. But she laughed right heartily."

Finally, Mary inquired of her minister when the Spanish Ambassador expected an answer from his master.

"The posts are slow: Spain is a long way off; and His Majesty the Catholic King does not make up his mind in a hurry."

Mary saw that there was nothing to be done but to wait and sigh. She dismissed the Baron with many expressions of appreciation, to be followed up in action.

She was as good as her word. The minister had not asked for rank but for property. Haddington, one of the richest abbacies in Scotland, fell in a short time afterwards. True, the house of Bothwell had, from of old, had claims to this property. But the Earl was far away, an outlaw, and his goods had anyhow fallen to the Crown. Maitland of Lethington rejoiced in his new possession. He had for some considerable time been wooing the Queen's fair maid-of-honour, Mary Fleming. Now he was in a position to offer her at least something of the splendours to which she had been accustomed from her youth up at the court of France.

★

Lethington had found his Sovereign disquieted on other grounds than the claims of the Queen of England. What really upset her was bad news from France. Almost on the same day, three of her six French uncles, the brothers of her mother, had been killed in the fighting with the Huguenots. François of Guise, the mighty head of the house, had fallen by the hand of an assassin. Mary wept bitterly and sincerely, particularly for her eldest uncle, who to her had always seemed the marvel of his sex: superior to all other mortals in beauty, brains, courage, a splendid freedom and subtlety of action and of speech. "And all that is gone, gone for ever," she moaned to her maids, who had been in France with her and knew all her friends and relations intimately. "For this life, at any rate, all that glory is gone from us for ever." She leaned, sobbing, on Mary Seaton's shoulder. "Before, if anything frightened me, I always knew that he was there, and would give me the best and wisest counsel of any one in the world. And now these godless and accursed people, who could not endure his being so splendid, have shamefully destroyed him. And I cannot even avenge his tragic death on them!"

★

Moreover, Mary was still under the disturbing influence of another horrible event, which, this time, had leapt out at her out of her own immediate circle. When she came from France, she had brought with her in her train a young French cavalier named Chastelard, a man of the most decorative personal appearance and a trick of spinning very pretty verse.

He stayed for a time at the Scottish court, finally going home with the Marquis D'Elbœuf. Then, however, he returned and became one of Mary's court attendants, in which capacity he was much distinguished by the Queen, who would talk with him confidentially, and call him out, at ball, the dance, or cards, to be her partner. She would stroll with him between the hedgerows of her garden, or call to him to read French poetry aloud to her. Every one at court knew who was meant in his quatrain—

> "While my heart dries,
> Shrivels and sears,
> Vainly love cries
> In your deaf ears."

The favours shown to the cavalier were said to be done him for the sake of his master, the King of France. But the Scottish lords hated the young Frenchman. The Queen, however, seemed not to notice their marked ill-will.

Late one evening, when she was staying in Falkland Castle, there was a sudden noise of shouting, followed by the clank as of armed men running. After a little the watch came, bringing Chastelard, pale, his hands bound together, but his face wearing an expression of almost rapturous scorn. In explanation of his arrest the following story was given. Some time before, the cavalier had succeeded, one evening, in making his way into the Queen's bedroom, where, however, he was discovered, before her retiring, by one of her serving women. When he was brought before Mary, he threw himself at her feet and poured out a flood of self-reproach for having, even in thought, cast a shadow on the radiance of her dignity. She motioned him to rise and go; his offence was pardoned. The cavalier, seeing that to remain about the court was become impossible, stayed shut up in his lodging for the next two or three days, so that he was assumed to be already departed or at any rate occupied with preparations for departure. On this evening the Queen, already in night attire, was passing out of her robing room into her bedchamber, accompanied by some of her ladies, and was in the act of approaching the bed, when Mary Beaton, with an ear-piercing yell, held up her arms before the Queen's face and pressed her away. There, there, there: she had seen it distinctly: it looked like a patch of shadow, but she was sure that she had caught the glint of eyes; there was a man under the bed! Gibbering with fright, and yet unable to stir from the spot, where, until one bent down, there was nothing to be seen but shadow, the women crowded round the Queen, stretching their arms out to protect her, until Mary Fleming bethought her of the watch. "The Watch! Call the Watch! I will go and fetch them." Before that, Lord James of Murray, roused by the shrieking, came in. The Queen left the room, that her brother might deal with the dreadful affair.

On the third morning after this evening the chevalier Chastelard was executed in the market-place of St. Andrews, the nearest town to Falkland Castle. He went to his death as though to a wedding, murmuring words of rapturous passion. As he laid his head on the block, he called out the Queen's name, as that of his patron Saint.

By now, there was no one in either kingdom who did not know whom Queen Elizabeth had suggested as a husband to her neighbour. Officially, however, she was modestly content with a repetition of her old principles. "The future husband of the Queen of Scotland must, of course, first be pleasing to her personally. It is then desirable that he should seem quite suitable to England. It would be best if the Queen of Scotland were to choose an Englishman of one of the great families. Any foreign Prince is entirely excluded." Finally, Queen Mary lost patience. She was, so she wrote to her kind sister in the neighbouring realm, independent, and did not feel called upon to please any one else in the regulation of her purely personal affairs. "What would you say, my good sister, if I were to prescribe to you what you are to do and leave undone?"

Whereupon Queen Elizabeth took offence, and wrote no more.

★

Mary, in her palace, was unhappy and ill at ease. What was to become of her and all her marriage plans, despite her countless suitors? Queen Elizabeth stood there like an ill-natured portress, whose narrow life knew no pleasure save to make agreeable persons feel that she and she alone had the office of barring the way to searchers after happiness, and above all after happiness in marriage, in the British Isles. Mary saw that she would have to appeal and even to apologize. She looked about her for a fresh emissary to whom to entrust the task of establishing new intimate relations with London. Lord Lethington was busy. Her choice finally fell on a young member of one of the minor Scottish houses, James Melville, who was prepared to put at the service of his country and of its ruler the fruits of a considerable experience and knowledge of men and things, gained in Germany and at the French court. She sent him to England, with letters in her own hand to Queen Elizabeth, her minister Cecil, and other great persons at the English court.

After three weeks, her envoy returned to report to his Sovereign. Of medium height, self-confident, ready and intelligent address, appearance and speech, Melville stood before her, and began at once with the main business. "When the Queen of England was pleased to summon me to her presence, I found her alone in the garden. She was walking up and down, but stopped when I approached. Kneeling respectfully on one knee, I handed her my credentials. After saying that I was welcome, and a few other words of course, she at once began to speak of the letter of Your Majesty, which so deeply offended her at the time, saying that it was expressed in terms that seemed to be explicitly designed, in their cutting offensiveness, to make an end of any kind of friendship. Indeed, she had intended to reply to it in a single letter, couched in similar terms. With these words she drew a letter from her pocket which she handed me to read. This, then, as I soon saw, was the letter, which she had already written. It did not seem to her sufficiently disagreeable, or she would have despatched it. I proceeded," Sir James continued, "to make suitable excuses for Your Majesty, somewhat as follows:—There had not been the remotest intention of offence. Indeed, Your Majesty was at a loss to understand how words so harmless in themselves and spoken in such entire good faith could have been so unfortunately misinterpreted. Whereupon Queen Elizabeth replied, 'Well, if that is really so, and since my good sister of Scotland has taken the first step to a reconciliation, I will not stand upon points, but will gladly tear up my letter'—which, Your Majesty, she there and then proceeded to do. I at once opened the proposal of our Government for settling outstanding difficulties, and above all, the question of Your Majesty's marriage to a cavalier of the Queen of England's choice, by a meeting between the responsible ministers of the two countries in some English border town, say beyond York. On our side, so I said, there was a lively hope that the English Government might send the Earl of Bedford and Lord Robert Dudley as their representatives. At these words, the Queen interrupted me, saying, 'You seem to think little of Lord Robert, if you only mention him second!' Her tone, here, was decidedly sharp. 'In a very short time he will be a much more distinguished person than Lord Bedford!' She then became almost impassioned, as she went on, 'I, I, I myself prize and honour him as a brother! He is the best friend I have in the world, and were it ever possible for me to make up my mind to marry, he is the only man I could think of raising to my side as a husband. As things are, however, I want my good sister, your Queen, to have him as a husband; for there is no one whom I would so gladly see participating in the right of succession. With him, and only with him, I could be convinced that nothing would ever be done to injure a good understanding between me and your Queen.'"

Sir James related how, on the same day, he had been present at the ceremonies at which Lord Robert Dudley was made Earl of Leicester. "The Queen herself invested the new Earl. Again and again, when she was putting the mantle on him, she could not refrain from stroking his neck, his head, and his shoulders, with her hand, although, apart from me, M. de Foix, the French Ambassador, and Monsignor della Quadra, the envoy of the Catholic King, were standing quite near her. At the close of the ceremony, she turned to me: What did I think of this gentleman now? She meant Lord Robert, now Leicester. I replied, if Lord Leicester be really so excellent a servant as he is reputed to be, he ought to count himself exceedingly lucky in having found a Queen who recognized and rewarded his service so magnificently. To which the Queen replied, 'Ah, I see this young sprig, with his slim waist, pleases you better!' She pointed to Lord Darnley, who, in accordance with his rank as first Prince of the blood at the English court, was standing right up by the throne. What was I to say? I was certainly in a quandary. I therefore replied that no woman of intelligence would prefer a man as a husband who looked more like a young girl than a man. I had to make a reply of that sort because her sudden question showed me that she had been rendered suspicious by the proposals that had been made to me in that quarter. Perhaps I might even be so bold as to say that my remark had some correspondence with the facts."

Sir James turned a questioning glance towards his Queen. He did not yet know how far one might go in making communications to her. She, however, was all attention. So he resumed: "The Queen of England, for the rest, treated me with the greatest possible attention. Not a day passed without my being commanded to her presence. Several times I had the honour of conversing with her no less than three times on one day. Probably the most important thing she said to me in all this was: Since, unfortunately, it did not appear that she was, in the near future, to have the pleasure of seeing Your Majesty, her good sister, face to face, she intended to open her whole heart, to its inmost recesses, to me, Your Majesty's servant, instead of to yourself. I was to learn that she had not really been so seriously annoyed by the tone of Your Majesty's letter, as by the fact that you seemed desirous of putting difficulties in the way of raising the Earl of Leicester to the position of your husband. . . . I replied that, although there had been unofficial conversations between Her Majesty and Lord Lethington, and hints from Mr. Thomas Randolph, there had, so far, been no really official proposition made to our Government by the English or even by Her Majesty herself. Further, how could Your Highness decide when there had been no approach to a settlement of the question of the succession? The Queen replied that Your Majesty had only to follow her advice and everything would be satisfactorily cleared up. In this connection she said that she herself would never marry, unless she found herself as it were compelled to do so by some line of conduct adopted by Your Majesty. To which I replied, Assuredly, her great position would prevent her from taking such a step. She was well aware that after marriage she would only be the Queen, whereas now she united in her own person King and Queen. After this, the conversation changed. Fixing her eyes on the portrait of Your Majesty hanging on the wall of the cabinet in which she was good enough to grant me this interview, she said that, while she was deprived of the sight of Your Majesty yourself, she could never look enough at the picture. She had, she said, other things to show me. Leading me into another room, she took from the middle drawer of a jewel-chest a number of miniatures, carefully wrapped up in paper, with the names of the persons represented inscribed on each in her own handwriting. On the first little packet, which she took out tenderly and held in her hand, stroking it affectionately, I saw the words: My Lord's portrait. Since it was growing dark, I held the candle for her, and ventured to say that I longed to know who was thus designated. She made difficulties: 'No, no, that cannot be. This is not for you. It is only for myself.' But I saw how the land lay. So I went on with my requests, until she at last gave way, and with a great display of sentiment un-wrapped the paper to show me the picture, which was a por-trait of the Earl of Leicester. I suggested that she should give it to me, for Your Majesty. Thereupon, however, she packed it hurriedly up again. 'Oh, no! it is the only one I have.' I suggested that the picture was but a copy of nature after all, and that she had the original in the Earl himself: I pointed to Lord Leicester himself, who stood in a window en-gaged in conversation with the Secretary of State, Sir William Cecil. The Queen, however, was not listening to me. She had taken up another picture, one of Your Majesty, which she pressed tenderly to her lips and cheeks and kissed repeatedly with the utmost feeling. Thereupon, by way of showing that I could fully appreciate the honour of such a display of friendli-ness on her part, I at this point took the liberty of raising her hand several times to my lips. She also showed me a ruby as large as a bullet; I begged to have it, with the portrait of the Earl, to which I thus permitted myself to revert, for Your Majesty. She merely replied: If Your Queen would only follow my counsel, she would find herself one day in possession of everything that now belonged to the Queen of England. At the same time she was good enough to give me a diamond for Your Majesty. By now it was late, so the Queen dismissed me, with instructions to come and see her again in the garden on the morrow."

Sir James asked the Queen to pardon the detailed nature of his recital; in view of the importance of the matter he felt he ought not to pass over even the most trifling incident. Con-tinuing, therefore, he said:

"When I reached the garden at the appointed hour on the following day, she asked me most graciously about myself and my travels. I told her about them, and, not unmindful of Your Majesty's counsel, introduced lighter matter here and there; for example, when I was speaking of the fashions of the various countries, I permitted myself to mention the ladies' corsets. She then told me that she possessed the costumes of every country in the world. Every day she would put on a different dress, appearing one day in the English fashion, another in the French, Spanish, Italian, and so on. Finally, she asked me which fashion suited her the best. I said, the Italian. This observation seemed not to displease her, perhaps because her thick, reddish-fair hair, which on superficial observation appears to be her own, looks best under the Italian cap. She then inquired of me, whose hair was considered to be of the more beautiful color—Your Majesty's, or hers? I hesitated; she pressed me, until I said that Her Majesty was the loveliest Queen in England, as Your Majesty in Scotland. This evasion did not satisfy her, however. At last there was nothing for it but to say that Your Majesty and she were anyhow the most beautiful women in your respective countries. By way of improvement on such commonplaces, I added that her complexion was perhaps even whiter than Your Majesty's, but that Your Majesty was also extraordinarily lovely. What else was there for me to say?"

Mary smiled and shook her head.

"She also wanted to know which was the taller. This I could easily settle; I could but reply, Your Majesty. Whereupon she retorted, 'Then your Queen must be too tall, for I am just right, neither too tall nor too short.' She asked how Your Majesty passed the time. I said that when I left Edinburgh and came to take leave of Your Majesty, you were just setting out hunting; that Your Majesty was fond of travelling, at present in your own provinces: that you were fond of reading, history and poetry; that you played the lute and the harpsichord—when you could find time from affairs of State for such distractions. She then inquired whether you played well upon the harpsichord, and I replied, 'Very well for a Queen.'

"After dinner on this same day, Lord Hunsdeen, the Chamberlain, who had looked after me while in London in the most friendly fashion, came to conduct me to a remote gallery in the castle. I heard the harpsichord playing within a room. It was Her Majesty, Lord Hunsdeen explained, but I must behave as though I had no suspicion of that. I listened for a moment at the door, then drew back the curtain. The Queen's back was turned to me, so I stepped in and stood quite quiet for some time, long enough to realize that she really did play extraordinarily well. At last she perceived me, or pretended to do so, for the first time, and at once stood up, as if exceedingly surprised, coming towards me playfully threatening me with her fists. She declared that she never played before a man; she only amused herself by doing so when she was quite alone. How in all the world had I come to be there? I said that, coming that way after dinner, I had heard such enchanting music that I could not resist it, and, before I knew where I was, I was in the room. I said, 'I can only implore Your Majesty to pardon a man who has sojourned long at the French court, where such freedoms are forgiven. If, however, Your Majesty cannot forgive me, I am ready to bear any punishment Your Majesty may think fit to impose upon me.' Or words to that effect. Thereupon she took a cushion, and sat down upon it, while I knelt before her, putting another cushion, which she pressed on me with both hands, under my knees. She then asked me whether Your Majesty played better than she did. To which I could only reply that she played far better than Your Majesty. I was glad to find something to say which pleased her, and was also true."

Mary smiled again. Sir James continued his narrative.

"In the course of conversation, the Queen said that she was glad I spoke French so well; did I also speak Italian? She spoke Italian and German to me, her German not being so good as her Italian. While she treated me with this extraordinary graciousness, I permitted her to see something of my desire to have my commission accomplished. Thereupon she remarked that I must find her very tedious if I thought of nothing but how to get away at once. I declared, on the contrary, I could have no conceivable ground for being anything but happy at her court. She then said that I must stay for at least two days more. I soon saw why I had got to stay—it was in order that I might

see her dance, as happened on the following evening. She then
wanted to know who was the better dancer, Your Majesty or
she. I replied that Your Majesty did not dance in such perfect
time or with so much stateliness as she did. She sighed again,
saying, 'Ah, if I could only see and speak with her!' At this, I
allowed myself to ask why should she not come privily to Scotland? Other Princes before her had ventured to make such
journeys—for example, Your Majesty's father, King James
V of Scotland, went incognito to France in order that he might
see the lady who was proposed to him as bride, and when she
did not please him, he refused to wed her. She shook her head:
'I cannot do such a thing. But be sure to tell your Queen how
tenderly attached to her I am and how I cannot allow even the
shadow of a suspicion to find room in my sister's heart henceforth.' I was then permitted to depart, and Secretary Cecil was
instructed to settle all matters of business."

Sir James had been taken from Hampton Court, the summer
residence of the Queen, where she had received him, to London,
by the Earl of Leicester, in his barge. The Earl had also spoken
to him of the marriage plan. "I parried his questions," said
Sir James, "but he assured me, with desperate earnestness, that
such folly had never entered his head as to aim at a fortune so
illimitably above a man who did not rate himself as worthy to
serve so great a Queen as my Sovereign even as a lackey. He
knew well enough that this whole plan had been hatched by his
arch-enemy, Secretary Cecil, as a cunning trap to cause him
to lose, at one stroke, the friendship of both Queens for good
and all. He implored me most earnestly to lay at the feet of my
Sovereign his most humble excuses and persuade her not to look
upon him as so criminal a fool."

Sir James Melville had also talked with those among the
English nobles who were devoted to the cause of his Queen.
Mary asked about the attitude of the other relations of the
English Queen who might, with her, have claims to the succes-
sion. There was Lord Henry Darnley, whose claims, like Mary's
own, derived through Queen Margaret of Scotland, but were

obviously inferior to Scotland's; the one great advantage on Darnley's side being that he was the solitary male claimant. Then there were the Princesses Katherine and Mary Grey, related to Queen Elizabeth in the same degree as was Queen Mary. Their importance derived from the wills of the last two Kings of England, Henry and Edward, in which both kings granted their Parliament free disposition over the Crown, and both cited the Ladies Grey as heiresses while expressly banning any claimant from Scotland.

Mary now heard that she had nothing to fear from any of the claimants. The Darnley family had been assiduous in attentions to her ambassador. Queen Elizabeth's attentions to them were confined to the bare minimum demanded by mere civility. For the Greys the Queen had no use: the less that they had once been given preference over herself in her brother's will. To prevent any trouble from this quarter, Queen Elizabeth had brusquely forbidden marriage, once and for all, to both ladies. Lady Katherine, however, the elder of the two, had secretly married a nobleman of the Queen's household. When the fact became known, Queen Elizabeth had the unfortunate pair shut up in the Tower. The marriage, which the prisoners had no opportunity to confirm, was declared null and void. While her wrath against this couple was still at its height, an action of the other sister, Lady Mary, fanned it to fury. In the deepest secrecy, she actually took the turnkey of the royal castle as her husband, on no better ground than that she was the smallest lady about the court, and the porter the tallest man in London. Wrenched apart, they too were for long confined under lock and key.

Mary asked her envoy, finally, whether he had received the impression that the friendly assurances of the English Queen were in accordance with her real feelings. Sir James Melville hesitated. "Do not be afraid to speak," said the Queen.

"If Your Majesty desires me to give my real opinion, and to speak according to my conscience, then, as a man to whom the truth is precious, I must reply 'No,' I do not believe that there is much reality behind all these pretty phrases. Rather they seem to me to mask a considerable degree of jealousy and spite."

"So I always thought," said Mary, sighing.

"It can hardly but seem suspicious," Sir James went on, "to have a man continually pressed upon you as your husband, whom the Queen of England, when it came to it, would be quite incapable of giving up. At the same time, it should be emphasized that Queen Elizabeth has, in the clearest possible manner, set herself against the tendencies in the Lower House of her Parliament which are hostile to Your Majesty."

"It is all very confusing," said Mary, thoughtfully. Then, after a moment's reflection, "Time will reveal what ought to be done. . . . You have often been in London?"

"This makes the second time, Your Majesty. I travelled to the Continent by way of Ireland, but I came back through London."

"What impression does the town make?" asked Mary. "I have never seen it. I was not permitted to return home by land," she added, smiling a trifle ruefully.

"London, Your Majesty," replied Melville, "is certainly a splendid city. It is very large, there are a great many rich houses, magnificent buildings, palaces, churches, towers; there is a tremendous sense of life. At every turn, you meet people from all parts of the world—Frenchmen, Spaniards, Germans, Dutchmen, Danes, numerous Italians. You can tell them by their clothes and faces, and also by their bearing. In the crowd, you hear every language spoken."

"What sort of people are the English? I mean, the people in general."

"They are more lively than our people; they talk more and laugh more often and more loudly. They are fond of music, and passionately devoted to the theatre. They are quicker at the uptake than our folk; you feel that they find nothing wonderful in the thought that in three weeks they could be in Paris and in six in Venice."

"Is London as impressive as Paris?"

"Almost, I think, Your Majesty."

"It cannot be so beautiful," said Mary. "Paris is wonderfully beautiful. The air there is like balm and the sky shines like opal. There, everything—houses, palaces, the streets, the squares, the bridges—is glorious. London can have no such churches as Notre Dame, Saint Germain l'Auxerrois, or Sainte Geneviève; no other city in the world has such. You know how the windows in the Sainte Chapelle glow? And then there is Rheims Cathedral—have you seen it? My mother is buried there. I shall be buried in France, too. Have you seen Rouen Cathedral?" Melville bowed deeply. "But I must not lose myself in these thoughts," said Mary.

"London is really very wonderful," said her envoy, encouragingly. "They have many fine buildings there and splendid works of art, paintings and so on."

"They cannot have such beauty, such art as they have in France," the Queen repeated. Two round tears fell from her eyes into her lap; she pressed her handkerchief to her face. "It is only that, there, when people spoke to me, I could read their faces and know what they thought, and everything was pleasant."

"But every one loves Your Majesty here."

"I know, I know," she said quickly, but the tears kept rising to her eyes. She said, in a minute: "By comparison with London I suppose Edinburgh is a small city?"

"Everything is different here," he replied. "But, Your Majesty, we have the sea and Arthur's Seat!"

"It is bleak," she said. "To have always to look at it is often very depressing." She collected herself and, after drying the last drops from her eyes, replaced her handkerchief. Smiling on him, graciously, her eyes still sparkling with tears, she said: "Sir James Melville, you have served me well and faithfully, with all the powers of a clever man. I thank you. I am glad that you have come home from abroad, and so given me some one on whose loyalty and efficiency I can entirely rely. I shall soon have other and more important commissions for you."

Sir James had to wait no longer than the next day, to know what it was the Queen had to ask of him. She then said, "I need all your courage, your brains, your uprightness in a place where such qualities are even more important to me than at the Court of London and with Queen Elizabeth. Sir James, I am going to ask you to assist me here at my own court, against my enemies at home and, it may be, against myself." His hand on his heart, he was about to assure her that all his powers were always at his Sovereign's service, but she interrupted him.

"Wait! It is in my mind to ask much of you. Sir James, you know how difficult my position is, inasmuch as I am of a different faith from that of the majority of my subjects. On that account I need an adviser, experienced, intelligent, courageous, upright, such an adviser as I have found in you. I want you to tell me when I do anything wrong, even if I only make a wrong movement with my right hand. So that I may alter it."

She looked with penetrating gaze at him as he stood before her, all confusion: his face normally so serenely indifferent, was suddenly suffused with colour.

"What is it that Your Majesty desires of me?" he said, at last. "So admirably educated, so marvellously gifted as you are, you ought rather to serve as exemplar to your subjects, and do so serve, whenever you appear."

"No, no," cried Mary, eagerly, "that will not do; you are evading! I know well enough," she went on, with a little sigh, "that I have often taken false steps without the smallest intention of harm. Are you going to leave me in the lurch? hand me over to all the evil gossips and to those who spy upon me? Oh," she signed to him again not to contradict her, "any one who is raised above the rest has spies and enemies—and a Queen! For such a task, there is no one suitable in my entourage. Either they are strangers here, with manners and habits that are more unfamiliar even than I am, or—with no lack of good will—a little too raw to serve me as useful teachers. You are upright," she repeated. "You are no flatterer. Look you, I know perfectly well what most people want of me. Those who are about me—what do they want? To serve me? No, themselves first. I am quite indifferent to most of them. You do not know how alone I am, really." There was a touch of real pathos in her tone. "Are you afraid that you will incur my displeasure, if you do as I ask?" she said, as he seemed still to hesitate.

"Your Majesty," he replied, "frankly, it is a dangerous post!" The Queen laughed, merrily. "Yes," he said, "it really is. Why does Your Majesty not turn to your brother, the Earl of Murray, or to Lord Lethington?"

Mary looked away from him. "That would not suit me," she said, after a moment's hesitation; then, turning again to him: "You do not mean to suggest to me that you have so bad an opinion of me as to fear losing my favour because you told me the truth? You should rather give me the opportunity to prove how serious my request to you is. Will you?"

She extended to him her small, white, very beautiful hand, covered with priceless rings, its beauty enhanced by the delicate lace of the cuff. Sir James knelt to kiss the exquisite hand. His mind was far from clear as he rose and went away.

★

Before Christmas, 1564, the meeting of the English and Scottish ministers took place at York, to discuss Queen Elizabeth's marriage proposals. Mary had nominated her two most distinguished counsellors, the Earl of Murray and Maitland of Lethington; the English Government was represented by the Earl of Bedford and Mr. Thomas Randolph. The result of the meeting was precisely what all those who took part in it had foreseen. The Scots said, "We must have guarantees, and above all a solemn, legally unassailable admission of our Sovereign's rights to the succession, before there can be any question of agreeing to the proposal of an English subject as her husband." The English replied: "So soon as Queen Mary of Scotland acts in conformity with the wishes of our Queen, she can count on her goodness." The Scots replied that such vague assurances could satisfy no one. At the same time, the matter must be settled, since it served to prevent their Queen from making any other decision. In fact, the uncertain attitude imposed upon her by the ambiguous motions of the English Government, exposed her to a serious danger of missing the opportunity of more important alliances. As a final formula they suggested that the patent right of their Queen to be completely free to choose the husband she preferred must be admitted. If she were to take England so far into account as to consider no one who might be hostile to England in views or behaviour, she must be compensated for such a self-imposed limitation by having her right to the succession to the English throne recognized.

The English had nothing effective to say in reply to this, and the meeting broke up. Its result was so meagre that there was not even an end of the futile proposal, by Queen Elizabeth, of the Earl of Leicester, which no one took seriously; on the contrary, it was continued through letters and verbal communications by Mr. Thomas Randolph.

Chapter 4

ADVENT OF THE LENNOXES

In the year 1562, when the Duke of Savoy, a near relative and friend of Queen Mary, sent envoys to her court to welcome her on her return to her native land, there rode in the Ambassador's suite a small, olive-skinned man, supple and powerful as a monkey in his movements, a Piedmontese of eight-and-twenty, named David Rizzio. No one took much notice of him as he moved about the court with his fellows, until, shortly before his departure, his master caused a musical performance to be given by his suite before the assembled court. Then David Rizzio stepped out, before the brilliant throng of lords and ladies, with a lute suspended round his neck on whose strings he plucked with his long fingers. Standing directly in front of the Queen, he opened to its fullest capacity a mouth that seemed to reach from ear to ear, and shaking back his thick mane of hair, sang, with singular vehemence, first one song and then, on the Queen's applause, a second and a third. Laughing heartily at the strange figure he presented, Mary encouraged him to go on by clapping her hands. On the following evening, at the Queen's request, the performance was repeated. Thereupon David was informed that he and his voice had pleased the Queen so much that she had appealed to his master: the singing at her court lacked a fourth voice. David's bass seemed perfectly designed to fill the gap—could and would Mr. Ambassador not leave his servant at the Scottish court? With infinite pleasure would Mr. Ambassador have granted far greater requests. David perceived that he was in a fair way to make his fortune. When his lord departed, he remained. The Queen had him sing. She sent for him, to talk with him of France and of

125

Italy, which, as his native land, he knew intimately. His coarse and clever repartee pleased her. When the secretary who did the Queen's French and Italian correspondence had to be sent home, ill of home-sickness, Mary found David well fitted for his post, perhaps the more so that, being an Italian, he had no sort of attachments in the countries with which she had most to do.

One day, watching some courtiers playing tennis, David was leaning over the rail with Sir James Melville beside him, a little apart from the others. The Scotsman turned to him suddenly with the remark that he had, for some time, had something to say to him to which, for his own sake, he advised him to pay heed; he proceeded to warn David to be more circumspect in his behaviour. The Scottish lords took it excessively ill that, for example, when he had to speak with the Queen, he would walk straight in to wherever she might be, regardless of who might be with her even if representatives of the nobles or the whole Council of State itself were there. David, who had listened with open mouth and wrinkled brows, at once replied that Sir James seemed to him to be entirely in the right. He was, anyhow, greatly obliged to him for the kindness of his warning. But, he added, with an embarrassed laugh, what was he to do? It was Her Majesty's wish to have it so, and no otherwise. In the evening, however, he came to Sir James's dwelling, in order to return explicitly to his warning, and inquire whether Sir James had anything definite in his mind. Sir James answered, No, nothing definite. He had merely spoken in general, from his own experience; he proceeded to amplify his advice by citing his own case, for he had voluntarily withdrawn from the special favour of the Elector Palatine to avoid bringing down the hatred of the local nobles on his own head and on that of his patron. After some reflection, David said he should do the same. A few days later, when he met Sir James in the Queen's ante-chamber, he detained him, however, in order to say to him that while he had, of course, been constantly occupied with the advice Sir James had given him, for which he was still heartily grateful, he had at last come to the conclusion that it was out

126

of the question for him to play the part of a coward and withdraw. It was the Queen's wish that there should be no limitations on the freedom of their intercourse. What could he do, but obey? Sir James wrapped the cloak he was in the act of putting on more closely about him. "Don't be surprised, then, if something unpleasant happens some day," he observed, dryly.

Mindful of the Queen's injunction to him to speak frankly, Sir James felt that the matter was of sufficient importance for him to go to her and tell her the comments that were being caused by the fact that she gave her confidence in most important matters to a stranger, to the exclusion of her own nobles, who were entitled to it. The disquiet thus caused was, he said, all the greater from the fact that David being a Catholic no one could be sure that he was not a tool of the enemies of the country in their constant plots against its religion. The Queen, obviously troubled by these words of warning, replied, after a moment's thought, that she was anyhow grateful to her servant for his loyal candour. But, she added, his concern was baseless. Only foreign correspondence went through David's hands, and he, like his predecessor, filled the part merely of a subordinate scribe. With domestic policy he had absolutely nothing to do. "I should have thought," said she, arching her delicate neck proudly, "that even an ill-disposed person would have admitted, after one glance at my ministers and counsellors, that I am dealing justly and fairly with my people! Yes, indeed. At the same time I shall always retain my freedom to give my confidence where it seems to be deserved, without consulting the humour of my dear subjects first." Sir James, however, did not allow himself to be put off. He went so far as to recall to the Queen the awkward affair with the Sieur Chastelard. "How much harm is come to Your Majesty from the fact that your goodness and patience caused you to go on forgiving him!" There was, even so, nothing ungracious in Mary's dismissal of Melville; she said she should think over what he had said. Yet at night Melville heard that she had spent the entire afternoon working alone with David in her closet. Moreover, no change was visible in her relations with the Italian, except that David became obviously more and more arrogant and wanton in his bearing.

★

About the end of the year 1564 Mary's plans for a proud Spanish marriage collapsed, for King Philip, after endless delays, at last brought himself to reply that in view of the physical and mental state of the Infant Don Carlos it was impossible to contemplate so dangerous and serious an undertaking as the Scottish marriage. Once again, the Archduke Charles of Austria came to the front as substitute, and his claims as the one suitable husband were pressed with lively insistence upon Queen Mary as well as on her neighbour, Queen Elizabeth, by relations and friends at the German, Spanish and French courts. Queen Mary, however, rejected the Austrian with an obstinacy equal to that displayed by her good sister Elizabeth.

She, on her part, was unwearied in pushing her own good friend and lover. In the end, however, it seemed as though the object of the Queen of England was merely to bar every other wooer's way to the lists for the hand of the Queen of Scotland.

For some decades now there had been living at the English court the family of Matthew, Earl of Lennox, closely related both to the English and to the Scottish Queen. Margaret, the elder of the two sisters of King Henry VIII, had, after the death of her husband King James IV of Scotland, entered into a brief second marriage with the Earl of Angus, a Douglas, whose issue was a daughter, named Margaret after her mother. On account of the disorders in her native land, the child had been sent to the English court by her mother, at a time when Margaret was still on good terms with her brother Henry VIII. There she grew up in friendship with his daughter, Princess Mary, a few months only her senior, and, later, was lady-in-waiting to each of her uncle's six wives in turn. When she grew up, the King of England married her to Matthew, Earl of Lennox, a Stuart in the second line from the royal house of

128

Scotland. Earl Lennox was given the Princess's hand as a reward for his having promised, after the premature death of King James V, to hand the kingdom and the person of his little Queen, Mary, over to Henry of England. This promise the Scottish Earl sought to fulfil by invading his native land with English troops who burned and laid waste everything on which they could lay their hands. His enterprise failed, and the little Queen was spirited to France, out of the way of English greed. The Scots then outlawed the Earl of Lennox, and divided his property among his foes, notably the Hamiltons, who, like him, claimed to be the nearest to the Scottish throne after the Queen herself.

The Earl now dwelt in England and his lady, as cousin and intimate of Queen Mary Tudor, played so important a rôle that there were many who strove for her favour as that of the future heir to the English throne. Times changed, however, and Queen Elizabeth ruled in England. She might not do any hurt to this near kinswoman; had, indeed, in view of the impeccable behaviour of the whole family, to allow her to appear at court. But that was all. The two sons of the family were brought up as though it were possible that, one day, they might be kings, somewhere, somehow. Nominally the family adhered to the English Church. Every one however knew that, at heart, ever since the days of Queen Mary Tudor, they inclined to the Catholic party. Many regarded them as its heads.

Meantime the family yearned for Scotland. The Queen Regent rejected all their advances. Queen Mary, for long, maintained the attitude of her mother. The Lennoxes though constantly rebuffed were not too proud to renew their petition every year. In 1564 their persistence had its reward: Queen Mary informed Earl Matthew that, in view of the need she felt in such disturbed times of gathering all her kin about her, she was ready to forget earlier injuries and feuds. Indeed, she contemplated doing all that was in her power to reconcile the Earl with his enemies. If he cared to come, Scotland was no longer closed to him.

Queen Elizabeth had to give her permission before one of her nobles might leave the country. When she was informed, she at first took up the attitude of never giving her consent to leave of absence for abroad in the special personal circumstances of her petitioner. But on the strong representations of her ministers, and, above all, of William Cecil, she at last gave way.

So, on a lovely afternoon in September, 1564, Matthew Earl of Lennox rode through the south gate into the city of Edinburgh, which for twenty years he had not seen. He rode slowly, looking about him, observing the changes that his long absence had made in gates and streets, houses and people. Richly attired, he sat his horse so well as still to deserve the reputation for a fine person which he had enjoyed ever since his youth in Scotland. Nothing in his exterior man betrayed treason to King and Country; on the contrary, he appeared a good, worthy, middle-aged gentleman, with nothing more in mind than a desire to win esteem by the correct modesty of his demeanour.

Next day, he appeared at court, in costly attire, with a magnificent train. He knelt before the Queen, who regarded curiously a man whom she had hitherto known by hearsay only. Graciously, she bade him rise. She said that she hoped his old home would bring him happiness; she would do all that in her lay to make it seem a real homeland to him. Earl Matthew presented the greetings of his wife, who ventured to lay herself, in humblest devotion, at the feet of her exalted young relative. He asked whether the Queen, in the plenitude of her grace, would deign to permit her passionately devoted relations and subjects to present some trifling little greetings as symbols of their faithful duty? All that they had belonged to Her Majesty. At the same time, perhaps she would look kindly on a token of affection. Earl Matthew took from a page a chest which he opened, revealing a lovely clock, in a gold case of exquisite workmanship, the face surrounded by a wreath of flowers executed in diamonds and sapphires, which a fat little Cupid, smiling gaily, was plucking. Mary looked at the gift,

130

then, overcome by its enchanting beauty, lifted it carefully with her two hands. "But this really is inconceivably lovely!" Blushing with pleasure, she showed it to Mary Livingstone, Mary Fleming, and the Countess of Argyle. "Even in France, we have never seen anything so fascinating!" "It is actually the most modern French work," said the Earl proudly. Mary displayed the details of the craftsmanship to her friends, and caressed the plump cheeks of the Cupid with her fingers. "And does it really keep time?" "Many, many blessed and joyful days of Your Majesty's wise and happy reign will have passed before it so much as needs to be wound." Nor was this all. His wife had selected a silver hand-mirror for the Queen. At the sight of this, Mary was quite beside herself. "You will fancy me a mere child, to be so pleased!" she said. "Just think: when I came here, they did not even know what a mirror looks like, far less did any such thing exist. Outside the ones that we brought with us, there were literally none in the whole of Scotland." Crimson with happiness, the Earl bowed again and again.

He had no idea what was being said about him by the ladies and gentlemen of the court, hardly separated from him by the widely open door. "He looks just such an old fool as my father's stories always made me expect," said Lord Minto, a dry little man with a parchment face and sparse lint-fair hair. "He has brought seven hundred pounds sterling with him, for the meantime," grinned the handsome young Earl of Sutherland. "No doubt he thinks that a lot for Scotland." The Earl of Argyle, a man of unusual height, with a face in which the appearance of a Hussite leader was crossed with a touch of the Oriental—a thick black moustache hung down with a melancholy air between his huge nose and a mouth like that of a Hottentot—laughed grimly. "He will have forgotten what it is like in Scotland. Dear sausage and lean bacon. Hanging no lower than anywhere else, for all that." "A fool, a fool, a cunning fool! Just look, do, at him twisting and turning like a teetotum! All the hairs on his bald pate are bowing too,

Doesn't his dagger look like a monkey's tail, sticking out all stiff with awe in this great moment of his life?" "In his whole life he has never fancied himself as much as he does now, not even when he led Lady Margaret to the altar as his douce reward for having put some sixty abbies, twenty towns and a hundred villages in Scotland to the brand!" "The reward was there all right, make no mistake," said the stout Earl of Atholl slowly. "Here he comes, to spread his happiness around." As Earl Matthew approached the groups of lords and ladies, he met everywhere deep bows and ready beaming faces. Here too he distributed the greetings of his absent spouse, and here too asked whether he might be permitted—his wife had ventured— the lords and ladies would not pain them by rejecting their gifts, which, modest as they were, came from the heart. . . . There was a rich diamond ring for Baron Maitland of Lething- ton, and for the Earl of Atholl and other gentry of the court. Only Lord James of Murray, so it was put about, went empty away. The Queen's four Maries displayed lovely lace, artistic fans, gold pins and scent bottles, all gifts of Earl Matthew.

The Queen interceded for him with his enemies. Before his arrival she had commanded the Hamiltons not to seek any kind of quarrel with the Earl on pain of her extreme royal displeasure. Indeed, they were not so much as to speak with the Earl save in her presence. She summoned the old Duke, who had been nursing his wrath in protracted absence from court, where she had for a long time left him to chew the cud of his bitterness against her and the world in solitude. Now he heard that for the sake of the State and of the Queen his whole house must make peace with that of Lennox. He was to arrange the restoration by his family of the estates confiscated from the Lennoxes; if this were freely done, there would be ample com- pensation from the Crown lands. Two weeks after the old Earl's arrival at court, the Queen summoned him and the old Duke before her, that they might both take her hands in the pres- ence of the entire court. "My Lords, if ye love our common country and myself, swear now between my hands that ye will

henceforth live in peace with one another and good will to all."
In high good humour, Earl Matthew wrote to his spouse that
a quite indescribable fulness of fortune and honour had been
poured upon his head. She should with all possible speed send
their son Henry after his father, equipping him with every conceivable elegance and richness.

★

There was but one word at court for the royal graciousness
to this elderly lord whom no one could abide. The only person
who on this occasion did not believe what every one said was
the individual who, in general, knew everything—Thomas
Randolph, Queen Elizabeth's envoy. He still believed in his
Queen's plan, that of her beloved Earl of Leicester. True, they
sought to open his eyes, saying, "Look at this repulsive being,
and our Queen not knowing how to do enough for his sweet
sake!" Randolph replied: "The Queen is far too wise not to be
perfectly aware that there is nothing to be gained for her there.
This Lord Darnley, about whom all at once every one is talking
as though he were a possible consort for so great a Queen,
what does he really amount to? A poor creature, who has nothing whatever but what the two Queens, out of the kindness of
their hearts, may be moved to give him. Apart from that, he is
nothing but a schoolboy of nineteen, and such a thick-head that
he cannot even understand his lessons." "So it may seem to you,
Mr. Randolph. Here Lord Henry Darnley has the name of a
very handsome young man, so well brought up that there is no
prince in the world to equal him for riding and sword-play,
dancing and playing on the lute. After all, the Queen doesn't
want to read Cicero with him! He is said to be exceptionally
well-looking." "A silly Maypole, as vain as he is long—that's
what he is," insisted Randolph, at first becoming excited and
then remembering that there was no need for that. "The
Queen will not look at him! She is far too clever for that."
"We shall see!" Randolph laughed, knowingly and grimly too.
He pressed the Queen to give him answer to his question: What

was her view of the Earl of Leicester's suit? She parried it.

Finally, she left Edinburgh with a small suite, for St. Andrews, the fair city on the east coast, on the invitation of a wealthy citizen. Randolph was told that, were he so inclined, he would be welcome there as Queen Mary's guest. He accepted, gladly. But he found the Queen in almost oppressive spirits. When he began to talk business, she waved it laughingly aside. "Mr. Randolph, are you already weary of our society? I would have you know that I have caused you to come hither that you too might enjoy some pleasant days and have a good time. Our idea is to live here like good, plain citizens. And then, when we are harmlessly pleased with life, you come and try to burden us with your great, great affairs of State? Look here"—mirth and seriousness danced in her eyes—"please, Mr. Randolph, go back to Edinburgh; pack up your great dignity and your great embassy neatly and properly in a great strong box, which is perfectly secure and can wait until the Queen of Scotland, who has gone on a journey somewhere or other, but must come back sooner or later, does come back to Edinburgh again. Meantime, do you come here and be merry with us. Are you not sometimes, Mr. Randolph, sick and tired of official garb and functions and solemnity?" But he, depressed and awkward, shook his head. "The letter of my exalted mistress!" He bowed still more profoundly, becoming quite grey from sheer distress. "Mr. Serious," said Mary, "Mr. All-Too-Circumspect, Mr. Ten-Times-Too-Safe rather than Once-Ready-to-Relax, is it really the case that one must have pity on you? Anyhow, be at ease: responsibility for all these matters falls on the Queen of Scotland."

On the following morning a message came to his lodging from the Queen to say that if he cared he might go riding with her that afternoon. He obeyed. Mary called him to her side. They rode by the sea, close to the water's edge; on their right was the mighty roar and plunge of the waves. Mary drew in deep breaths of the strong air. At first they rode fast: then Mary slackened her horse to a walk; her suite remained a little behind: only Mary Fleming and Mr. Randolph rode by her side. The jesting humour of the previous day had quite passed. As she gazed out over the ocean, she became sorrowful, losing herself in memories of the home of her youth and her happy days in France. There she had been honoured, so much so indeed that she had been chosen to wife by a King as great as that of France. As if to comfort herself for the change in her fortunes, she said that after all she was not altogether forgotten there, for her friendship was eagerly sought after. "You have no idea of the offers that are made to me thence," she assured Mr. Randolph, hinting that she had only to choose to ascend the throne of France anew as the wife of her brother-in-law, the new King. "But I would put it all on one side, every prospect for the future, every honour in the present: neglect everything, everything, that the world has for me in the way of friends and relations, if your mistress would treat me really as her sister or daughter; then I would give her all the obedience and respect I would have given an elder sister or my own mother. But if she insists on treating me merely as a neighbour, merely as the Queen of Scotland, and forces me back upon myself, then I may have no choice, greatly as I care for her friendship and for peace, but to look for friends and allies after a fashion that perhaps neither she nor I might wish."

While the usual assurances flowed from his lips, Randolph looked at his royal companion, sitting her horse like Diana herself, light, proud, happy in her conscious mastery of the lovely animal she rode. He thought of the shy, repressed young woman who, three years ago, after bitter experiences in a distant land, had returned to her home as though to some hostile alien region. Now, she seemed to him to have blossomed out into such beauty that even in his heart the question stirred, poignant, had the earth ever seen anything so perfect since first beauty shimmered over its surface? Perhaps Mary knew how the radiance of her splendour touched what did duty for a heart within this inhuman time-server. She stretched joyously in the saddle. A smile curved her delicate scarlet lips. "Mr.

Randolph," she said, with a glance that made even him feel his steed bound with Olympian grace, "doubtless it is folly on my part to contend with you, for of course you are far too subtle for my unschooled simplicity. What can one do save state quite frankly—it seems to me very right and proper, nay even necessary, that we two, your mistress and I, should really live together in sisterly friendship, being as we are kinswomen, Queens, neighbours and alone on this island. Oh, of course I know that at a crisis even our good will might be of no avail." She sighed. "What are Queens if their people do not stand behind them? At the same time, look about you. You know as well as I do—although proud England may feel entitled to look down upon us and despise us as poor and unimportant—that we have time and again been a thorn in your flesh and have compelled you to recognize that we have sufficient might to do you very sensible injury! By which I mean merely that the Queen your mistress and I must redouble and treble our efforts to do all the good that is within our power, and consolidate our countries against all others. That done, we can adjust whatever points may be in dispute between ourselves. . . . What do you say?" she asked, finally.

He could but express his delighted agreement. That, in this conversation, he had at last been given a definite answer to his Government's propositions, he did not perceive until much later.

★

After this Mary was the guest of her brother, Lord James, in Wemyss Castle. The old fortress, traditional home of the clan Macduff, was perched in a wild spot above the Firth of Forth, whose wide waters beat with a loud roar against its rocks. Towards evening, Mary stood in the embrasure of her window; a cold wind was blowing: she looked up to the sky, heavy with vast cloud masses, tossing and turning under the force of the gale: she looked down to the Firth, a mighty unison of streams heaving like a black sea under the force of the tide. With a shiver she stepped down from the window back into the room. Here her Maries were waiting to array their Queen for a great reception. They clad her in a robe of lilac silk, covered with silver and pearl net, passing over it a black satin over-dress edged with grey fur, with a wide and costly collar rising high from the décolletage. On the Queen's hair they placed a net of gold, leaving the front clear, with delicate curls about the temples. The Queen bowed slightly towards Mary Seaton, who hung round her neck a beautiful chain with a miniature of the dead King of France dependent from it. Mary took her gloves, her fan, and her little lace handkerchief, and, accompanied by her pages and followed by her lords and ladies, entered the great hall of the castle, where a brilliant company awaited her. With a silken rustle, the rows of ladies and gentlemen ranged along the walls bowed deep in greeting as she entered. On the arm of her brother, the Queen passed along the broad pathway between them, smiling on all sides, to the carpeted dais at the further end of the hall, where she seated herself beneath the canopy to receive the greetings of the newly arrived guests. She knew whom she was to see today for the first time: knew that the young man whom Lord James of Murray was bringing up to her was Lord Henry Darnley. With mien at once assured and modest, he approached, dropping his beret so low that the great feathers almost swept the ground, clad in a close-fitting doublet of silvery grey velvet, slashed with pale pink satin on the hips and round the sleeves, a short cloak of silver-grey velvet lined with pale pink and trimmed with swansdown hanging from his shoulders by a chain of gold. As he approached he looked taller than any of the proud cavaliers in the hall. Beside him, Lord James looked almost like a sombre monarch of the nether world, while Henry Darnley, with his regular features, was all light: light hair, light eyes, light complexion, and light shimmering attire. Mary had heard him described as the handsomest youth in the British Isles; anyhow the best dancer, the most skilful fencer, the most accomplished tennis-player and lute-player at the English court. As James Murray, the host of the house, presented him,

and he sank upon his knee before her, Mary bent towards him
with a gracious smile. He stood up in response to her gesture,
and answered her questions calmly, in an agreeably soft voice.
She asked after the health of his mother, after the Queen of
England, whether Henry Darnley himself had had a very unpleasant journey in the winter cold, whether his impressions of
Scotland, during his ride, had been agreeable, whether he were
comfortable here in the castle. Her eyes shone with pleasure,
as after greeting the new arrivals, she stepped down among the
company. The musicians in the gallery, decked out with green
larch, raised their instruments in readiness. The Queen sent
for Lord Henry Darnley, that she might open the dance with
him, the most distinguished of her guests.

★

A few days later, Lord Henry Darnley left Wemyss in order
to visit his father, who had betaken himself to his recently recovered estates. He was at pains, however, to be in Edinburgh
before the Queen's entry. She soon returned, and festivities,
hunts, balls, concerts and theatrical performances followed one
another in dizzy succession. Darnley was perpetually at her
side. A modest assurance marked his behaviour to her; he was
courtesy itself to every one. He, too, had brought full pockets
with him. They held friendly letters of recommendation from
the English Queen, from her Minister, Cecil, and from the Earl
of Leicester. And there were costly presents, for the Queen, for
her ladies, for the leading men of the court. Wherever he went,
he pleased the people of the town, of the streets, throughout
the country; first he was fair to look upon, next, he was atten-
tive in his greetings, and appeared every Sunday at kirk, side
by side with that fervent patriot and blameless Christian, Lord
James Stuart of Murray.

At court there were bets. "Will our Queen marry this long
fair fellow, or will she not?" "She will marry him." "Not she!"
"Nonsense, she has been burning for him like a pine torch this
great while. Any one can see it. The fires are all lit, for this

lad. And he, at any moment, is not sure whether there is any difference between spirit and spectre." "Just so. Do you imagine she does not know whom she has to deal with? A woman in love! Has she not said that in all her life she never saw a better built man? Six months ago, she would have been writing apologies to France and sent any one who libelled her with such a story to the stocks. But Lord Henry, if she could get him to say, 'Ah, je vous aime, ma belle Marie!' she would put him in a pretty hole!"

Henry Darnley dwelt in Holyrood, although there was too little room there for the court. The Queen's servants waited upon him; the horses in the royal stable were at his disposal. What could such distinction imply, if not the highest favour? His worst enemy could not deny that the young man was well, even extraordinarily well, bred. The Queen's friendliness might be no more than courtesy to a near relative of the English royal house. "She will not wed this sponger! Truly, you know our Queen well, if you really believe she will demean herself so far." "Of course, she is all graciousness and sweetness and loving-kindness to every one. But in her heart she thinks that even the greatest King is hardly worthy to stand by her side. A subject, twice a subject? her own? Never. Never will she take him."

It was said that the Queen had spoken confidentially to Sir James Melville. She knew well enough that the Lennox family intended Lord Henry to be her husband. But this intention of theirs was an old story. In the very early days of her widowhood, Countess Margaret had proposed her son Henry as an admirably suitable husband for her. He was fifteen at the time. Such a notion could hardly have astonished her more at the time than did this present wooing.

Sir James Melville had come forward on behalf of the young man, suggesting that every gift, every circumstance, made him exceptionally suitable as a consort for Her Majesty. He had set out his views in detail: Lord Henry was both a Scottish and an English noble, and close kin to both royal houses.

Though a Protestant, he was in close touch with the leaders of the Catholic Party; at twenty, he was young enough to be easily adaptable; the Queen evidently found his bearing and personality not displeasing. Queen Mary listened kindly, but did not continue the conversation. About this time, Lord Henry was frequently to be seen arm in arm with David Rizzio, whom he further distinguished by visits in his lodging, where he would stay chatting for hours. The two went together to the chase. David, who was likewise on most friendly terms with Lord Robert and Lord John Stuart, the younger illegitimate brothers of the Queen, undertook to introduce Henry Darnley to the pleasures which Edinburgh offered to gentlemen of the court.

★

Whatever the Queen's feelings, she had little leisure to indulge in sweet dreams. One day, after a brisk ride in the company of Lord James Stuart, she dismounted in the courtyard of the palace, and with the train of her gown thrown over her arm, was about to enter the hall to ascend the stairs, when a squire approached the Earl to whisper a message in his ear. As she stood, the Queen saw a veritable flame of wrath pass swiftly over her brother's dark brow. He bit his underlip hard, sure sign that he was struggling to master the tide of passion that devastated him. "What is it?" asked his sister.

He approached her. "Incredible, Madam!" His excitement was so great that his voice broke: he was hard put to it to muster enough self-command to speak. "The Earl of Bothwell is in the country again."

Mary looked at her brother, upset in her turn. Troubles rushed down over her mind, like the loose stones that break from a crevasse when the wall gives that has held them back. Angry and disturbed, she knit her brows. Her brother spoke quickly: the Earl of Bothwell was still outlawed; he had broken the Queen's prison. A warrant must be issued at once.

"He has earned death a thousand times, the worthless, treacherous, perjured rascal, the traitor, the ruffian!" said

Lord James, every glance betraying the flames of a destruc-
tive hatred that brooks no delay. "The world holds no more
devilish tongue, no more utterly abandoned nature, than this
man's. Search Scotland, England, France, Italy, you cannot
match him for evil."

The Queen, however, her eyes on the riding-switch with which
her hands were playing, said no word in reply.

He continued: "Without question, a warrant must be issued!" Apparently he did not realize that he had overstretched
his bow. For the Queen replied now, coldly, "Tomorrow will
be plenty of time for that." His wrath still blazing, Lord James'
shoulders shook. "No, there is no time! Your Majesty cannot
comprehend the abyss of vice that opens on the mere mention
of that name." "Well, he will not storm Holyrood this evening," she said, "and if he did we are surely more than safe
under your guard." Turning icily away, she went into the
palace. That day the Earl spoke to her no more. Next morning, however, so soon as he thought she was awake, he came and
stood by her bed, and said: "Madam, I have reflected on the
news of the arrival of Earl Bothwell. I had time to do so, since
the news kept me awake all night. I come now, since it is my
duty to inform you: You may permit the Earl of Bothwell to
stay in the country. That is your right, and no one can gain-
say it. But there is not room in the country for me and the
Earl. If Your Majesty desires this man's presence, so be it: I
cannot alter, nay I cannot so much as contradict it. But in
that case I ask Your Majesty to release me from all my offices.
Such is the choice before Your Majesty." Mary had sat up in
bed. "Why do you hate the Earl so extraordinarily?" she
asked her brother, in amazement.

He laughed. "I do hate him—yes, I do. I hate his every
movement, every gesture. I cannot endure him when he laughs
and all his teeth flash like a wild beast's. I cannot bear to look
at him, when he throws himself backwards, so insolently, as if
nobody in the world existed but him. Wherever he appears, in
he marches, as though he alone counted, and every one else

141

came after him. Arrogance—he has been made up of that ever since his boyhood. It was arrogance made him go against us, his peers: that, and not the famous loyalty to the monarchy of which he is for ever prating: arrogance based on no services, for there can be no talk of service with such a man: arrogance which simply is, asserts itself, insists that everybody else is mere rabble in comparison with him. When has he shown any sign of so much as knowing the meaning of discipline or shame, order or morals? The final proof of his consummate insolence is the way in which he regarded himself as entirely free to take advantage of the moment which once forced him, under sheer necessity, to restrain, his brutality under some sort of pretence of decent restraint! Nothing in the world is sacred to him, and that forced laughter of his spares nothing. Yes, I do hate him, absolutely, and to destroy him, absolutely, should be my life's work, so long as I, James Stuart, draw breath, and am permitted to live and work. For everything obscene, everything barbarous, everything that violates and undermines discipline, morals and decency, everything that works destruction in this world, is incarnate in him or sings anthems to him as its master spirit. It would be just like him . . ." James Stuart would have gone on, but the Queen interrupted him. "What in the world has the Earl done, to give you such an opinion of him?" James wanted to reply, but, with a gesture indicating that she did not desire to be interrupted, she continued: "I am no more attached to the Earl than to any other of my cavaliers. He has shown courage more than once. So have many. But he stood by my mother, and in that he did not find so many comrades. You say, he did so only because —well, what you have said. That has nothing to do with me. He did it, and I am not likely to forget it. As for the stories about the Earl of Arran, nobody believes all that. Anyhow, whatever there was in it, he has paid for it, paid in full; for I hear that he has fared very ill in his exile." Lord James was almost speechless from the rush of words that came to his lips, when he at last had a chance to speak again. "Your Majesty speaks of the Earl of Bothwell as your modest and faithful servant! Well! I shall say nothing of the fact that this accursed man, as I know from all too certain sources—I am not referring to the crazy Earl of Arran, though, at the same time, it is easy to distinguish, with an insane person, those things which are the product of his mental affliction purely and those which bear the stamp of truth—I know, unfortunately, from other, quite reliable sources that this man has sworn to do me and Baron Lethington to death, whenever and wherever he meets us ; I have exact knowledge of the fact that he has constantly laid the most treacherous traps for us both and that it is only by the most wonderful exercise of the Providence of God that his shameless plans did not succeed. Naturally, we are, both of us, a thorn and a stumbling-block in his way, for he knows that, so long as we are on guard, he can never lay his ruthless hands on Scotland, which is and always has been the single object of his black ambition." The Queen sought to speak, but her brother was in full train of passion: "I do not speak of such plans and designs, for they concern us only and have no significance for Your Majesty, provided it is not ultimately made impossible for us to act as Your Majesty's eager and loyal servants. But does Your Majesty know how that other true and loyal servant, the Earl of Bothwell, has dared to speak of yourself and of Her Majesty the Queen of England, in open tavern, in front of all sorts of base and ill-conditioned persons? Do you know that he has said that Scots and English were on all fours so far as the virtue of their rulers went, and that there was not enough of it in the two Queens together to furnish a single decent woman? Such is Your Majesty's modest and loyal servant, and I am of course the malignant enemy of such incomparable services !" Mary had gone deadly pale. Falling back into her bed, she drew the cover close up over her, shivering. Earl Murray went on: "Your Majesty will say to me, 'Have Scots heard that, and this man still lives?' He does. You yourself have held your hands over his head." "Such an insane attack cannot be made without witnesses," said Mary at last,

evading her brother's eye. "There are only too many of them,"
he replied, naming various names. "I must think it all over;
leave me alone now," she said at last. He went.

At noon he heard that during the morning the Queen had
wept bitterly. At night, however, he had a message from her
instructing him to call a day of law on the Earl of Bothwell,
bidding him present himself before it on a specific day on a
charge of breaking the royal prison. Until then he should leave
her in peace.

★

A fresh source of trouble was the continued intractability
of the preachers. Mary had come to the country at a time when
a law was in force forbidding every form of Catholic worship
under heavy penalties to life, freedom and property, a law
which she had had expressly to accept. For her own part, she
was allowed to celebrate Mass for herself and the Catholic
members of her household in the ample church attached to the
palace. John Knox thundered against this licence, as though
to burst his throat. Soon he was pointing with his finger, and
asking: How many inhabitants of Edinburgh, who had no connection, not even the remotest, with the court, were going every
week, nay, every day, to make sacrifice to Satan in the papis-
tical Mass? The Queen's presence was stretched like a mantle
over all these evil-doers. His preachers announced far and
wide every progress made by the Catholic Party: When the
Queen was absent from her palace, on the chase, or on journeys through her provinces, the congregation still came to
hear Mass, to have their children baptized, their marriages
blessed, to celebrate evening prayers. The preachers roused a
storm; thereupon it was communicated to them by the Cabinet:
The Queen, at the suggestion of her Privy Council, and notably
of the Earl of Murray, had assigned considerable sums from
the private revenues of her own Crown lands for payment to
the Protestant ministers, who seemed like to perish of starva-
tion if left to the resources of their own parishes. It was now
her desire to see the two confessions exist without persecution,

144

side by side. She left every liberty to her Protestant subjects. But it was by no means her desire to have her Catholic folk troubled in their consciences.

John Knox preached in the Cathedral: "So has everything come to pass that Thy servant, O Lord, has foretold, though no one in this blinded generation would hearken to his words. Now they cry—Toleration! Soon they will be crying—Strike dead! Burn, banish, put to shame every child of God professing the true faith!" He prayed—"O Lord, give at last Thy Blessing, purify the heart of the Queen of the poison of idolatry, and free her from the bondage of Satan, in which she has grown up and to which she still adheres. That she may escape eternal damnation, and the pestilence and the destruction that must inevitably follow on such worship of false gods as, against Thy clear commandment, she seeks to maintain in the obstinacy of her heart!"

John Knox was called before the Privy Council, to answer a charge of high treason. But even in this assembly there was no majority for a judgment against him. Lord Lethington exhausted his eloquence and wit in hours of controversy. At last the preacher yielded so far as to agree to an address being despatched to Calvin, the Swiss Reformer, whom even John Knox recognized as his master, to inquire, Should a Catholic prince be obeyed in spiritual matters?

Meantime attendance at Mass in the palace continued to grow; they were assiduous in Communion. The preachers declared they could not be silent in the face of such iniquities. The Queen's decision to leave every one to his own conscience in matters of religion led straight to Hell. "How is it then? Are there two roads to salvation? No, never. The worshippers of Baal, who sacrificed their children to their idol, maintained that they were in possession of the true knowledge of God." The preachers declared: The Queen's vain dream of freedom of conscience was sending thousands and hundreds of thousands of souls straight to perdition. Therefore, cost what it might, it must be broken. Or Scotland was lost, body and soul.

At the moment the Queen was away from Edinburgh. One morning, when Mass was being celebrated, an artisan, who had once worked for the court but for some time had been afflicted by progressive softening of the brain, suddenly burst into the chapel in a fit of madness. Shrieking that he was the Queen's husband, and was going to her embraces so soon as he had overthrown the princes of Hell, he threw himself, with drawn sword, upon the priest at the high altar, who was terrified out of his wits. Roaring louder and louder, he chased him from the choir into the sacristy, where the priest tried anxiously to barricade himself. While the terrified congregation was pressing its way out, the madman smashed the furniture of the altar, tore down hangings and curtains, and hacked at pictures and reliques until they lay about him in a mass of ruins. The whole watch had to be called up before the maniac could be got under control.

A few days later, the Catholic owners of a well-to-do middle-class dwelling were, with one or two like-minded persons, celebrating the Holy Office in their own house, when suddenly, with great noise and shouting, a crowd of young men, armed with swords, scythes and knives, burst through the door, and without any parley, threw themselves upon the priest and the master of the house and dragged them out towards the market-place. There they tied them up to the market cross; by the Queen's law, the accursed idolaters had deserved to die! Their houses should be burned and their wives and children pushed out into the streets for their sin in daring to pollute the city by brazenly practising their accursed idolatry in the open light of day! They forced the chalice into the priest's hand and then, held high, bound it fast. For an hour the unfortunates stood thus, tied to the market cross, surrounded by a yelling mob that rained a hail of rotten fruit and vegetables and bad eggs upon them. Then, still bound, they were dragged to the Town Hall: judgment was speedily passed, and, on a subsequent day, they were again subjected to the martyrdom of the stocks, this time for several hours. The rage of the mob against them was so

146

savage that they must certainly have perished if the Town watch, commanded by Lord Archibald Douglas, the Provost of Edinburgh, had not come up in sufficiently strong force to snatch their prey from the yelling fiends.

The Queen was in Stirling at the time. She heard of the incident with the addendum that the priest had been stoned to death. In anger such as no one had hitherto seen in her, she cried: "If the priest is really dead, I shall have the whole town sacked and the murderers hanged!" She received the official report from the Provost, with an account of what had passed, and wrote in reply:

"We can never be satisfied until all the ringleaders of this disgraceful plot have been properly punished. What will become of a State in which each individual takes into his own hands the vengeance that properly belongs to us alone? To what purpose are good laws and decrees issued? Never have we failed in punishment of any guilty person, no matter what his station. For that very reason is it our will that the law, in all its rigour, be set in motion against these brawlers. For that you, Mr. Provost, are in your own person held responsible. So much so, that proof shall instantly be given, should you fail in this duty, that we have no mind to overlook any such disregard of our authority."

After a few days' detention, for his own safety, in the Town Hall, the priest was released. The Queen soon found a rich cure for him. Some of the ringleaders in the affray were banished, others came off with heavy fines. At Easter, Catholic service was celebrated with much pomp at court.

★

The day of law on the Earl of Bothwell was fixed for May 2nd, 1565. As complainants, there appeared the Earls of Argyle and Murray. But when the accused was called before the court, one of his friends, Lord Riccarton, appeared in his stead, and in a loud voice declared: My Lord the Earl of Bothwell finds himself compelled to refuse to appear in person before this court: he sends in his stead his friend, to enter protest in his name: his absence shall in no wise be held as prejudicial to his cause. The bravest must agree that it is impossible for the Earl of Bothwell to appear before an assembly where an all-powerful foe, in the person of the Earl of Murray, will simply annihilate every opposed opinion. It is not only that the Earl of Murray is, next to the Queen, the most powerful man in the realm: he has, for this court, gathered unto himself a following of between seven and eight thousand armed men, and the forces of the Earl cannot possibly equal his, least of all after he has, for a whole year, been driven out of his own country by a hostile conspiracy.

The Queen herself attended the day of law to hear the judgment of the assembly. But the court had been informed that she would in no circumstances tolerate extreme measures against a resolute supporter of her party. It had therefore to content itself with taking note of the protestation entered by the friend of the accused, and the lapsing of the bail deposited by the Earl's supporters for his appearance. A new day of law was to be proclaimed, later. The Queen forbade the posting of the Earl's name on the stocks as that of a proscribed outlaw. The lapsed bail was repaid to those who had produced it. Bothwell himself withdrew to his castle in the Debatable Land, known as the Hermitage, which no one, so far, had dared to attack. There, under the pretext that, after such marked signs of royal good-will to him, his restoration was only a matter of time, he attempted to gather a body of desperate fellows about him.

But the settlement of his affairs tarried, and, as a proclaimed outlaw, his life was not safe for a moment among men so reckless as those of this region. He was, at last, compelled to leave his native land once more. Once again, he betook himself to France.

★

Meantime, matters at court were developing on lines that caused almost everybody there to see in Henry Darnley the accepted bridegroom of the Queen. He himself was no longer quite so modest, of quite such distinguished restraint in manner, as at first; had no longer so much need to control himself. Since Mary, patently, had no eyes save for him, he had become for most people quite a different person.

The Queen's favourite brother, Lord John Stuart, the Queen herself, Henry Darnley, and Mary Livingstone, were playing billiards one day. At first Queen Mary said: "Ladies against gentlemen"; then she had another idea: "Lord Henry, you must play against me for once." Signing to her brother to come over to her side, she raised her cue and began; then Henry Darnley took her place, and, being a very good player, was in play for a long time. In a corner of the great room Mary Fleming sat with her admirer, Maitland of Lethington. Glancing at Darnley, she said: "The idiot! Look at her gazing at him, as if, for sheer love, she could eat him up! And it doesn't upset him in the least. He just takes it all for granted . . . It is a shame," she went on. "It makes me furious, to think of it." "Why?" asked Lethington. "Because I simply cannot understand how such a woman, such a marvel, such a creature as appears once in a thousand years, can throw herself away on that stupid lump! And yet, he has only to hold out his hand to take her!" "It is his long legs that do it," said Lethington. "She has always been so," the girl went on. "She has always had to have some one to worship. In France it was her uncles. Of course they all just made use of her. They treated her as a cipher, in France—but they saw what a glorious being she is. But this creature is utterly bad. Not only stupid. That he is by nature. Of a hair-raising stupidity. But also, quite simply, evil, evil!" "Of that I have no doubt," her admirer agreed. "Yes," said Mary Fleming, "you are perfectly right. There is nothing to be done. None of us can stand him. But what is the use? The only result is that, for weeks, she simply has not seen any of us. Mary Seaton practically went down on her knees to her, to beg her to let him go. For her, he is an arch-heretic. As for him—he is far too stupid and too cowardly to have any opinion of his own. He will be Protestant today, Catholic tomorrow, if any one tells him that one or the other will remedy the bulging eyes he has got from wearing tight boots in order to look pretty . . . They have finished, and he has actually collected enough sense to let her win in the end. What in all the world is he up to now?"

Mary Fleming rose and approached the others. Henry Darnley was in the act of drawing a ring from his finger and presenting it, with a profound bow, to the Queen, as a token of his defeat. Mary held the ring in her hand, while blushes spread over ears, throat and neck, and right up into the roots of her hair. She looked uncertainly at its giver, who stood before her, half embarrassed, half with the air of one who has performed a heroic action; her glance travelled over the others, standing round her in a circle, unconcealed curiosity in all their faces— what was she about to do? "My Lord Henry," she said, holding the ring out to him with a rapid movement, "I am afraid that we have by no means won the right to so great a favour!" Astounded to the point of speechlessness, he took back the gift and dropped it into his pocket. As though at a signal, all the others at once began to talk loudly among themselves; every one laughed, chattered, while their cheeks shone with sheer heat. The Queen had taken Mary Livingstone's arm, and walked up and down the room with her, talking eagerly. In so doing, however, she, casually, as it were, and without intention, approached the embrasure of the window where Henry Darnley was standing alone and cast down, his hands behind his back, his mouth half open, apparently engaged in looking at a picture. "A beautiful painting, is it not?" said Mary, letting go of her friend's arm, and drawing near her wooer. "It belonged to my grandmother—to our grandmother, Cousin, Queen Margaret, and represents Mary Tudor as a quite young girl. I am told that it is a very good likeness. You must have seen many pictures of her; did she often look like that, do you think?"

Mary Fleming left the room, followed by Lethington. "I cannot look on and see her throwing herself at that donkey's head." "At least, he is young," Lethington remarked, bitterly —the man of forty, whose lady imposed such long-protracted trials on him. "By that token she might as well marry her guard. The pretty boy who stands on guard all day under our windows is exactly nineteen."

★

Henry Darnley began to assert himself among the gentlemen of the court, and two camps formed. Those who thought that they were looked down upon by the powers that be at court, the Earls of Murray and Argyle and Baron Lethington, and made little of by the Queen, in particular the Earls of Caithness and Atholl and Lord Ruthven and Lord Hume, sided with Darnley and his father. The Queen's two younger illegitimate brothers, who had never been able to endure their elder brother, added their weight to this party. Those on the other side said that Lord Henry behaved as though he were already king of Scotland, or, at least, the Queen's declared fiancé. It was reported to the Earl of Murray that, one afternoon, Lord Henry Darnley had got Lord Robert Stuart to show him a map of Scotland. Lord Robert showed him: "This is the territory of the Earl of Argyle, this here belongs to the Hamiltons, here to the north is subject to the Gordons; here is the earldom of Murray and the other lands of Lord James." Henry Darnley laughed contemptuously. "And he holds all that of the Queen?" He looked at the place marking the property of his own house, and became yellow and red with anger as he looked back over the lands of Earl Murray: "What! All that belongs to him? It is far too much!"

Lord James betook himself to his sister, that she might demand an explanation of these words of Lord Henry's. She summoned the young cavalier at once. Assuredly, he had never said anything of the kind. Suffused with red, he stood before his challenger; appealingly, he looked towards the Queen. "Lord James asks no more of you, cousin, than to say to him expressly that what you actually said has been completely misinterpreted and wholly distorted," said Mary very gently. He stood in helpless shame and fury. "I am satisfied," said Murray, in a tone of cutting contempt. Darnley understood, and apprehension loosed his tongue. "Of course, it is nothing but an impudent lie," he cried. "Really, sir—there is my hand on it. You are satisfied?" "I must be," said Murray, with a constrained smile, taking two fingers of the hand extended to him. "Nay, truly," exclaimed Darnley, now quite at his ease. "Really I would take nothing from you!" "I admit I do not see how you could," replied Murray.

Mary was aware of the growing dislike of the young man. She appealed to Lethington, to Sir James Melville, even to her brother, Lord James, to try, for her sake, to make the best of a young man to whom much must be excused on the ground of his inexperience. They replied politely that they would assuredly do all that lay in their power. But the success of any such efforts must depend on the good-will of the Prince himself. "Oh, he is good and kind at heart," said Mary, "only so young."

★

Lord Henry fell sick of the measles, and Mary's concern was obvious. She was not satisfied with sending her own physician to the invalid, and surrounding his sick-bed with every comfort and distraction. Regardless of herself and of her royal station, she went, when the period of infection was still at its height, every day to see the patient; saw that he lacked for nothing: inquired as to his wishes: comforted him when he grew impatient: later, when he began to recover, sat for hours by his bedside to amuse him with talk or with games of one sort and another. On such visits, she came alone, or, at most, accompanied by David Rizzio, who spent every moment of freedom from his duties in the sick-room. The most singular rumours spread through the palace, the town, the whole country. A servant had reported, so said one, that the Queen was already secretly married to Lord Henry. David had come in one time and found Darnley trying to put a ring on her finger, which she rejected, crying, "Cousin, cousin, it will not do! It is not yet time for that!" Thereupon David: Why in the world should she not accept so pretty a present? The poor gentleman would die of pain and longing, if she would not listen to him! What was Her Majesty waiting for? Had she not, long ago, settled irrevocably, in her own heart? With a sigh, the Queen was said to have replied: Ah, it was not enough for her to consult her own heart. There were so many things to consider—her French relations, other foreign powers, above all, the Queen of England; any unseemly haste would cause much justified feeling. But David, growing with zeal, buzzing to and fro, disposed of every objection. If, so far as the outside world was concerned, the Queen had perhaps got to behave as though she took some small heed of the opinion of these foreign potentates, at home she could do just as she liked. David was like one possessed: he was deaf to all the Queen's objections. He was off, at once, to fetch a priest to say a blessing over the pair. Then, Her Majesty could visit her dear friend as often as she cared, and so far as the public was concerned, she could, later, celebrate her marriage with all possible pomp and ceremony. With one glance at the face of the invalid, all aglow with longing, the Queen actually agreed to this mad proposal. David fetched a priest, who, at least, spoke a blessing on a betrothal.

This story spurred those Lords who were not of the Lennox faction to take precautionary measures. The Earls of Murray, Eglinton and Argyle formed an alliance, and called on the old Duke of Châtelherault to join it. Though outwardly reconciled with the Lennoxes, he had withdrawn from court to his estates, full of mistrust, depression and a sense of injury. The alliance was sealed by the signing of a solemn undertaking to the effect that the Lords herewith bound themselves together for mutual defence for any fight not directed against God and their ruler. Marriages between the houses were to strengthen the new alliance.

A great gathering of Scottish nobles assembled in the dwelling occupied by Mr. Randolph and complained to him that the

Majesty of England had tied a most noxious fellow round their necks. "Your Queen thinks she can recall him at any moment," said the Earl of Eglinton, "but it is too bad that she ever loosed him upon us. What will your Queen do if he does not remove?" The nobles agreed that Lord Henry was at least as stupid as his father, but surpassed him notably in vice and pusillanimity.

Randolph had as a matter of fact received no instructions from his Government in the matter of the Prince. He tried to calm their excited spirits. He repeated his old story: How could the great and wise Queen of Scotland ally herself with such an insignificant fellow? one who, apart from what the two Queens might choose to give him, was a mere beggar? Surely those who hitherto had found no King good enough would know how to block a mere subject in either kingdom? he added. "Ah, but women!" replied the Earl of Argyle. "She is a woman, after all, and a woman who always wants her own way." Randolph recalled that, so far, Darnley had always proved an obedient servant of the Queen of England. Without doubt she would speedily recall him, if only to attach the Scottish nobles to herself. That would finish him off. "Perhaps," said one. "Certainly he is cowardly enough." "But he is growing too big for his boots," said another. The Earl of Argyle grinned under his thick moustache. "If the lad does not mend his manners I can prophesy that those of this country will not give him too many years in it."

Chapter 5

HENRY DARNLEY

QUEEN MARY sent her minister, Maitland of Lethington, in person to London. He appeared in grand audience before the monarch there, and said: His mistress, the Queen of Scotland, in pursuance of her marriage plans, sought to be completely assured of their being agreeable to her sister, the Queen of England. She was happy in the conviction that she had always sought to meet every wish of the friendly neighbour Government in the most punctilious fashion. Thus, the special distinction of the husband on whom her eyes had at last fallen was that he was as much a member of the community of English as of Scottish subjects, that he was as near of kin to the English Queen as to the Scottish, that his heart's devotion was extended in almost equal warmth to the two Queens, and gave to her of Scotland that preference only which a Queen was entitled to ask of a faithful husband in return for her own affections.

From him there was no danger to be apprehended to the security of the two realms or the form of religion professed in either; on the contrary, rather the consolidation of peace and security between them. So, mindful of the fact that it was her good sister herself who had sent Lord Henry Darnley with the warmest recommendations to her sister, Queen Mary, the latter counted confidently on meeting, on the part of England, with a speedy and joyful agreement in her plans. Lord Lethington handed over the letter of his Sovereign, in which stood, written with her own hand, what he had just reported verbally.

Queen Elizabeth, however, replied with frigid mien: "Mr. Ambassador, you have come in a bad cause. The Queen your mistress knows well how different was the sense of our proposals. This choice of hers causes us the greatest possible astonishment: indeed, a veritable shock. A document shall be prepared for you, Mr. Ambassador, by the skilled hands of our Privy Council, in which you shall find the reasons set out why this marriage must absolutely not take place. We further intend sending a special envoy to Scotland, who shall express, in the most solemn fashion, our opposition to any such foolish and over-hasty step." Lord Lethington stood, dumb. "I am to lower your Queen to a mere subject," Elizabeth continued, while her eyes blazed like those of a cat in the dark, and she laughed angrily, "She, for whom positively no King on earth was good enough!" A quick movement of the Queen's fan indicated that the audience was at an end.

That evening he visited the Spanish Ambassador, and next morning, the French. To both gentlemen he said that his mistress now looked on their Governments as her only friends. She was determined on this marriage, for the sake both of the Protestant and of the Catholic cause. Provided only she were assured of some support from outside, she would go ahead regardless of English opposition. She was not afraid of civil war, since she could count on a very large party both in her own country, and in England. To the Spanish Ambassador, Lord Lethington made a specific appeal—King Philip should furnish monies. The Pope had already granted aid in this form. His envoy only awaited the time for bringing it over to Scotland. The Spanish gentleman, however, had neither power nor instructions to do this; he shook his head in helpless perplexity and said that no one had the faintest idea of what the mind of his master would be or knew what he was going to do. As for the Frenchman, M. de Foix, a Huguenot, he raised his hands in amazement. "My Lord Lethington, do you not see that your mistress is about to pursue an openly Catholic policy? Are you yourself not a Protestant, then? or have you become a Catholic?" Coldly and definitely, he said: "Your Queen has no support to expect from us. Does she not know with what a hydra-headed revolution we are struggling at home?" he added. "No one in Paris will hear of this marriage of your Queen's.

LORD HENRY DARNLEY

She knows this: His Eminence the Cardinal of Lorraine wrote her explicitly—the young man is impossible. One does not marry such a fool."

Next day, Maitland received a copy of the statement of the English Privy Council, whose original was to be conveyed to the Queen of Scotland by Sir Nicholas Throgmorton. In this document, prepared by Mr. Secretary Cecil, it was stated:

"After long and mature reflection the Privy Council of the Throne of England is unanimously of the opinion that the marriage of the Scottish Queen with Lord Darnley is, in existing circumstances, wholly inadmissible, indeed incompatible with the maintenance of friendship between the two kingdoms and the continuance of good mutual understanding. Therefore, in so far as the marriage depends on the good-will of Her Majesty, the Queen of England, it is, so states the Privy Council, to be definitely and energetically opposed. On the other hand, the Queen of Scotland is offered the free choice of any other nobleman of this island or either of the two countries, who may be so pleasing to both realms as in no sense to jeopardize by his elevation the continuance of a happy friendship between the two States."

Maitland was received a second time by the Queen of England. "Your mistress has, I know, great confidence in you, Mr. Ambassador," she said. "Read therefore in my despatches from Scotland how she mocks at us! She is already married to our subject!"

Maitland travelled home in company with the English envoy, Sir Nicholas Throgmorton. After an arduous ride, throughout a whole very hot day in May, they dismounted in an inn not far from the border, and sat down together to talk in the best room of the place. Their commissions were neither simple nor pleasant—but, there it was. Lethington said that he had always found his ruler accessible to reasonable propositions. Already old acquaintances, the two talked of this and that.

157

Lethington, deep in an armchair, his legs crossed, bending forward with his chin sunk in his hand, declared that he did not see the fearful dangers which this marriage was said to threaten for England. "It is perfectly clear," he said, thoughtfully, while his fingers, sparkling with many a diamond ring, restlessly combed his long red beard, "that the English Queen simply wants to force one of her creatures on us. She would be on velvet then, while we had her spy on our Throne."

Sir Nicholas replied: "Our Queen absolutely detests the Lennoxes. She believes the worst of them—from secret plots against her person upwards. We know what our wars of succession cost us. We don't want that sort of thing again. The Queen of Scotland wants to be accepted as heir. In that event, she must accept the disagreeables of close kinship. Our Queen was never a comfortable relative. Queen Mary knows that as well as any one."

Lethington repeated: "And this young man is supposed to be dangerous? Although he is too stupid for anything but tennis and dancing?"

"Other people may be clever on his behalf," replied Sir Nicholas. "His mother, for example, or his wife. He is there; that may suffice. Such is the view of our Catholics, anyhow."— "Who are anyhow in our hands."

"Inasmuch as Queen Mary marries the other claimant, she strengthens her own claim." Sir Nicholas added: "What will be, will be; all this talk is idle. The one point is that my Queen simply will not have this marriage. And she has the power to make her will and her will-not effective."

"Her will, her will-not!" replied Lethington. "Is it her marriage, or ours? What sort of marriage does she graciously deign to offer us? She presents her lover. An affront we might well resent. The more offensive in that it was all done without the least trace of serious purpose. No purpose but to injure us. Oh, I admit we have made bad mistakes. We have let ourselves be put upon, boundlessly." Lethington went on: "Henry Darnley is impossible. Granted. We all know it. Unfortunately she does not. A lout, a silly ass. Stupid, unmannerly, cowardly. But his great dangerousness? For us, yes, if we marry him. But for others, for you, for England? God in Heaven! Unfortunately, for us, you have fixed them both, first the old man, and now the young one, round our necks, knowing perfectly well what you were about. That mad proposal of the lover was a jest for you, as well as for us. Suppose we accepted him? What a pity, it is impossible! Then you are told: Over there, they are thinking of the Lennoxes. Once again, you can rejoice! Here is a nice way out of your awkward dilemma. So, you let first the old and then the young one on us, with many sweet words of your wondrous graciousness. We are to take them up, compromise ourselves. Which we immediately proceed to do. It worked like a laxative. Then you beckon. The Lennoxes hurry away. As for us, there we are, empty, naked. We have exposed ourselves before the whole world. And England, at the last minute, has saved us. Or showed us up. But there is no thought of a wedding, for at least a year. Meantime, you can think out excellent new devices. The Queen of Scotland may not marry. You do not do it either! Why? You may know. But the Queen of Scotland is, on no account, to produce the heir. What a policy! One that cannot possibly lead to anything but ill feeling. For you must know perfectly well that, in the long run, no one can stand such interference. True, you may count on miracles. Why not? They are not excluded. But it may well be that the resistance to which you have committed yourselves will merely show you your limits. . . . If only it was somebody else," Lethington added. "But, so it is, and we are now up against a man who has absolutely nothing in him, no power of resistance—not even an average intellect. I shall try to make things clear to her. She is certainly very much in love."

It was nearly midnight, and they were still talking. The bustle of the inn had gradually subsided. Suddenly, however, they heard the noise of many new arrivals. Doors banged; there were voices down below; at last the clank of spurs came up the staircase and along the passage.

"This will be for us," said Lethington. There was a knock at the door. "Come in." A squire appeared. The Queen of Scotland sent an urgent message to her ambassador. Lethington called the messenger into his own room. John Beaton, one of the Queen's most trusty servants, entered with various letters. Lethington, breaking open the one addressed to him, found, as reply to his report of his experiences in London, the command that he should use every means to prevent the English envoy from pursuing his journey. He himself, on the contrary, was to turn back to London and go thence to Paris in order to present holograph letters, enclosed from his mistress, and communicate the fact that the marriage of Queen Mary with Lord Darnley was to take place within the next few days.

Lethington returned to Throgmorton's room. There, beating his brow, he strode up and down, crying incessantly, "Sheer lunacy!" Standing at the table, he smote it with his fist, repeating, "She must, she must be prevented!" He moved towards Throgmorton: "What in all the world can have happened?" Throgmorton, sitting on the couch, looked at his usually discreet friend, without saying a word. Finally they agreed to start very early next morning, and to make, both of them, for Edinburgh.

★

James Stuart was passing the afternoon in the Queen's antechamber, in polite conversation with various ladies and gentlemen, when, towards the end of the time which he thought himself entitled to pass thus leisurely, Queen Mary herself appeared. After she had spoken a few friendly words to this person and that, she signed to her brother to come with her into her workroom. To his unpleasant surprise he saw Henry Darnley approaching him from the further end of the room, and extending his hand to him with facile heartiness. Lord James barely touched the tips of his fingers; Lord Henry dropped his hand: his face flushed dusky red. The Queen then turned to her brother with a sweet smile. She had it in her heart to make a great request of her brother which would be a mere trifle, a mere empty form on his side. Out of a portfolio lying ready on the great table there, she quickly took a sheet already covered with writing and placed it before him; ink and pen were ready beside it.

"See!" she said, appealingly, her eyes brilliant with delight, "You must help me. What can I do without you?" She told him that he surely already knew that both out of pure inclination and of consideration of the welfare of the State, she had decided on marriage with Lord Henry Darnley. She now begged Lord James to append his name to this paper, where it was stated that he approved of this marriage and would support it with all his power.

Lord James looked at her, in the act of dipping the pen in order to hand it over to him. Behind the soft gentleness of her appeal he recognized a determination that would yield to no resistance. From her he looked across to Henry Darnley, separated from him by the breadth of the table, and standing opposite to him, expectant, embarrassed, suspicious. In a flash James Stuart felt that everything that repelled him in this lanky, pretty youth was as it were summed up in the uneasy insolence of his bearing at this moment. Involuntarily, every atom of his being was up in arms against him.

"Your Majesty must pardon me, but I cannot do as you ask," he said, hoarsely and slowly.

Mary's face flushed instantly. She still held the pen in her hand.

"I cannot possibly decide so quickly," the Earl continued, with laboured breath.

"What am I to wait for?" asked Mary sharply.

Then, as though recollecting herself, she laid down the pen and came over to him to take his hand. "When I beg, nay entreat it of you, James!" She placed her exquisite hand softly on his arm. "You are a Stuart, too, like us, like Henry and me. Don't you want the crown to stay in our family, with all the greatness that may come? That would have been our father's wish, always." He was perturbed: the colour mounted to his face; he wiped his brows hurriedly with his handkerchief.

"Madam, on my life, I cannot do it! It is too hasty! The Estates must be asked, and Parliament. Who of the nobles has given his consent?"

She looked as though she must burst out laughing with amazement. "I am to ask my Estates whom I am to marry? My nobles?" Then, suddenly, "I am beginning with you—if so!"

With genuine anxiety, he blurted out: "What will foreign Powers say?"

The Queen laughed, scornfully now. "Oh," she said, "of a surety I shall go on asking my good friends and faithful neighbours whether and whom their goodness permits me to marry, until I have no more teeth in my head and no more hairs upon it, and my neck waggles back and forward with age!" Angrily she stepped close up to her brother. "Don't you understand what they have done to us? Oh, these people, these people!" She raised her little fist. "James," she said, "you must see that they have nothing else in mind, nothing, but to pillory us in shame and mock before the whole world." She marched up and down the room, and then paused before Murray. "It would be treachery, if you would not help me! You must help me! You will. If you were to leave me in the lurch . . . I could never forgive you! Never, never!"

Lord James stood without moving, his eyes on the ground, saying no word. Henry Darnley had removed himself from the table to a corner of the room, where he leaned against the now fireless chimney-piece.

"What have you got against him?" said Mary, standing straight in front of her brother. She was so tall that she had to look down into his eyes.

"I cannot answer for it in my conscience. Any other man, whom Your Majesty's choice presents to us. . . . Only not him."

"May I not know the reasons why precisely not him?"

"He is an enemy of our purified faith," replied Murray, driven into a corner.

"Any other man," said Mary, her voice clear and high in anger. "Any other, to be sure, so long as he is in the moon!" She laughed, contemptuously. "I certainly ought to present you with any other, he might infuse a little more respect into you, by coming with a regiment of heavy cavalry behind him!"

She threw herself into a chair, and sat so, her chin in her hand. Lord James stared in front of him, his face averted.

Suddenly the Queen leapt to her feet. She began to speak, very rapidly, words pouring from her lips like the waves of the sea, tumbling over one another. She declared that she had had to put up with nothing but insults ever since she set foot in this country. Nay, before, even before, indeed, long before! She drew herself up. "Have I or have I not been Queen of Scotland from my cradle? Is it or is it not the case that these people owe all they have and are to my favour? Of course it is. But one ought to take scourges and beat this race till the blood flows, for kindness is utterly wasted on you. Oh, far worse than wasted: far, far worse. For kindness in you simply feeds wolves and leopards! They grow, they lurk there, greedily waiting for the moment when they can take me by the throat and tear me to pieces!"

James Murray opened his lips to speak, but she would not permit it. "Oh, yes, oh, yes!" she cried, "I know it all!" She waved her hand contemptuously in the air. "How admirably you rule my land! How peaceful it all is, thanks to your merits alone! How you sacrifice yourself, give up sleep by night, pleasure by day, simply and solely in order that I may revel in peace and happiness." She looked him up and down, taking in his costly garments of violet velvet, and the heavy chain of gold hanging round his neck. "Truly, your great sacrifice becomes you well! That ought to be a comfort to me!" Turning away from him, she sat down again, and for a time fell into silent brooding: then burst out again, bitterly: "Oh, of a surety it should please you, you and your like, my obedient and trusty subjects—for there are my false friends for ever with their hands on my head, making sure that my pride never shoots up on high!" She drew herself up, straight as a die, to her full slender height. "But I will not have it, will not, will not! And you shall see that you have still got me to reckon with! . . . For your sake," again she turned directly to her brother, "I destroyed the Gordons. What is to prevent me from treating others as I treated them? My good sister, my dear friend in England knows perfectly that, if I choose, she can have civil war in her land tomorrow. . . . Your religion!" she continued, letting her hands drop in a gesture of scorn, "Your religion, which is for ever on your lips! How agreeable it must be, this poor starveling religion! They all shout 'Religion!' and all their greed, all their falseness and treacherousness, their black ambition, everything, every vice is covered up under its cloak! And yet—your priests were starving, and I gave them food out of my own pocket." She rose, stood before Murray once more. "What have you against Henry Darnley? You had better take care lest you get a man of quite another sort put over you! You ought to be down on your knees, every day, giving thanks to God and to my patience that you are only given Henry Darnley as your king! He will never be any danger to you. But thanks? What does this race know of thanks! I may be glad if I do not get high treason from you in return for my good deeds! Why was I so foolish as to fatten your wolvish greed?"

Lord James, his eyes cast down in wrath, his teeth gnawing alternately at his upper and lower lip, was silent while her words poured over him.

The Queen paused. "Well?" she said. "I am waiting for your answer."

"Your Majesty is hardly in the mood at the moment to listen to reasons," he replied, speaking with difficulty.

She rushed at him. "You shall not speak, then! I want none of your reasons. You are to obey! Obey! Do you hear me—obey!" Lord James again felt for his handkerchief, to wipe the perspiration again from his brow. "Your Majesty can have me killed," he said, "but to an answer contrary to my conviction you cannot compel me."

"You, you! . . ." She was like a flame.

"Moreover, this is not the place in which I can speak," he said contemptuously. "Your Majesty has not deigned to allow me to speak with you à deux. Therefore I shall put my reasons before you in writing."

"Spare me your twaddle," she replied. "I have had quite enough of that already." He stood, dumbfounded.

"You may go," said the Queen, over her shoulder. She had moved towards the window.

He left the apartment.

★

The news of the hurrying on of Mary's marriage, which had caused such painful surprise to her Ambassador and to the English envoy, had been preceded by other events at the court in Edinburgh.

In the solemn assembly of all the knights, Henry Darnley was elevated to the Earldom of Ross. Clad in the hat and cloak of an earl, he knelt before the throne, where the Queen sat in splendour surrounded by her foremost nobles, raised his hand and said:

"I swear to protect the Christian religion with all my might.

"I swear fealty to my Sovereign and exalted ruler, the Queen of Scotland.

"I swear to defend her body, her kingdom, her allies, with the last drop of my blood.

"I swear never to leave my Sovereign or any of my knightly brothers in arms shamefully in the lurch;

"to defend all orphans, widows and maidens;

"to exact vengeance, within the limits of my powers, on murderers, robbers and impudent thieves who oppress the people;

"to uphold the honour of the noble order of knighthood in

the equipment of horse and weapons and knightly garb, so far as my means permit;

"So help me God, as I swear by His Holy Gospels, by my own hand, and by God Himself."

★

After this Henry Darnley, now Earl of Ross, sat with David Rizzio in his room in the palace, where he still was put up as a guest at the expense of the royal household. They drank out of great beakers, and filled them again so soon as they were empty. With both elbows on the table, David listened to the new Earl, who was, within a few days, to be still further elevated, to the Dukedom of Albany. "Ho! how they envy me!" said Henry Darnley, with his loud laugh. "I could see it well enough. Just what one would expect of them—they are a shameless crowd. But they shall wonder at me yet. Yes, indeed: they shall wonder. I tell you, David, they shall certainly wonder yet. I tell you . . ."

A page entered, announcing Lord Ruthven, one of the Lennox party. "Show him in, of course, of course." The elderly man who appeared was tall and dry-looking: very dark eyes burned with a sort of melancholy fire in a face that had the yellow shiny surface of antique parchment. At his entry David slowly got up. Henry Darnley held out the full beaker towards him. "Good idea, truly, Ruthven! Excellent! Sit. There. Fresh wine coming." The cavalier remained standing. "I came at Her Majesty's bidding."—"That is charming! What has our sweet Sovereign to command?" Darnley smiled as though at the recollection of some secret intimacy.

Lord Ruthven replied: "Her Majesty's greetings, and I am to inform you that your nomination as Duke of Albany must be postponed. The Queen of England is against it." Darnley's jaw dropped. "That is not true," he said, at last.

"My Lord!" said the cavalier.

Darnley flew into a rage. "Sir, the Queen of England has no command over me!" he screamed, as red as a turkey-cock.

166

He came right up to Lord Ruthven. "Do you fancy I am to be treated so shamelessly? No, I shall go to the Queen, now, at once! I shall make a complaint—yes, at once, a complaint. . . ."

"You cannot go now to Her Majesty," said the cavalier, placing himself before the door.

Darnley seized his dagger. "You will! . . . What, what? Who do you think you are? Who?" It looked as though he would fall upon Ruthven. In a trice the latter seized his hand, and the dagger fell with a clatter on the ground.

David sprang up: "Holy Mary! Your Highness!" Darnley, his arms cast round his friend's neck, lay sobbing on his breast.

When, a few hours later, he betook himself to the Queen, he was still quite beside himself. He sobbed: "Your Majesty will never marry me! I know it; I know the Queen of England will not allow it. And now Your Majesty has begun listening to her! Never, never, never, shall I be your husband!"

Mary, bending tenderly over him, attempted to soothe him. "I stand by you, I love you. Poor dear heart! No power on earth shall take you from me."

He wept on. "You do not know the Queen of England! You do not know her at all. She never gives way. Least of all in such matters. And now you are listening to her, and I shall be driven away from you!"

Mary kissed and fondled him; wiped away his tears, kissed him on the mouth and on the wet cheeks. He lay on the ground beside her, his arms wound about her body, and wept aloud. "I shall die! If I cannot have you, life has absolutely no value left for me. Let me be, let me be; I am a lost soul." He believed in none of Mary's assurances. "You do not know the Queen of England; she will never allow it."

In the morning, the Queen promised him to send messengers to stop the approach of the English envoys. Instructions were sent to Lethington to go to London and Paris as the herald of a *fait accompli*.

Next day, however, the Hamiltons, the Earls of Argyle,

Glencairn and Eglinton, came to ask the Queen's permission to withdraw to their estates, where their presence was urgently required. And Lord James of Murray approached his sister with a similar request.

★

Sir Nicholas Throgmorton and Baron Lethington reached Edinburgh only to learn that the Queen had departed to Stirling. They ventured to follow her thither. The Provost, however, refused to open his gates for the English Ambassador, from whom Lethington had finally separated; to his lodging outside the gates there came to him one or two noblemen to warn him that he would do well to withdraw into the English Ambassador's quarters; Her Majesty would receive him so soon as he had somewhat recovered from the fatigues of his journey. Mindful of his instructions, Sir Nicholas tried to insist upon being received at once. Politely, but firmly, the visitors told him that, heartily as they regretted it, they could do nothing against the express commands of the Queen. On the same day, however, these gentlemen came down to the town, where Throgmorton had meantime installed himself. He did not allow himself to be perturbed by the turn of events; he was a man of the world, and had learned to take things as they came; what would be, would be, and many an event which was heralded as about to set the world in ruins did not come to much in the end, after all. The gentlemen of the court said: If the Ambassador were ready, he might come up with them to the castle. They led the English gentleman through the inner court-yards, conducted him to the palace, and showed him the way to the great reception room. When the doors opened to admit their small party, Sir Nicholas saw the Scottish Queen under the canopy on her throne, in full state pomp, with veil and jewels, surrounded by all her knights—they were all there, even the old Duke of Châtelherault, even the Earls of Argyle, Eglinton, Murray, and Morton. Throgmorton knew Scotland, its Queen and its nobles, its burghers and its priesthood, intimately, and also his own country and its government. He presented his commission, with all due external formalities. He recited how the Queen of England loved the neighbouring Sovereign like a sister, yea, almost like a daughter, and how she had given proof, of the most striking kind, of this tender affection. What then must be the feelings of the Majesty of England, when she saw all her faithfully-meant advice rejected with silent contempt? Lord Henry Darnley and his father had simply displayed a gross dereliction of duty. English subjects, attached to the English royal house, they had not so much as thought of securing the consent of the head of their family before taking so vital a step! And yet without it, according to the laws of every State in Europe, no member of a reigning house was in a position to contract a valid marriage.

Queen Mary replied to the Ambassador immediately after he had pronounced his speech, without giving any sign of excitement either by the smallest alteration in her face or the slightest raising of her voice. She said: "Mr. Ambassador, it must seem singular to us to hear, as has been stated even now, that we ourselves, and our relations, Lord Lennox and Lord Henry Darnley, should have neglected the respect due to our exalted neighbour and kinswoman, the Queen of England. Assuredly there is no obligation upon us either to consult about or even to communicate our decisions. Rather are we, as an independent Sovereign, entirely free to do whatsoever may seem to us good. Even though we were prepared to leave this our right, as self-evident, entirely on one side and took the ground that, for the sake of mutual and sincere friendship, a certain attention, in the case of all reasonable wishes, is due to our good sister the Queen of England, even in that event we should find it impossible to comprehend the claim made by our good sister in the present instance. Rather, in view of the very warm recommendation of our kinsfolk on the part of the Queen of England, we have thought that no choice we could make of a husband could be more pleasing to our good sister than that of Lord Henry Darnley. He possesses, in greater measure than any other, all the qualities so often set before us by the English Queen as indispensable for the maintenance of a good understanding between the two Kingdoms."

The Queen ceased; the Ambassador bowed; the audience was at an end. There was no more confidential conversation. After Sir Nicholas had spoken with various lords, and found little in the minds of most of them but disquiet and suspicion, he saw that there was nothing for him to do save return to London.

Hot on his heels Mary sent her own Ambassador after him, Mr. John Hay, who replaced Lord Lethington, obviously under a cloud as the consequence of his disobedience. Hay was, in the most courteous fashion, to convince the Queen of England afresh of the immovability of her young kinswoman.

★

Dark, dapper, discreet, Mr. Thomas Randolph presented himself, first in the dwelling of Earl Matthew, next at the palace to Lord Henry Darnley, now Earl of Ross, to remind them that the leave of absence granted them by the English Queen expired yesterday. What did the gentlemen intend doing? With some embarrassment, Earl Matthew replied that he was, of course, aware that his leave expired yesterday. But Her Majesty here had herself applied in their favour to the English Court. So that he did not imagine they would take it ill in London. Her Majesty the Queen there would assuredly grant them an extension, in view of the fact that nothing to her detriment was being done here.

Randolph shrugged his shoulders: he was aware of no extension. Since the gentlemen were of that opinion—it was at their own risk—he made off.

A few days later, when, as he anticipated, neither father nor son gave a sign of departure, Randolph again waited upon them, this time bearing letters from his Queen, which, shortly and sharply, commanded their swift return, under the threat that if her subjects showed disobedience by remaining away, they would be declared rebels, and their kin in English territory taken and held. Earl Matthew, to whom, as before, Randolph paid his first visit, was dumbfounded: "But Her Majesty here sent word! We must wait and see what sort of reply Mr. Hay brings from London!" Randolph, again shrugging his shoulders, replied that, for good or ill, he must abide by his instructions. He pressed to know what the Earl was going to do? He pulled at his scanty beard, looked again at the letters, and said, at last: "Mr. Randolph, you must see that I cannot answer right away!" Randolph, however, was not to be put off. Just because the matter was so important, it must be decided, one way or the other. "My Lord, you have already thought it well over. You knew when your time expired; knew the danger that threatens you. You cannot tell me that you are surprised."—"I shall give you your answer in an hour"; the Earl rose at last, sighing deeply, folding up the paper and putting it away.

Next, Randolph went to the son, who spread the letter out before him on the table, after he had read it, and stared at the envoy with round eyes of astonishment. "Mr. Randolph, this is a bad business!" He reflected. "What would you do, in my place?"—"That is not for your lordship to learn from me. Rather, I am to know what your lordship intends."—"No, no, you must tell me what you would do in my place. . . . Yes," he continued, looking helplessly at the envoy, "of course I have no desire to return."

"Am I to take that back as answer?"—"Oh, no, no," replied Darnley, desperately rumpling his hair. "I do not say that. Surely you can give me a little time, enough for me to collect my thoughts!"—"I thought you had your answer all ready. Speak. You can do it as well now as later." "No, no," the other evaded it. He felt for his beret and dagger. "Wait a bit; I cannot give it to you yet."

It had been Randolph's intention to wait a few days before giving his Sovereign's letter to the Queen herself. But he heard that Queen Mary intended going for five or six days to her city of Perth. Therefore he determined to execute his commission at once. He sent the document ahead of him. When he came before the Queen, she was in the act of reading the letter in a low tone to Baron Lethington. She greeted the envoy with a nod as he entered but continued her occupation undisturbed. She finished reading: Mr. Randolph stood, waiting dutifully at her side. Handing the letter over to Lethington, she at last gave her attention to Randolph. "So, Mr. Ambassador, what have you to communicate to me?"—"I think that the letter of my gracious Sovereign contains all that Your Majesty needs to know. If Your Majesty will meet the wishes of my gracious Queen, I have nothing to add." Mary looked at him with a smile. "I am convinced that my good sister, the Queen of England, has long been aware that she was insufficiently informed. And, even if I were to dismiss my kinsmen, do they desire to go?" Randolph smiled. "They have hardly a choice!" "Indeed!" said Mary. "I can assure you that my good sister, your ruler, has long been of a different opinion." Randolph, with a bow, replied, "Doubtless, Your Majesty is right. My Sovereign will be the more delighted by obedience."—"But they have no mind for it, Mr. Ambassador!"—"In that case I am afraid that they will draw my mistress' vengeance down upon themselves."—"We might let it come to that," replied Mary. "But disquiet is superfluous. My good sister has doubtless changed her mind by now."

It was said at court that evening that the Queen had been weeping. Earl Matthew went about with a sombre face; Henry Darnley's manner showed a proud, pallid uncertainty. The ladies and gentlemen stood about in the rooms and passages. The Queen did not appear at table, dining in her own apartments with the two Lennoxes and David Rizzio. Even her Maries were not there.

Any one whom his office did not compel to come to court stayed away, in his own house. The Protestant nobles were very busy.

★

The news Mary's Ambassador brought back from London

was that the Countess of Lennox, Henry Darnley's mother, had been sent to the Tower by Elizabeth as a high traitor.

★

The Queen went north to the city of Perth, to hold an Estates Assembly there. It would make grants for the eventuality of her marriage. After it, Queen Elizabeth must change her tone. What did she want? War, because the Queen of Scotland was disinclined to marry her royal neighbour's pet?

Queen Mary had seen enough to know that her faithful and devoted nobility had no love for her betrothed. Perhaps she had thought—all the same they will not venture to murmur openly. In Perth, however, she learned that she had accomplished no more, in her four years of rule, than any of her forebears; if she wanted obedience, she had got to compel it. Whenever her will did not chime with that of her nobles.

She had gone to Perth in order to cut off her recalcitrant or wilful vassals from their support from the capital, never too docile. The heralds who summoned the Assembly, went throughout the country and came to every town. But the knights either excused themselves or were silent. Mary saw that there would be too few of her vassals at her Assembly to give the force of law to a single decree. She had only got the Earl of Atholl, Lord Ruthven and one or two lesser nobles, like Lords Seaton and Livingstone. Her counsellors were the two Lennoxes and David Rizzio, who seemed to be gathering up into his hands what Baron Lethington and the Earl of Murray had unwillingly abandoned. The Earl of Morton, whose mighty energy rather than his estates made him important, sat, deep in Scotland, in his own domain. He said that he should not oppose the Queen's marriage, because he was related by marriage to the Lennoxes. But he was not going to risk his peace on their account.

★

In Edinburgh, there was tremendous excitement. A great Church Assembly was summoned, which went off better than that of the Queen. Queen Mary sent messengers to put it off.

But the Assembly met.

The armed men of Earls of Argyle and Glencairn surrounded the Town Hall, where they met. From every side, the lesser Protestant nobles marched in. All came eagerly, with a defiant air, at the head of their forces, as though to proclaim: We are ready for the great day when we stake life and property and all else against tyranny and oppression. Every one wore an important mien on that account.

The town watch, greatly increased, exercised daily in the meadows and slopes round about the royal palace.

From early to late, the preachers were at it. They said: "Ye children of God, behold the enemy. Hitherto the Queen, in seeming gentleness and sweetness, has merely stood on the threshold of the temple of idolatry, but now the day and hour have come when she casts off the cloak. Listen to the commandment warning the children of truth to gather their forces and sharpen their swords."

They deliberated from morning to night. Finally, they agreed on six Articles, to be carried through in a royal decree. These Articles demanded:

(1) That the Mass, papistry, etc., be abolished not only in her subjects but also in her own person, with due punishment, and the "sincere Word" be received instead.—That the people be compelled on Sundays to resort to prayers and preaching, as formerly to the Mass.

(2) That due provision be made for sustenance of the ministers present and future, duly admitted by the superintendents.

(3) That none be permitted to have charge of schools, colleges, or universities, but those so admitted, or tried by the Visitor of the Church sound in doctrine.

(4) To sustain the poor, that all hospital lands be restored, and emolument of all friars and priests of whatever order be so applied for the poor.

(5) That horrible crimes now abounding here—as idolatry,

blasphemy of God's name, Sabbath-breaking, witchcraft, sorcery, and enchantments, adultery, incest, manifest whoredom, maintenance of "burdelles," murder, slaughter, "reife and spoile," etc., may be severely punished by Act of Parliament.

(6) That some order be devised for the ease of the poor labourers of the ground, concerning reasonable payment of their "teindes," and setting their steadings to others over their heads without their consent.

The Six Articles were sent to Perth.

★

The Queen received the delegates. She appeared perfectly calm, as she answered their questions. She merely said to them that she certainly could not decide by herself on such momentous regulations. She would consult her Privy Council, and send them a reply in a week or so.

★

Meantime John Knox preached daily in the open air at St. Leonard's Mount behind the royal palace, his hands raised to heaven: "May God give a righteous victory to our cause, since at last the day has dawned when we may fight and suffer openly for the righteousness of God."

To the nobles who had poured into Edinburgh there came a letter from the Queen of England, in which it stood: We observe in many letters from you that your minds are disturbed by this marriage with Lord Darnley, as though the cause of religion might thereby be overthrown and danger created to the peace that has prevailed between the two kingdoms in the last few years. In view of the importance of the cause, we can but praise and encourage those who take this matter to heart. In view of the fact that it must be of the utmost importance to our good sister to have her realm continued to enjoy the peace which has blessed it during the last few years, we can but allow and esteem those who are concerned to warn the Queen, our good sister, against the false counsel of those such as regard

only their private estates. We shall support them in so far as is
most useful to our good sister and her realm, and do not doubt
that they shall finally gather the fruit of their truth and their
trouble, to the honour of God, the comfort of their ruler, and
the happiness of their whole land.

★

Queen Mary, almost exclusively surrounded by men, was still
in the city of Perth, and without intermission messengers came
and went with missives from the Privy Council, and good or
bad news from without. Mary had convinced her kinsfolk in
France and Spain that in this marriage there was no question
of a mere passing fancy. It represented rather the completion
of the first stage in a series of well-thought-out political plans
of a far-reaching character. From Perth she wrote earnestly
to the French court for the renewal of the true and close alliance of the past centuries; to the Spanish, that now was the
time for the forging of an inalienable bond of steel between
Scotland and the lands of the Catholic King. For what was
at stake was the destruction or salvation of the religion shared
by both and so precious to both, which stood in such danger
in these fearful times, and nowhere in such danger as in Scotland.

Her appeals were not without success. France had always
profited greatly by the Scottish alliance. Such a request was
not to be put aside. True, neither troops nor money were sent.
But other, less costly, efforts were made, which at least showed
good-will. At the moment, lively discussions were going on between the French and English courts, about a suggested marriage between King Charles, aged sixteen and Queen Elizabeth,
aged one-and-thirty. Nevertheless, the French Ambassador in
London went so far as to make specific representations on behalf of his master and of the Queen-mother to the effect that
the Scottish Queen had entered a complaint that she was being
molested in her most private concerns by the English Govern-

ment. The King of France himself, in a holograph letter, asked
Queen Elizabeth to release the Countess of Lennox.

Mary was still in Perth, but intending to return south next
morning. Towards evening, just as she was on the point of
seeking some refreshment in the views round about the castle,
David Rizzio came to announce that a messenger was just
arrived with important news. The Queen absolutely must see
him. Mary was ready. David brought the man in; he stood
before her in her apartment, his face, grey with exhaustion,
showing how hard and fast he had ridden through the dusty
July day. He came from Her Majesty's most devoted servants,
the Earls of Seaton and Atholl, he said, to say to Her Majesty
as from them: Tomorrow about eight o'clock, at the time when
Her Highness, with the Earls of Ross and Lennox, would be
passing through the glen of Kinross on their way south, the
Earls of Murray and Argyle, with three hundred horsemen,
would be waiting there, to surprise the Queen's train, in order
to take the Queen prisoner and transport her to Lochleven
Castle, which belonged to the Earl of Murray's brother. There
the Queen was to be held prisoner for life. Mary stepped back a
pace; David, standing behind the messenger, raised his hands
to heaven. "And Earl Henry and Earl Matthew?" asked the
Queen, quickly collecting herself.—"They too are to be taken
captive; or perhaps they may fall in the fight." The Queen
bethought herself, shook her head. "Earl Murray is said to be
a party to this? But I know that he is lying sick in Lochleven."
—"At all events, so I am to report, munitions and artillery
have been taken to Lochleven. Here are letters for Your Majesty from their lordships." The Queen inquired once more, holding the letters in her hand, how many men the others were
supposed to have. They were put at some three hundred, said
the man. They had also taken some field pieces from Dunbar
and Edinburgh. "Cannon! It sounds incredible," said Mary.
The man repeated that she would find it all in the letters. The
Queen moved to the window, to open them: she read the sheets

twice through, then, throwing them to David, who seized upon them greedily, came back to the messenger: "We shall see to it."

Next morning, when the troops of the Earls of Murray and Argyle actually reached the glen of Kinross, it was only to learn that the Queen had ridden through with Earls Henry and Matthew, at the head of eight hundred spears, at five o'clock in the morning. They had left Perth before midnight.

Mary refused to be overwhelmed by this. In accordance with her plans, she made a detour to the west of the Edinburgh road, to go to the castle of Callender, which belonged to Lord Livingstone, the brother of one of her Maries. She had promised to act as godmother at the christening of the new-born son of the family. Unlike the Queen's maid of honour, Lord Livingstone and his wife were Protestants. Nevertheless, the Queen attended the whole christening ceremony, including the sermon. Simply to make it quite plain to show the head of the house how dear he and his must be to her heart. She had never before shown so high a mark of favour to any one.

★

Thereafter, accompanied by as many troops as she could gather, she resumed her journey to Edinburgh. The lords, who had assembled there for the Kirk session, marched out on the news of her approach. Those who dwelt near by took to their castles, the others to the houses of their friends. Queen Mary did not go to Holyrood, but took up her quarters in the castle.

Thence she despatched letters to all the Protestant lords who had not yet displayed hostility to her cause. The letters signified her sincere meaning to all her good subjects in the exercise of their religion and conscience, notwithstanding evil bruits spread by seditious persons to the contrary, and desired the person addressed to have no dealings with such. To the letter a postscript was appended to the effect that though she had hoped not to issue any sudden summons, she now prayed the recipient with his kin, friends, etc., to come in "fear of war," provided for fifteen days.

In Edinburgh, four prominent citizens, merchants, were apprehended and brought to the castle. Their houses were closed, after all the inhabitants had been put out. The Queen's Council, which consisted in the main of Lords Atholl and Seaton, fiery Catholics, together with some of the minor Protestant lords, with the support of the Queen's two illegitimate brothers, Lords John and Robert Stuart, accused the prisoners of having sought to provoke uproar and conspiracy against the Queen. But no good grounds for their execution could be proved. Their imprisonment for a time long enough to serve as a warning to other unruly spirits had to suffice. In the territory of the Earl of Atholl, who had a special feud with the Earl of Murray, the fiery cross blazed night and day, as a signal that every one who wanted to be safe against hostile attack by his neighbours, should be on guard and under arms.

★

Terror now shook all the friends of England. Swift messengers were on the way to their arch enemy, the Earl of Bothwell, to summon him home with all speed to his Queen, who stood in urgent need of his determined aid.

★

Once again did his sister urgently and solemnly appeal to the Earl of Murray to adduce reasons for his hostile resistance to her marriage. He replied, in writing, in which form her last appeal had been addressed to him, since he had for some time entirely withdrawn from court: Apart from the fact that, despite all his professions of religious toleration, Henry Darnley, at heart, was nothing but an embittered Catholic, full of hatred for the sincere Word of God, and wholly determined on its destruction, the Earl of Murray possessed all too certain proof that Her Majesty must expect, from her betrothed, everything up to murder by treachery. Together with his

179

father, he had suborned murderers to remove himself, the Earl of Murray, guardian over Scotland's weal and woe, out of his path.

Queen Mary was informed: "It is a fact that the Earl of Murray has received monies from the Queen of England. Day and night he has but one thought—before Your Majesty came into the country, and he stood at the head of the rebellious lords, he had his first taste of the experience of looking down from aloft on all men, like a King, and concentrating all men's powers of love and hatred on himself alone. So, now, his ambition will never let him sleep until Lord James stands under the regal canopy. Nothing short of this can satisfy him, and however he tries, it leaves him no rest." Mary knew that Margaret Douglas, the mother of Lord James (while her lover, King James V, still lived), had married with the Lord of Lochleven, a Douglas." Bitterly, however, she gave every one to understand that she had always regarded herself as the King's rightful wife. Her son James Stuart was, in the eyes of God, King of Scotland, and Mary the illegitimate bastard.

Nevertheless, Mary sent again to her brother. Her messenger was John Hay, who had recently proved his loyalty in London. He was commissioned to say: Of a surety, neither Earl Matthew nor Lord Henry had any evil will towards him. If, as Lord James complained, he had been given intimation of a murderous attack planned upon him by the two lords, Lord Henry only asked for a chance to meet his calumniator in a single combat and force the black lie down his dying throat.

But Lord James replied: As a loyal vassal, he would, at any hour, gladly honour the Queen's command to him to come to her. But with those about her he would never have anything to do. Once again Queen Mary sent, that she might know exactly where he stood. Her herald rode into Lochleven, where the Earl still lay, and proclaimed the Queen's command— Within eight-and-forty hours the Earl must appear before the face of Her Majesty, there to answer the charges made against him, on pain of being punished as a traitor.

Two days later, the name of the Earl was posted as a rebel. The same fate befell the Earl of Argyle. The Queen, so it was said, had sworn that these people should now know the taste they had so often prepared for others.

★

Mary sent to the fortress of Dunbar, where George Gordon, eldest son of the Earl of Huntly, still lay prisoner. Her messengers now brought him to Edinburgh. There, his relations awaited him—above all, his mother, his sister Jean, and his brother Adam. With tears, the Queen clasped him in her arms. All his lands and honours were to be restored to him, with heavy interest, to repay him for the grim years of his suffering.

★

Mr. Thomas Randolph still went up and down about the court, when he was not occupied in writing, hour after hour, reports to his court of all the talk and gossip of which he could lay hold in town or country. The Queen was, he wrote, as good as finished, so serious was her position. Even externally she had changed. The gracious gentleness that had once made her so lovely had gone; all her features had hardened into a kind of cold pride.

He reported to his Government the imminent arrival of the Earl of Bothwell. His return from France, whether by land or water, should be watched, and he himself held captive, on pain of grave peril to England. This warning he repeated thrice.

He received the reply of the Lennoxes to the Queen of England's summons to them to return home. Old Lennox said, After the shocking treatment of his wife, Countess Margaret in London, any idea of returning thither on his own part seemed to him sheer lunacy at the moment. Henry Darnley drew himself up proudly, when Randolph appeared before him. He recognized duty and obedience to one Queen only, he said, the Queen of Scotland, whom he served and honoured. With a scornful smile, he added: "The Queen of England seems to be in sad need of me, since she makes such a fuss of my return!" Randolph raised his eyes to heaven—such an answer to such a Queen!

★

On the next day, Henry Darnley was formally raised to the status of Duke of Albany.

On July 28th, in the evening, three heralds rode in the soft dusk of summer through the wynds of Edinburgh, halted in the market-place, and blew to all the four quarters of the heavens, while the crowds thronging in the streets were so still that only one soul might have been breathing there. The heralds proclaimed:

"We, Mary, by the Grace of God Queen of Scotland, to our vassals, our marshals of nobility and heralds, our lieutenants and judges, all and sundry, friendly greetings! Since we intend, in conformity with God's holy will and in sight of Holy Church, to enter into a bond of marriage with the exalted and high-born Prince Henry, Duke of Albany, we decree That in view of this our contract of marriage, and for the period of its entire duration, the said Prince Henry, Duke of Albany, be from now on known as King in our Kingdom. All our letters and decrees, issued by us after our marriage, shall be valid only when to our name, that of Queen of Scotland, the name of this exalted Prince, our future husband, is joined. So that we united together appear as King and Queen of Scotland."

The herald rode on, to publish his message at other places. Behind him swarmed the crowd, which could not tire of so remarkable a show until it had been repeated for the last time. Then, as they sat in the wineshops, in the houses, drinking and talking endlessly, the heart of all their talk was: "She has consulted no one, neither Parliament nor the Estates. From today we have got a King, as though he had fallen from the skies! And the Queen of England cannot abide him!"

182

At court it was well known that Queen Mary would gladly have waited until Parliament offered her husband the name of King, perhaps on the day when he attained his majority. But she had given way, at last, to the desperate agonies of her betrothed. "He is still so young," she repeated, in excuse, to the members of her Privy Council.

★

On Sunday morning, July 29th, 1565, Mary was married to Henry Darnley. She knelt at his side before the altar in her chapel, clad in the black velvet she had worn at the funeral of her first husband. So soon, however, as she had greeted her young husband with kiss and handshake as King of Scotland, she retired with her ladies in order to change her garb, and reappeared among her guests clad for the first time for five years in colours—a dress of rose-red satin, embroidered all over with gold, pearls and precious stones, the crown shining above the veil on her fair head. Beaming with pride and happiness, she sat beside her husband, on whom she had poured out all she had to give in the way of honours, and even more. From the galleries of the hall the trumpets of the royal chapel blared forth in jubilation. Queen Mary watched the empty face of her consort in order to note whom his eyes distinguished and show further grace to the fortunate ones. He sat, magnificently dressed, his hand on his hip, gazing about him with an air of triumph. The Earls of Atholl, Morton, Crawford, Eglinton and Cassilis were in charge of the service of the royal table. Many lords were raised to higher rank on this day.

But Mr. Thomas Randolph wrote that evening to the Earl of Leicester in London: That the Queen of Scotland might well find it harder to move her husband to do anything that he had not a mind for than he, Thomas Randolph, would, to let himself be hanged at the word of his lordship!

Chapter 6

In Edinburgh Castle, the men of the watch threw open wide the doors of their rooms, so that the mild air of the August evening might blow in. In one corner sat a group of soldiers playing cards; opposite, another group was chatting. They talked of the guest that day expected at the castle, the Earl of Bothwell. One young fellow, sitting with his legs stretched far out in front of him, and his hands driven deep into the pockets of his wide hose, said, decisively: "Anyhow, he is a Sodomite!" An elderly man of sickly aspect said thoughtfully, "Oh, no, he goes with women." He declared that the Earl had had at least twenty; Lady Reres had been his mistress, and also her sister, Lady Buccleuch. Indeed, when he was quite young, only eighteen, the Earl had married Lady Buccleuch, or so it was said, though no one knew for certain. Anyhow, both Lady Buccleuch and her sister, Lady Reres, were undoubted witches, and knew every point in the black catechism. And they had instructed Lord Bothwell in their magic arts. Another gave a different story. Once the Earl, when still quite a young man, one- or two-and-twenty, had gone on a journey to Denmark. In Denmark, he had persuaded a young, lovely, very rich and high-born maiden to run away with him. "But when they got into the Netherlands, he left her, but her money was all gone. And the lady came all the way here, looking for her lover, who was, she said, her husband, and also for her money, and she went to the Queen, but the Queen knew nothing. For, by then, the Earl had been banished. His mother would have nothing to do with the Danish lady, and said the marriage was not legal. So the lady had to fare back again."

184

They went on talking, and the last speaker always knew the most. The soldiers who had been sitting with their cards, finally stood by and listened, too. At last, one of them, with coarse, black hair hanging in strands over his stolid, red face, said: "In my opinion, all that talk is lies. A great lord may take some of her money, one time, from a rich maiden. And she may be pretty near done in. And she may go so far as call herself Countess over it all. And here folk call that a great shame. I have seen a bit more of the world, for I have been in Italy and in France, and of course in England too. And I see nothing in it. And I can tell you that the folk I got to know out there would see nothing in it either. And they were all folk who thought a lot of themselves."—The others now said, that they thought nothing of it, either. And therefore they praised the speaker. He continued: "Here, the Earl of Bothwell is said to be a Sodomite, and to have three wives living, and to practice magic. That is the story. Well, to begin with, I don't believe any of it. I was in England, as I told you, and I heard there, and on the very best authority, for his lordship said it to me himself, that is Sir Henry Percy told me, that no man bore himself better and more honourably than the Earl of Bothwell then did. And it was Sir Henry Percy who held the Earl a prisoner in England. That was before my time, of course. And Sir Henry told me that he had imagined the Earl quite different. Before, every one had been afraid of him. No boy was supposed to be safe with the Earl of Bothwell, and no girl either. But Sir Henry said, when he came he was simply cleverer than the others, and knew more than they did."

The speaker went on: "For my part, I prefer Bothwell to Murray. Murray will never give a soul so much as a bloody groat, unless he is absolutely forced to do so. A man gets tired of working for him for ever and never getting a thing out of it. He has simply squeezed the Queen dry. Bothwell would never do a dirty trick like that. He knows what a man needs, and a decent man and a soldier can talk to him and be glad to do anything for him. At least that is my opinion."

One of the others chipped in: "His sister is married to the Queen's brother." The sickly-looking man said: "There is no love lost between him and the Lennoxes." Every one looked at him on this, and he went on, with an important air: "That is an old quarrel. Thus. When the Queen was a wee thing and was sent into France, and her mother ruled here, and was a notably beautiful and clever woman, there were ever so many lords who sought the hand of the Queen's mother. Of them, the two whose chances seemed the best were Earl Matthew of Lennox and Earl Patrick of Bothwell, the father of the young Earl. They were both very rich and powerful, and at that time both were young and both were handsome men. But Earl Patrick was far the handsomer of the two. He was absolutely the handsomest man in all Scotland, and was generally called simply the Handsome Earl. If you said that, every one knew he was meant. Well, neither of them got the Regent, and Earl Matthew went and betrayed Scotland for the sake of Countess Margaret and went off to England. But every child here knew that the Regent liked Earl Patrick and would have gladly married him, and only did not do it for the sake of her daughter, the Queen. And Earl Matthew hated Earl Patrick with a deadly hate, and they fought a duel together, and Earl Patrick struck Earl Matthew's sword out of his hand."

They talked of all sorts of things, until the whistle for the watch sounded shrilly outside; then they rushed out to take their places and droop their spears in greeting. With a small following, Earl James of Bothwell rode into the court. He was mounted on a fine black horse, whose spirit he curbed with happy ease, and was clad in a jerkin of dark red silk. He smiled as he passed by the watch, and his white teeth flashed out suddenly in his dark face. He nodded a greeting to the soldiers, and reined in his horse. One of his squires had already dismounted and came running up. The Earl swung out of the saddle. For a moment he stood, bending back his tall figure, and looked about the yard: gloomy banishment over, he returned, in honour, home.

Breathing deep, he turned to the page who appeared in the door that gave entrance to the royal chambers, and followed him rapidly up the staircase. In the antechamber several pages were waiting; Her Majesty was ready to receive his lordship; he would find Her Highness almost alone. The door flew open; Queen Mary sat in the window, occupied with her embroidery, with Mary Seaton opposite to her. The Queen wore a robe of light brown silk with small gild embroidered spots upon it; her hair was hidden under a golden net. She extended a friendly hand to the Earl, across her work, and then pushed the frame a little to one side. Falling on his knee, he bowed deeply, kissed her hand reverently. Then, with profound emotion, he raised his eyes, and said: "How I thank Your Majesty!" Mary signed to him to stand up. As he drew himself up stiff and straight before her, she looked up at him; in his eyes she seemed to read a cold, steely calm: in his features, that this man, in the bitter years of exile, had freed himself from every trace of vain imagination and fear, nay even from hope and from feeling, so that he was now and for ever simply ready to meet any and every necessity forthwith, as it came to him. Recollection of her own recent experiences smote her heart with pain. High hopes rose exultant, and drove this feeling down. She said, quickly, "We have been through much, my Lord. And I am afraid that the worst is still to come—so that we are much in need of a really loyal servant."

"Your Majesty knows that nothing but the extreme bitterness of my deadly enemies' hatred could drive me from Your Majesty's feet," he replied. "If Your Majesty will again permit me to put my powers at your service . . . I have learned what the alien is!"

Mary said that she should receive him, in the course of the next few days, at the solemn session of her Privy Council. The decree quashing the process against him and restoring him to possession of all his properties, was already drawn up and signed by her and her ministers. She hoped that her trusty vassal would again take his place in her Crown Council. Of course his rank as High Admiral of Scotland was there for him. But she had thought he might be ready to take over the command of the troops on the southern borders. She then bade him go very soon to the King her husband, to offer him, too, his services. If it were agreeable to him, it would give her and her husband pleasure to see him that same evening at the royal table. "We are still living very quietly," she said, smiling rather sadly.

The Earl stood before her, about to take his leave, when fastening her glance on him, she added, suddenly: "How tall you are, sir!" In that instant, a quiver, the shadow of a singular smile, passed over his mouth, only to die away at once: he stood before his Queen, his face as rigid as though cast in bronze. But she had flushed a deep purple-red right up to the roots of her hair. Her heart was contracted, almost stopped; she felt again the sickening pain that had invaded her on the day she had been told the hideous insult this man was said to have uttered about her. Unconscious of what she did, she raised her hand to her temples, pearly with sudden sweat. Then, collecting herself, she calmly dismissed him. "Till this evening, then, at dinner."

★

The Earl of Murray, with all the lords of his party, came from Lochleven Castle to Glasgow, to summon the country to open rebellion in defence of religion, threatened by the new and disastrous tendencies of the Queen. In his declaration to the people he entered his own defence. Had not the Queen shamefully and scornfully dismissed all the Protestant counsellors who had, hitherto, sacrificed their personal interest and concerns to the service and protection of the country? Had she not more and more openly supported thousands and tens of thousands of her subjects in partaking of an idolatrous worship that was detestable to God, and of the Mass which must be avoided in peril of eternal damnation? Had she not more and more sought to base her power on friendship and alliance with the Pope and the King of Spain, Hell's foes to true religion, whose minds were set, day and night, to seeing the blood of the children of God flow amid the pangs of martyrdom?

★

Henry Darnley, now King, having throughout his life, so far, been accustomed to serve both Confessions, went to the Cathedral in Edinburgh to hear Master John Knox preach. He sat on the throne, under the canopy, opposite to the pulpit. John Knox preached from the text: "Woe to the land that is ruled over by boys and women!" Henry Darnley did not dare to leave his seat suddenly. John Knox talked for over an hour.

True, he was subsequently called before the Council, which forbade his preaching for three weeks under terms so severe that even he had at last to make up his mind to obey. But the public amends the King thus secured was by no means equal to the injury done him.

★

Queen Elizabeth sent yet another envoy, to convey how deeply she was injured. As a visible proof of her anger she sent, this time, a man of low birth and education, who had hitherto only been employed on quite subordinate tasks. He had a long document from his mistress, in very unamiable terms. Queen Elizabeth began by recounting that her astonishment knew no bounds; she had again and again been asked for advice by the Queen of Scotland, only to be confronted at the last by action taken without any regard to her. Nor could the Queen of England at all understand how the Queen of Scotland could have been induced to retain subjects of a foreign power at her court when their return had been expressly demanded. The Queen then went on to say that she wanted an explanation of certain words in Mary's last very bold letter, where she stated: I had never dreamed that you could possibly take such an action, and shall, without seeking any further revenge, turn to all the princes my allies that they may show you who

I am by blood relationship! Further, Queen Elizabeth said: All the actions of the Queen of Scotland have, so far, had but one purpose, namely the sowing of disquiet between the two kingdoms. The Queen of Scotland must, however, now cease secretly stirring up trouble among the subjects of the English realm, and rather give a little attention to vassals of her own who have done her much good service. In England, the Queen of England will look after justice. In return, she asks of her neighbour of Scotland at least not to pursue the poor Earl of Murray with such harsh ingratitude as to persecute a man whose love to her is so great, lest, driven to despair, he is compelled, merely to save his own life, to take to weapons that might haply bring the whole realm to ruin.

Such, so the document ended, were the main points in regard to which the Queen of England felt herself to have been injured. She concluded by asking the Queen of Scotland to be pleased to reply to them.

It did please her, and she wrote:

"On all these points the Queen of Scotland has already given information again and again, through Lord Lethington, through Sir Nicholas Throgmorton, through Mr. John Hay, and through other envoys, as well as through the French Ambassador. Who could upbraid her with not giving up her husband, who was, moreover, so very warmly recommended to her by the Queen of England herself? Of dealings with the subjects of her Majesty of England she knows nothing; as for the advice proffered her on how to deal with her own vassals, she would remark that she has never been curious to know what the Queen of England does at home with her own subjects, in obedience to the common rule of courtesy among princes which forbids her to interfere in the internal affairs of her royal colleague. The Queen of England surely does not wish to break so just and reasonable a custom."

Further, Mary observed that she was astonished to find false reporters for ever representing her as seeking to make forcible changes in the religion of her country. If the Queen of England

had said to the French Ambassador that the Queen of Scotland
cherished a whole nest of idle fantasies in her head, she, the
Queen of Scotland, could calmly await the time when God
ripened her purposes, and those of her neighbour.

Mary closed by saying that she was ready, at all times, to
enter into a bond of friendship and amity with England on any
just basis.

★

Mary could build golden bridges for her opponent, for when
she wrote this letter, she had victory in her hands.

News came to her: "The rebels are making a nest in Glasgow." Thereupon, she marched out with her troops. The Earl
of Bothwell rode on her left hand; on her right, her husband.
Queen Mary was shining with purpose: "I will lose my Kingdom rather than let these men escape me!" She was magnificently attired in red-purple velvet, with a beret, also of purple
velvet, on her proud little head. Pistols were ready in her
holsters. Her husband was resplendent in golden armour and
rode a superb horse. If the Queen wanted conversation, however, she had to turn to the man on her other hand. She drew
to one side, while the Earl of Bothwell led the army past her.
They bowed in greeting, as they passed, and the soldiers cried,
"Long live!" in heady enthusiasm. At night, the Queen sat in
the tent in the midst of her captains; the map of Scotland lay
before them on the table; they talked eagerly. The Earl of
Bothwell led the discussion. The Queen uttered her opinion
quickly; Earl Bothwell replied: "No, that will not do. This is
the only way." He pointed to the map with his finger, and
Queen Mary, all aglow with understanding, cried: "Yes, of
course! of course, you are entirely right!" Henry Darnley,
in his golden armour, sat at the head like a magnificent table
decoration, silent with boredom, and injured because he had to
be bored. His wife rose, to go through the camp accompanied
by the Earls of Huntly and Bothwell. She stood by the camp
fires, talking with the men and promising them rewards. She
said, With such an army, who could doubt of victory?

Suddenly, the troops were before Glasgow, and found it empty. On the news: The Queen is coming! She will be here in two hours! the rebel lords had hastily ridden away. The Earl of Murray, their general, went south, where, in the shelter of the woods, he awaited the Earl of Argyle's reinforcements. His ally delaying, he sent to him thrice daily: The campaign is lost, they are all ruined, if he does not keep faith. The Earl of Argyle told the messengers, in reply, that the matter was by no means so simple as the Earl of Murray seemed to think: and made no move to come out of his castle. Thereupon James Stuart collected his courage and determined to make a dash for Edinburgh. The town was Protestant. It thought it had a thousand reasons for bitter wrath against its ruler. It would supply them with the money, weapons, food, and shelter that they needed.

The rebellious lords stood before the town. So many citizens were on their side that the gates were opened. The troops came in, grey with exertion and fatigue, and made at once for their quarters. Next morning, drummers went up and down the streets, first beating loud upon the drums and then suddenly falling still to let a soldier step forward from among them and roar out hoarsely the goods and honours promised to every man who took arms under the fortunate standard of the great Lords of Scotland, who were fighting for the weal of all, and stood guard over the religion and law of every Scot. Every one listened to the promises. When it came to testing them, there were only a couple of emaciated boys and one or two broken-down vagabonds, of no use to any sergeant. Later on came other drummers, down from the castle, and their pursuivants announced: "From six o'clock tomorrow morning the castle cannon will be trained on to the town. Because of the shameless rebels who attack our gracious Majesty the Queen. Until the aforesaid rebels and shameless traitors are driven out of the town."

Every one in Edinburgh passed a night of dread. Next morning, when the cannon actually crashed down from the heights,

192

nobody was asleep to be waked up by them. The shells fell, roaring, in every quarter of the town; in many places, the wooden houses blazed up like bonfires. The screaming inhabitants tumbled out into the streets, only to find death whistling about their ears when they emerged into the open.

Before evening, the Lords retreated, left the town. Two hours later, the Queen entered, riding to the Town Hall, where she dismounted and entered. She sat in the Hall of Justice in the midst of her counsellors and knights, and well-to-do citizens of good repute were brought before them for judgment. In view of the proofs of their guilt in the testimony of witnesses, and, even more glaring, in the documents lying there on the table in front of their Sovereign, any attempt at lying must have seemed to them both useless and unworthy. After a brief process, the soldiers took them away, and they were promptly strung up in the Lawnmarket. Their goods fell to the Crown. The town itself had to pay a heavy money fine.

Queen Mary only spent one night in her capital. At daybreak on the following morning, she was again on horse, in pursuit of the fleeing lords. They fled southwards, in open and anxious flight before their irate Sovereign, seeking a precarious safety in the neighbourhood of the English border. Once across it, they could, for the first time, pause and draw breath, though they still hardly dared to look about them. The pursuit was stayed at the frontier, since Queen Mary wished to spare the territory of the neighbour State. It was inclining her way, and not a hand in it had been raised in support of the defeated rebels.

Now the Queen's proclamation was sent out in all directions. "To all, gentle and simple, who cast themselves repentant at her feet, the Queen will show mercy." The only names excluded from pardon were those of the Earls of Argyle, Murray, and Glencairn, the Lords of Rothes and Ochiltree and the knight Kirkaldy of Grange.

Sadly perceiving that their cause was hopelessly lost, the rebels had no choice; some must humbly take the hand of mercy stretched out to them, others, beaten, isolated, without troops, must creep over to England in the timorous hope that some obscure shelter might be granted them there.

From the heights of her Castle of Edinburgh, Queen Mary looked down upon a subjugated country; in her hands she held the submission of all the lords east and west, north and south, through the new inviolable oath they had sworn in return for their recognition and humble abjuration of the sin of rebellion they had committed against her. The suspected towns of Glasgow, Hamilton, and St. Andrews sent deputations which cast themselves at the Queen's feet, to purchase her pardon at the price of great sums of money and the surrender of important privileges.

A messenger from the English Queen announced the advent of an Ambassador bearing assurances of friendship.

★

Lord James of Murray was now in England, without resources and accompanied merely by a handful of friends in misfortune. He recalled the fact that the Queen of England, both in special letters and through privy as well as through express instructions to her envoys, had continually encouraged him in resistance to his ruler. More than once had considerable sums in money been supplied to the lords in the field by the English Government, and the Earl of Bedford, the commander on the English border, had assured them at the same time, that, if his Queen still hesitated to send troops, the sole reason was the painful embarrassments to which she was subject in her own court, where both Spain and France were continually making the most pressing representations through their Ambassadors to the effect that any injury to the Queen of Scotland would be felt by their rulers as an injury to themselves.

Lord James had proceeded on his journey to the English court as far as the neighbourhood of London, when he was halted by a messenger from Queen Elizabeth, who came to command him to retrace his steps at once. An icy chill penetrated the Earl's soul. If the Queen of England did not support his cause, he would have to take refuge in the air to find a place in which he would not be branded as a traitor. As a declared and outlawed rebel against his ruler, who was at peace with all countries, there was no power which would tolerate his presence. On the contrary, any one who met him would seize and deliver him to his own country. In sheer despair, he continued his journey, the message, notwithstanding, that, once actually in London, he might forthwith inform the court—here he was; to turn back was impossible; the Queen must receive him! After a secret parley, Queen Elizabeth acceded to his request.

She actually received the fugitive in solemn audience. Her entire Privy Council, with the French and Spanish Ambassadors, stood around her throne, where she was seated, magnificently attired, sparkling with diamonds from head to foot; a lace ruff as large as the top of a table stood up all round her head, which was itself adorned with pearls and precious stones. So Lord James perceived her, on his admission to the throne room. He himself was all in black; dropping humbly on one knee before her, he entered his plea for protection, speaking in Scots. Queen Elizabeth interrupted him somewhat sharply: he should speak French, that the foreign gentlemen might likewise understand what he said. When he excused himself, saying that his command of that language was not adequate to so alarming an occasion, Elizabeth replied, still in the same unfriendly tone, that, in that event, she would speak in French, while he adhered to his Scots. He went on with his speech, describing his pitiable position and saying that his sole hope now was in the kindness of the Queen of England, who surely, in her inexhaustible graciousness of heart, would not refuse shelter and protection to a man who to all intents and purposes was excluded from the entire world. Then, still on his knee, he fell silent, longing for the gesture which should at once permit him to rise and assure him of support and protection. But Queen Elizabeth did not at once reply. Waving her jewel-bespangled fan to and fro, so that sparks from it flew about the room like shining seeds, she looked down at the man kneeling before her, and went on looking, till the blood overspread his cheeks and circles, fiery and black, danced alternately before his eyes. With a sudden movement, the Queen let her fan drop. Sitting up very erect, she began to speak, slowly, in an almost mocking tone. She began with an expression of her surprise that the Earl of Murray, a declared rebel, lawless and outlawed, had so much as ventured to appear before her. Turning first pale than red, the Earl was too much taken aback to utter a syllable in reply, and the Queen continued without a pause. True, she said, there had been certain slight misunderstandings which had temporarily somewhat troubled the otherwise altogether sisterly and entirely friendly relations between her and her good sister of Scotland, but thanks to the kind offices of the French and Spanish Ambassadors, these had been altogether cleared away and remitted to entire forgetfulness. For that reason, she had asked these two gentlemen to be witnesses of her statement, made with all possible clearness and definition, that she had had no sort of connection with the people who had given her good sister, the Queen of Scotland, more than justified ground for the greatest possible indignation. "The world is in the habit," she said, "of whispering that the true focus of every disorder that occurs anywhere among my neighbours lies in my Kingdom. Even in this rising in Scotland, I am said to have been involved. Well!"—she spoke in clear, distinct and slow voice, so that every syllable of her speech must have been heard throughout the great room—"may God, who is, as I know well, a just God, punish me with a similar rising in my own realm if I have ever stirred up the subjects of any prince whatsoever to disobedience or encouraged them in it!" With a cutting glance for the Earl, who trembled so violently with shame that he was near fainting, and a coldly ironical glance for her suite —for she knew perfectly well that if they could have spoken their thoughts, they were, at this moment, all struck dumb with astonishment—she went on: "So far as we are informed, there are two reasons for the disturbances in Scotland. First—

the Queen there has married without the consent of her Estates, and has neglected to give her princely neighbours sufficient warning of her intentions. The Earl of Murray sought to oppose these irregularities, and for this reason fell into disfavour. Second—the Earl of Lennox and his house are not in favour of the Reformed religion. Thereupon, the Earl of Murray, in agreement with his friends, preferred to risk his life rather than tolerate the destruction of the truth as he sees it. Now the Earl of Murray appears before us, to secure our good offices between himself and his ruler, and get a hearing for his defence of himself. Certainly, he has committed grave offences—treason against the person of the Sovereign remains treason—and if we had to assume that there was here a case of intentional treason, we should not hesitate for a moment to punish the traitor as his treachery deserves. Yet, in former times, we have known the Earl of Murray as so true and loving a subject of his ruler as to incline us rather to the view that he has erred in this instance out of an excess of love and loyalty. At the same time, to count upon any kind of support from us is an idea so perverse that, as we have already said, we do not know how sufficiently to express our amazement. There is nothing for the Earl to do save to remove himself from our presence and to consider whether he cannot find some way of softening the just wrath of his injured ruler against him."

With this, she turned from the Earl, who rose, staggering, from his knees; everything swam around him and he hardly knew how, under the guidance of two pages, he managed to make his way out of the audience chamber.

On the same day, he left London, and took refuge with some English friends, made in the days of his former prosperity, where he might drag out the wretched existence which he had purchased at the price of such frightful personal humiliation.

★

Thus had Queen Elizabeth restored superficially good relations with the neighbouring State. Henceforth, polite letters

197

passed, while trifling irritations, of one kind or another, were used to keep tempers hot. Queen Elizabeth's messenger refused to accept a safe conduct for his journey through Scotland to the English border, countersigned with the names of Queen Mary and her husband. Therefore, the Scottish Queen caused him to be apprehended and held captive on her border, on the ground that he was travelling without a passport. Queen Elizabeth, on her part, expended her wrath on the Countess of Lennox, whom she kept in the Tower.

★

Meantime the preachers of Edinburgh were passing a wretched time. No cavalier now ventured to interfere with the Queen when she wanted to exercise tolerance, as she understood it. Earl Morton was at court, and on the Privy Council. He was a Protestant. But who would trust him in spiritual matters? Unless he saw a personal advantage: only then. The preachers were aware that last Easter ten thousand persons had partaken of the Communion in the royal chapel. What Catholic now took any pains to be secret if he wanted to celebrate service according to his own confession in his own house? They celebrated christenings, buryings and weddings, publicly, after the fashion that pleased them. The great bishoprics had been overthrown or filled by mere shadows, concerned mainly with keeping their activity as far as possible hidden from the people. Queen Mary re-established the sees, endowed them, and filled them with zealous and competent priests. She fetched learned priests and monks from Italy and from France, who preached openly on their religion and its tenets. Was it not only a question of time, and of a short time, before the Cathedral of Edinburgh, where the services had already fallen back into idolatry, would be decorated again with pictures and filled with the fumes of incense?

The preachers cried: "Fifty-four holy men and women were burned last Witsun in Madrid, at a festival, a great show in honour of the court, for which people had been saving up for

weeks beforehand. They were burned slowly on bonfires artis-
tically built with terraces and stages so that the pangs of the
human torches thus set up to God were visible, on all sides, up
to the last minute, as a marvellous spectacle, a feast for the
eyes of the gorgeously decked lords and ladies and a joy to the
heart of the servant of Satan, King Philip, the accursed of God.
Two hundred and fifty Protestant sailors from England sailed
into the harbour of Cadiz. The treacherous Spaniards threw
them into the maw of that Hell-upon-Earth, the Inquisition.
When the Spanish servants of Moloch, who calls himself King
Philip, could no longer refuse Queen Elizabeth, eighty were
yielded up by the Spanish dungeons. What became of the others,
our brothers in Christ? They perished of hunger and thirst.
In the Netherlands, a hundred thousand men, women and girls
have been beheaded, hanged, tortured on the wheel, burned, or
buried alive by the Emperor Charles. His son, Philip, is doing
things there so awful that all his father's cruelties are forgotten
in comparison. In France, any children of truth that fall into
their hands, all those whom they have not crushed by the fear
of their weapons, are hanged. In Italy, the streets run with the
blood of the slain children of God, and the sky is dark from
the smoke of the fires in which our brothers have burned. And
Antichrist, incorporated in the bloody tyrants of these lands,
in every case took from those who fought for God everything
they had in the way of property. When will they set up the
Calvary for the servants of God in Edinburgh?"

Many citizens of Edinburgh had lived through the times of
King James V and of the Regent, and seen Scottish preachers
burning, in the square before the entrance to the castle, about
the hour after dinner, as though to afford an agreeable entertainment during the fat prelates' pause for digestion.

The citizens said: "Hitherto, our Queen has been gentle, for
her nature is good. Now, however, Queen Catherine of France
and King Philip of Spain, her son-in-law, have made an alliance
at Bayonne, under whose terms they mutually pledge themselves to destroy all heretics in their lands, not even sparing the

child in the mother's womb. And our Queen has entered into this alliance. The Pope has sent her a hundred thousand pieces of gold to fight heresy with, and an ambassador, who is here already though he goes about in disguise, to seek out who is first to be burned. Twenty ships are on the way here from Spain, with more soldiers on board than there are men in Scotland. And when all the Protestants in Scotland are dead, then the Queen will march on England at the head of the Spaniards to thrust Queen Elizabeth from the throne, and all the Protestants in England will be burned, too, and it will be a thousand times worse even than it was in the time of Bloody Mary."

Yet when Queen Mary rode through the town, bowing in friendly fashion on all sides, she looked so gently and smiled so sweetly on everybody, that folk shook their heads and asked How could she find it in her heart to murder her subjects on account of their faith? When she had passed by, however, folk came out of holes and corners, and said: "Is not the Court more Catholic than ever? At Christmas the King spent the whole night in the chapel on his knees. True, he was alone; for the Queen must e'en play cards all night with David."

★

Shortly after Christmas, on a mild, frosty day, Queen Mary went out riding with a small retinue. She rode merely for the sake of getting a little exercise, taking a north-easterly turn round about the town and approaching the road that led to Craigmillar Castle, set among its lovely hill country, a place of which she was very fond. Today, however, she intended leaving Craigmillar on one side, and returning directly to the palace. Just, however, as she had given the sign to turn, she noticed that her horse was losing one of its shoes. At the point where they were, a few houses grouped together, on either side of the road, to form a hamlet. "The roads are glassy with frost, and I do not want to fall," she said. "Probably there is a smith somewhere near here." Sebastian, one of her servants, said, Yes, there was a smith. They rode through the single

short street of which the place consisted, and at the end, in
an open house, there was a fire blazing away, and the smith
came out to the distinguished company.

Queen Mary explained to the man what was wanted, dismounted and, as a fine rain had come on, went into a little
house close by the smithy, which she and her suite—Mary
Livingstone, David, and the servant Sebastian—took to be the
smith's abode. From the street they stepped straight into a
room which served at once for dwelling, sleeping, and cooking.
Here, too, a bright fire was burning on the hearth; a stout,
black kettle hung down over the fire on a chain from the
chimney. As the company entered, an old woman and a girl
with a dense mane of black hair tumbling over her face, turned
sharply from the fire, and stared at the Queen, silent, motionless, as though they were facing a messenger from another
planet.

The Queen, interpreting such obvious amazement as embarrassment, spoke a word of greeting; her servant fetched her a
rush-bottomed chair, since the women made no move, merely
stood there, staring; the Queen sat down, they still stood like
pillars. Then, the younger woman turned so suddenly that her
skirt flew out in the air. With a shrill laugh, she stepped to a
door at the back, and disappeared through it, while the door
crashed to behind her.

"A very pretty creature," said the Queen in French, to her
companions, "but apparently somewhat wild."

The old woman had withdrawn into the shadow of the chimney, where she crouched, only sending forth a baleful glance
now and then at her visitors. Outside it was raining: drops
could be heard pattering on the windows. The dark, low room
was sparsely furnished—a large rude table, a few rush-
bottomed chairs, a closet bed with dirty blankets, and, on the
walls, some utensils in wood and pottery. This only made it
more surprising to see, opposite to the Queen, a great leathern
arm-chair, and hanging over one arm of the chair, a dress of
red satin whose glowing colour seemed to fill the whole room.

201

Beside it, on the seat of the chair, was a pair of light satin slippers, covered with embroidery. In order to quiet the obvious trouble of the old woman, Queen Mary sought to be thoroughly friendly. So she said, "That is a very beautiful dress, and those shoes,"—she rose to approach and inspect them more nearly, "I really think that I have a pair that . . ." With a shrill cry the old woman burst out of the darkness. "Those are my daughter's things." But the Queen had the slippers in her hand. "It is very odd," she said, turning to her companions, "for they really are mine . . . or . . . that is to say . . ." She stopped, suddenly; her gaze seemed to turn inwards; she went white as a wand. For a moment, she stood as though broken, the things still in her hands. Then, without another word, she set the shoes carefully back on the chair. Mechanically, she moved towards the door. No one dared to address her, not even to remark that it was still raining. It was only when they had got outside that Mary Livingstone said, "I fancy we shall have ice." The Queen made no reply. Not until her horse was brought did she seem to come back to awareness of where she was, or to hear the words that had been addressed to her some time back. "We shall ride, all the same," she said, quietly.

On the way, Mary Livingstone remarked: "We must inquire. This person certainly stole the slippers or bought them from a thief."

"Certainly," the Queen repeated.

Mary Livingstone, who had meant well, dared say no more.

That evening, Queen Mary sat in the small room next to her bedroom, almost in the dark, before the fire. Mary Livingstone was again with her. Contrary to her habit, the Queen sat quite unoccupied; rested her feet on the edge of the fender, leaned her head on the back of her chair, with her arms extended along its arms; she sat, so, motionless, staring into the fire, burning low and quiet round the great beech logs. Mary Livingstone, likewise unoccupied, sat behind her, rather to one side. The maid thought of many things: of the Queen's hope, lately become a certainty, that she bore a child, and of all the proud wishes connected with the birth of such an heir: of all the pomp that had once surrounded her Queen, and which, in the view of all those round about her, was her due. She gazed at the quiet figure before her, and suddenly, without herself being able in the least to say why this was, she felt nothing but pity—a pity that made her, Mary Livingstone, who was always gay and always liked to laugh at any signs of soft-heartedness, feel inclined to get up and go to her Queen and kneel down before her and take her face tenderly between her hands and caress it, to make up for, to console her for—what? The knowledge that Mary Livingstone had acquired this morning, at the same time as her royal friend, seemed to her far too much matter of course for her to be especially moved by that.

There was a knock at the door. She opened it. David was there. The Queen turned her head a little. "I have the shoes here," he said, holding out a packet to the Queen.

Mary took them in her lap, and then sank back into her old position. "Good," she said.

"Anything else?" he asked.

"No," she replied. "Good. I thank you."

He went. As he was in the act of opening the door, she spoke to him again. "There was nothing else? I mean, that was all?"

"Yes, Your Majesty," he replied.

She was silent.

After a moment's hesitation, he finally departed. It was quite quiet in the room again. Mary Livingstone watched the singular pattern of light and shadow cast by the fire on the wall, as though there were a sort of fight going on between them.

She bent down, to throw fresh twigs on the fire. Thereupon the Queen raised herself from her semi-recumbent position. She took up the packet in her lap, and began slowly unwrapping it. It contained the shoes, carefully wrapped in the light grey paper used in the royal household. Mary held up the shoes, looking at them in the firelight. Then, slowly, she threw them, one after another, into the heart of the flame. Leaning forward, her elbows on her knees, her chin buried in her hand, she watched the fire first fuse all the colours of stuff and embroidery into its own glowing red, so that the pattern stood out with extraordinary clearness for a moment. Then, suddenly, the clear flame broke through the light stuff, and with a crackling noise, it was soon gone altogether.

Mary Livingstone had recognized the shoes in the morning. The Queen had herself embroidered them and worn them, and then, when Lord Henry Darnley, in a particularly lover-like mood, begged passionately to have them, she had given them to her husband.

A few days later, when Mary Livingstone, under a strong impulse of curiosity, went by the smith's house, she perceived that it was empty.

★

Mary accepted the invitation of a wealthy burgher to celebrate the housewarming of his new abode with him and with his family, and came down from the palace to the town with her lords and ladies, and with the King her husband. She was in lively and friendly mood, both at table and afterwards, when she withdrew to an alcove in the banqueting room, still surrounded by almost all the guests at the party. The King remained seated at table, lying, stretched out, his long legs in front of him, his chair pushed out from the board. Again and again, he lifted his wine-cup, without ever removing his hand from it, to the pages who stood behind him, to be re-filled. Only the son of the house remained at table with him, a stupid, blonde youth of some eighteen years. The King drank to him, "Holla! young sir! Are you a cavalier? Long live all those who wear the dagger!"

"My Lord," stammered the youth, awkwardly propping himself up on the arm of his chair. "Your Majesty!" He wanted to smile, but it turned to a grimace; the cup, which he sought to clink with the King's, fell out of his hand on to the table, and spread a dark red stain there over the white damask.

Whimpering, the lad sank down. "I have no one in the whole world." The King laughed, uproariously.

Mary, who had turned slightly pale, rose, and stood for a moment as if uncertain what to do. As she stood, the signs of her approaching motherhood were obvious. At last she went to her husband, and touched him lightly on the shoulder. Was it not time to go? Her smile was friendly, but a trifle uncertain. Without altering his comfortable position or looking round, he answered, over his shoulder, that he at any rate was going to stay where he was. Mary stood in doubt; one or two of the older people were occupying themselves with the host's son, who listened to none of them, but went on sobbing aloud that he was a cavalier, above every one else, and the King had honoured him with his notice. The Queen, observing the grave and uncertain air of the lad's father, bent over her husband. "Dearest," she said, softly, "I think you had better come with me. . . . Look at that poor young man. . . ." Darnley turned sharply round; his face was suddenly white as ashes and his eyes travelled over the Queen's figure, with a light in them like sudden leaping hatred.

"If you wish to go, my dear . . ."

"You must come with me," Mary, now desperate, insisted.

He sprang up abruptly. Crashing on the ground, the wine-cup fell at her feet and the wine spurted up into her face, "I will go, go, go!" he shrieked, bursting with rage. "To Hell—that's where I'll go." Snatching up his beret and dagger from a small table beside him, he rushed to the door. Before any one in the room had grasped what was going on, they heard the door slam below; then the King's sword rattling against the plaster.

The Queen, her pallid lips smiling, turned to her hosts, who pressed about her, assuring her that they could not sufficiently thank Her Majesty for having done their poor house the highest possible honour and pleasure by her gracious visit. Of that and of that alone the hearts of all were full, they repeated: how their heart-felt devotion might repay Her Majesty's kindness.

★

Queen Mary summoned her Parliament for the first half of March. This Parliament would pass sentence on the traitorous lords: death, or, at the very least, banishment and the loss of all their property.

But there were other demands to be made of this Parliament. Henry Darnley desired to have his Queen set the crown matrimonial upon his head. With it upon his head, he would be King and could transmit Scotland to his heirs, as now his wife alone could do. Queen Mary had demanded this crown for her first husband, and had received it for him. To her second she said, "My Lord, you are still too young."

Whereupon he replied: "How old were you, when you took upon yourself to reign as Queen, my dear? And how old was your famous French husband?"

"Times are different now," said Mary.

He left her with a bitter laugh.

★

Queen Mary was surrounded by petitioners, imploring her to show mercy to her poor banished lords. Queen Elizabeth of England was not put off by negative answers to her repeated interpositions; she went on writing, to this noble end, and knew why she was exercising so much forbearance. Only, Queen Mary also knew. Jean, Countess of Argyle, came to put in a good word with her princely sister for her outlawed husband. Mary replied, "The Earl has been as neglectful as a husband as he has been insolent as a subject, and you have complained of him to me a hundred times." She went on: "They have brought upon themselves what they are now experiencing. It was they who proved to me, unmistakably, that force alone could compel them to obedience." She remained firm. Parliament was to meet. So she had determined.

Sir James Melville came to his Sovereign.

206

He was feeling very unhappy, for he believed that David Rizzio's influence was still growing. David was said to take money wherever it came from. Even were he a model of all the virtues, he was a Catholic alien, and every Scot chose to regard him as a spy of the Pope. They all said: David had gone on appealing to the Pope until, at last, he sent Queen Mary another great treasure, this time something beyond counting, a veritable shipful of gold.

Sir James knew that the Pope had not sent a shipful of gold. He had, however, sent help, about which Sir James was fully informed. For the ship that carried it was cast by an extraordinary storm against the English coast, and dashed into a thousand pieces on the rocks. Next morning, the inhabitants of the coast, vassals of the Earl of Northumberland, found, lying on the shore, a dead man with a heavy leathern girdle about his body. On its being taken off him and unrolled it was found to contain ten thousand pieces of gold and letters from the Pope in Rome to the Queen of Scots. Soon after this, Mary sent emissaries, among them Sir James himself, to the Earl of Northumberland.

To him, so it was said in Edinburgh, the money had been brought, as Lord of the Manor. As a good Catholic and devoted friend to the Queen of Scots, the Earl would, doubtless, account himself fortunate in having been able to rescue so valuable a treasure for her. The Earl of Northumberland received the emissaries with marked courtesy in his dark castle by the sea. But after they had dined magnificently, he put before them a primeval law in Norman speech which he could not read nor his guests understand. He could be all the more punctilious in saying, thereupon, that according to this sacred rune, he was absolutely obliged to hold any property thrown up by the sea in his domain.

So, Queen Mary did not get her gold. But the secret of her friendship with the Pope was exposed to all eyes.

Sir James shook his head; what was to become of Scotland if the great Protestant lords never came back? He resolved to go himself to his Sovereign. He began by making certain admissions. It was true that there had been, among a very considerable part of the Scottish population, much mistrust of the good intentions of Her Majesty, at the time when she came back to her own country, was known to none, and arrived almost a stranger. "But Your Majesty, in your wisdom and goodness, succeeded, very rapidly, in creating in your subjects a universal, great, deep and genuine affection. I am now entirely at ease on this head. Today, let any external enemy whatsoever harbour evil or treacherous designs, he would find our Scottish nation against him, to a man."

"Sir James, what are you driving at?"

He placed his lance in rest. "And now Your Majesty could be in a position utterly to uproot, crush, destroy the small, surviving fragment of an opposition that still perhaps, in silence, does exist. Your Majesty could have the opportunity to weld all such hostile elements as still, perhaps, do persist, into a fraction that operated to strengthen you. If only you could decide quite simply to allow your own kindness of heart to speak. To do one thing, and one thing only—to forgive the rebel miscreants, the banished lords, the fugitives, their grave sin." He saw the gentle face of his Sovereign harden to stone, and went on, quickly, "Of course they must give guarantees of inviolable allegiance."

"Guarantees!" replied Mary. "Oh, I know only too well what those are worth with rebels! I know these people, know them well. Listen. It pleases them to rise against me. Against me, to whom they owe all they have, all that gives them a mind to rise and pleasure in rising. And, at last, they think, the hour has come, now it is time to do it. Oh, it is so awfully simple! They need only declare that I am the enemy of my own kingdom. And they, who betray me, are, at once, the self-sacrificing benefactors, the saviours of my country and my people!"

"If Your Majesty would postpone this Parliament . . ."

"I daresay that they are beginning to think of me now. They

208

are not finding the bread in England to their taste? I am very glad to give them time to get used to it."

Sir James did not allow himself to be over-awed. "I have no desire to protect such miscreants. I am thinking of Your Majesty's weal and welfare. If only Your Majesty would be good enough to consider my arguments. They are all of advantages to Your Majesty. The Queen of England, thanks to her black double-dealing, has lost any hold she ever had anywhere. If Your Majesty, now, were to take back these wretched men, you would simply knit all hearts to you for ever! For now they have learned how things are. And then they would know that, in the whole world, there is only one place where grace and mercy are to be found."

Queen Mary, however, replied only: "Sir James, what you say does not touch me. Are they children, who can only be taught through punishment what may and what may not be done? I was never other than good to them. Yet they betrayed me. They will do it again tomorrow, if tomorrow it seems to them that the hour is ripe."

It was on the tip of Sir James's tongue to say that it might be wise to do, freely, what, sooner or later, was certain to be forced upon her. But he contented himself with saying, "The people look upon the Earl of Murray as a leader whose mere presence near Your Majesty reassures them if any stirrers-up of strife suggest to their minds that anything is being planned against the religion of the country."

"And who," cried Mary, "are these stirrers-up of strife? The very people whom my wrath removes."

Sir James finally sought support through the medium of a letter which he brought to his Sovereign. Sir Nicholas Throgmorton had written it; Mary had a regard for Sir Nicholas and knew him for an intelligent man and as upright as his diplomatic profession allowed. In this letter he said:

"Your Majesty has a great following in England, as the heir to the English throne. Both on account of your incontestable

209

claim and on account of your personal qualities. You have friends both among Catholics and among Protestants. Of course, Your Highness also has opponents. Many of these latter, however, could be won over by wise statesmanship. It is of advantage to Your Highness that you have not married a stranger but a native Prince, whose equally incontestable claims now support those of Your Highness. On the other hand, too close a friendship with Spain and France is certainly not to be recommended, in view of the difficult religious conditions in the British Isles, which only the greatest wisdom can prevent from bursting forth into the flames of religious war. Hitherto Your Majesty has shown marvellous wisdom and moderation in every step taken. Thousands of hearts that are still uncertain will turn to you, thousands of timid ones will find the courage to admit your rights and demand their recognition by Parliament, if Your Majesty can demonstrate, by a fresh act, that your heart holds nothing but magnanimity and faithfulness even towards ingratitude and faithlessness. No one could speak here of weakness. You, a glorious conqueror, forgive wretched fugitives, who lie smashed at your feet.

"It must certainly be recognized that my Lord of Murray has given Your Majesty just cause for wrath. But it may nevertheless be very difficult, indeed, impossible, to convince the mass of Protestants that the division between him and Your Majesty is not rooted in difference of religion.

"If Your Majesty thinks that the grant of so complete a pardon is too great mercy for so grave a crime, you might nevertheless postpone the stringency of the penalty on the exiled men. Instead, opportunity might be given them, at some distance, to give proof, through service to Your Majesty, of their keen repentance, their still deep devotion and, in future, inflexible loyalty to you.

"Above all, these lords will never again commit themselves to the Queen of England, not even so far as to apply to her good offices for an appeal to Your Majesty's grace."

Sir Nicholas ended by saying that he enclosed, in cypher, for Queen Mary, the names of the most important English lords who would, so long as she did not declare herself an enemy of Protestantism, stand by her so strongly that no resistance on the part of the Queen of England could affect them. Through their aid, Queen Mary could, without any foreign help, at any time secure the rights that were still improperly withheld from her.

★

Queen Mary, with David Rizzio and her friend Mary Fleming, followed by one or two servants, went walking, and came right round the mighty base of Arthur's Seat to its distant and quite lonely slopes. Somewhat fatigued, she sat down on the dry grass: the day had the clear mildness that sometimes comes after spring rains. David stretched himself out at his Queen's feet; the lackeys waited at some little distance. Mary Fleming walked up and down. The Queen said to her, "Won't you sit down, too?" With a piece of grass between her teeth, while she hummed a tune, she merely shook her head without speaking, as though nothing would induce her to give up her piece of grass. The Queen said: "What a distance one can see from here! There are the Carberry Hills, quite distinct, yonder, and there, the sea."

"Yes," said Mary Fleming, at last bringing herself to throw away her grass. "All that is always there."

The Queen sighed. "If only it were ever warm here!"

"In February one can hardly expect that," said Mary Fleming.

"Everything is queer here," complained the Queen. "In winter, it is not cold: in summer, it is not warm; misty it is always."

"In summer one often has little enough air," said Mary Fleming, by way of encouragement.

In their walk between the cliffs they had come upon a ruined chapel, facing towards the palace; recalling it, the Queen now remarked: "There is said to have been a light once at St. Anthony's—a machine, I mean, for that, in the tower."

"A useful thing, certainly," Mary Fleming agreed.

"But the Protestants have removed it," compained the Queen.

"And the last lighthouse-keeper, the Hermit of St. Anthony, perished at the same time," said David.

"A somewhat stormy removal," remarked Mary Fleming. "Never mind—the holy man was doubtless pretty old, and would have been dead by now in any case. So do not let us torture ourselves by pitying him. Let us rather allow him his well-earned death, since there is nothing to be done about it now."

The Queen played with her glove, first drawing it out long, and then stretching it broad. Suddenly she asked her friend: "Would you like to be a Protestant?"

"Oh, no," she replied at once: adding, "It is so coarse, and loud, and troublesome."

"In what way?" asked the Queen.

"Oh," answered the other, "I can tell you, His Reverence is there for that—he has nothing else to do, it is his profession to consider it all, and so, in short, he looks after and arranges that tomorrow, or the day after, or in a week, a month, a year, as you please, my nice, cosy, easy-going little pony is all nicely saddled and fitted out and arranged to trot straight along the smoothest, safest and nicest road right into the Heavenly Kingdom. I rely on that. That's why I go to Mass every morning. It doesn't take too long, and one knows—what has to be done is done and that's that. For the rest, I can spend my time as I like. But Protestants! Who can answer for anything, there? I? You? He? Perhaps Master John Knox? We must ask the Bishop of London. They know nothing. How can they be of any use to one?"

David joined in the conversation. "Anyhow we cannot become Protestants. . . ."

"Who thinks of such a thing," the Queen interrupted him; and Mary Fleming took him to task.

"Keep your beak shut, little David; you know I don't like it when you get loud in my presence. And if you talk at all, I get that feeling. No doubt, in that miraculously clear intellect of his," she turned to the Queen, "he means that, if we were to become Protestants, we should, thereby, have to recognize our good sister of England for evermore as most just, legitimate, correct and regal. Her existence means that every heretical heresy has replaced every proper ceremony at betrothals, weddings, births, and removed god-parents and preceptors. Strange, a country where everything is turned topsy-turvy for the sake of marrying a woman whom you behead two years later, after wooing her for fifty months! Stranger that all this story concerns a gentleman of three-and-forty summers, who, up to then, lived virtuously for four-and-twenty years with one wife! Suddenly, he goes crazy, runs through six wives, two of whom he has beheaded, two of whom he gets rid of, while two are lucky enough to die—or one still survives him perhaps. And yet, in spite of all these exertions, he only gets three children out of his six wives, and they only amount, really, to one and a half. What really is delicious, though, is that, at bottom, our good sister of England, in the depths of her soul, simply cannot abide all this respectable Protestantism, though it has been so extraordinarily useful to her. Good Heavens, she would sacrifice all her eighty wigs, and be satisfied with her own tail of hair, if only she could claim a nice Catholic mother, say Madam Katharine of Aragon, instead of poor dubious Madam Anne Boleyn! We at least have the satisfaction—even if our dear Scotland may be a wee bit shabby and even plunderous by the side of England—of coming of a good family! Quality is quality—one knows it, and, of course, remains Catholic."

The Queen sighed deeply. "You may look at it like that," she said.

"True," replied her maid. "Life really is an odd dance! Extraordinary—there are a hundred thousand threads, all hanging down from the ceiling. And there are little puppets fastened to their ends, with lead in their feet and in their heads. And, swish! one of them runs his heavy head against his precious neighbour's and crack! he is broken, beyond repair; smash! there is an arm off; crack! again, off goes a leg, and the fellow's heart is done. Merrily, merrily they are flying, all together, a hundred thousand puppets, with two hundred thousand arms and two hundred thousand legs and a hundred thousand leaden brain pans. Hallo! right away! merrily! all together! hurrah! what a jolly life! And wise folk chat about destiny and character and all that happens to them, and it is all to make them look clever in their own eyes—but there is no other purpose in it. Often the whole thing seems to me utterly unreal, and all these great cliffs which they call King Arthur's Seat here seem to me no more substantial than the sickle of the horns of the moon, which haunted me as a child. What is it, after all? One has one's day, and there are four-and-twenty hours in it. One can sleep for eight, and lie in bed for another two, but what about the other fourteen? I am lucky, I am still in quite an amusing place. Of course, it was more amusing in France. But here is not too bad. I still have the most interesting people by me," she turned her sparkling eyes on the Queen, with a smile.

"When I hear you talk like that, I don't find myself at all interesting," said Mary, sadly. "Once, yes; but now?" Tears sprang up in her eyes.

Mary Fleming flung herself down on the grass beside her. Taking her in her arms, she cuddled her. "Ah, don't be sad! Our baby is coming, and is a lovely little son, and we call trumps, and our good sister in England is green with envy. That does not suit her, anger makes her greener and greener, till she turns into a frog and the game is ours, *Victoria!*" She kissed the Queen on her soft, warm, delicate cheeks. "No one is looking," she said. "For David doesn't count, and the servants don't matter. After, I will 'Your Majesty' you, all over the place!"

The Queen pressed her close to her, with both hands. "I believe that you are the only living soul who really loves me," she said, and the tears ran down her cheeks, one by one. Soon, however, she collected herself. "Here, I mean."

Mary Fleming shook her head. "Mary Seaton would let herself be roasted alive, not only for her faith but for Your Grace and that with a solemn joy: and Livingstone too, and even Beaton, as far as in her lies. But it is far too cold here for my Queen, and little David's nose is quite shiny, he longs so for his warm slippers."

★

An extraordinary event took place.

One day, Mr. Thomas Randolph was summoned instantly before the Scottish Privy Council, which he found in full session, with the Queen herself sitting beneath the canopy at one end of the hall, her consort by her side. And before them was standing, in a respectful attitude, a little, stocky man in drab attire, whom Mr. Randolph recognized at a glance. This fellow with the dirty complexion and straightforward air was a Scot called Johnston, of whom Randolph had made use, at the time of the late rising, for the purpose of transmitting English money to the Scottish rebels. Randolph was not given long to digest his disagreeable shock. The stout Earl of Atholl, in his level voice, began recounting to him that this man, in a very full confession, had seriously compromised the English Ambassador. He had reported having received from him on various occasions large sums of money for distribution among the rebel Scottish lords in the field.

Randolph, seething with anxiety, began to defend himself. How could the testimony of such a man be allowed against that of a man of honour, the Ambassador of Her Majesty, the Queen of England? On a sign from the Earl of Bothwell, who was presiding at the session, two servants brought forth several great sacks, with the seal of the English Crown still upon them, and the exact amount of their contents inscribed in heavy ink.

Randolph's brow was icy cold, and sweat stood on it in beads; in despair, he tried to speak. The Privy Council passed judgment upon him, as though he were a common malefactor. The Ambassador of the English Crown was guilty of a double sin— a sin against the Crown of Scotland, and against that of his own country. For since the Queen of England had stated, repeatedly, in the most solemn terms, that there had never been the slightest connection between her and the Scottish rebels, her ambassador must have acted contrary to her will in his criminal attempt to stir up strife on his own initiative. Therefore he must at once, on this very day, remove himself from the court of Scotland, and from Edinburgh, and within forty-eight hours from Scotland altogether.

In a high, shrill voice, that broke and then rose again, almost in a scream, Randolph cried that only his Queen, who had appointed, could recall him. But Queen Mary retorted contemptuously that he had got to go; she would inform his mistress. She wrote to Elizabeth:

"MY GOOD SISTER,—

"With the frankness I have ever employed in my relations with you, I do not now hesitate to inform you of the conduct of your Ambassador here, Randolph, as it has come to my knowledge. In the midst of our worst embarrassments this man has dared to assist my rebels not only in various minor ways but actually with a sum of three thousand pounds sterling. Immediately on the information of this fact, I had him called before my Privy Council to meet the charge made against him. No answer could be got from him save that as your subject and servant he was responsible to you alone. I believe that I can promise myself that you will not permit any one who so perverts to its converse his commission to do good to be regarded as worthy of your confidence. In that assurance I have taken no other measures against the man than to send him back to you."

Queen Elizabeth replied at once, but not to the Queen of Scotland.

"Since it has seemed good to the Queen of Scotland to disregard the comity of nations in this scandalous fashion and, in this, to take advantage of the too-long forbearance of the Queen of England, the latter will, in future, think long before she enters into any exchange of letters, and, meantime, will take such measures as may seem needful in her own defence. So far as concerns the Earl of Murray, the Queen of England, to speak quite frankly, cannot, in consideration of her own honour and of the good opinion which she has of his uprightness and of his devotion to his native land, refuse him the necessary alleviations of his stay in England, of which she herewith informs the Queen of Scotland. If disorder results, she trusts to God to let the evil of that fall on those who are guilty of its origin."

Mary replied:

"MADAM,

"MY GOOD SISTER,

"It has been communicated to me that you have given detailed assurances both to the French Ambassador and to the Spanish, to the effect that you have never given any kind of assistance to my rebellious subjects, whether by encouragement of their rebellion, or by actual support. I have never doubted the sincerity of this assurance, and need no other proof of it than your word. Nevertheless, despite this assurance, whose sincerity, as I have said, I shall never question, I have in my hands proofs that my rebellious subjects have been assisted by a sum of three thousand pounds sterling, handed over to the Earl of Murray by Mr. Randolph. I find such conduct on the part of this ambassador quite extraordinary, in view of the fact that his office lays upon him the obligation to seek peace and ensue it. My advisors and I could not do otherwise than condemn such conduct. In the conviction, therefore, that he had acted contrary to your will and your commands, and quite

217

aside from the purpose for which you sent him here, I took this opportunity of dismissing him. Any other ambassador will be well received."

Upon which Queen Elizabeth was silent.

★

The news of this proceeding made the Scots turn pale. Queen Mary had risen up like a Goddess of revenge who will not rest until she has exacted the penalty for every act of unfaithfulness.

In Edinburgh they said: "No one is to blame for that save only the Earl of Bothwell. He is the deadly foe of every Englishman and every friend of England, and the Earl of Murray and he hate each other to such a degree that if they have to be in the same room for five minutes together each is all eyes to see where he can get a deadly blow in at the other."

Others retorted: "No, it is all David's work. Scotland has got to be Catholic within the year."

Meantime there was hammering and carpentering in the Town House, to make worthy preparation for Parliament if it met within the next few days.

★

Mr. Randolph had an unexpected encounter, before he left Edinburgh. He was riding with a few companions towards the outer gate, sunk in gloomy astonishment. It was really possible; it had really happened; there he had stood, in the semi-darkness of that room which was good enough for the Privy Council of this accursed, barbarous State, and these savages, these so-called nobles of the Crown, these Scottish lords, had sat there, heavy and huge: and, above them, in the full blaze of light that came over sidewards, had sat that proud young Queen, no barbarian but as full of pride as though the angels and archangels, under the command of Raphael, Gabriel, and Michael, stood ready at every moment to do her bidding. And there stood the stocky, common little man, turning his cap in his hands, looking at once cheeky and straightforward, and on the sight of him, his own heart, yes, his, Randolph's, had actually lost a beat. It had come to this! They had determined on it, and every one of them knew beforehand how it was to be. The harsh voice of the Earl of Atholl resounded in his ears, reading out the accusation, yes, the accusation, against him, Randolph, the accredited ambassador of the Queen of England! It was set out in the most direct and casual terms, as though they were taking no pains to show the smallest consideration. Randolph heard, again, the cutting voice, full of cold contempt, with which the young Queen drove him out of her kingdom, and ground his teeth. The young Queen had dismissed him, pushed him away, as though he were some loathsome worm, and she had dared to do it, dared, in face of his Government! Yes—it, too, was included, in the contemptuous aversion she felt for both, as though his Government too, had behaved in a contemptible, ridiculous fashion; that was what she meant; and this young Queen had permitted herself to show her abominable opinion!

And Scotland still stood!

The noise of hooves woke Randolph out of his broodings. He turned and recognized the Earl of Bothwell, who came galloping up on a superb horse. Yes, he had been a lackpenny, but now he went about in state, at the cost of the decent folk whom shameless tyranny had driven out of their native land. But Randolph knew that the Earl had some business with him, and he was afraid, much as he might inwardly curse his fears. What did the man want with him? Yet the Earl approached, with a friendly gesture of the hand. Randolph's fear was transformed to amazement; here was the most powerful man at court, today: he could have no request to make; he himself, Randolph, was a mere cypher, at least for so determined a foe of England. The Earl was by now at his side. Drawing up, laughing because his brief gallop had left him so out of breath, he at once began to speak with the utmost frankness. Mr. Randolph must not refuse him a great favour. "I assure you, I shall not detain you.

It can be done on the way. Quite easily. It is a question of a couple of words only." Randolph set his horse in motion again. The other remained close to his side.

"You will know," said the Earl, "the sort of means that have for long been employed against me. No lie was too base. Among the mass of such that they have served up to my damage, they have actually dared, in their impudence, to assert—I assume, and no doubt correctly, that you know all about it—that I allowed myself to speak disloyally of my Queen, and also of yours, the Queen of England. Obviously, it has never occurred to me to do any such thing!" The Earl threw his head proudly back. "Here of course no one dares to whisper anything of the sort now. I would let them hear about it, if they did. One thing, however, I want to ask you to do—to inform your mistress, the Queen of England, of the truth in this matter. And further, to inform every one that I challenge to single combat any man who dares to cast such vile aspersions on my honour. Any one in England, Scotland or France to combat, till one of us be dead. Will you do this?"

"I shall do whatever is in my power," replied Randolph dryly, though he was flattered. Fate, after all, gave him this— the proudest of all these proud devils of barbarians must recognize that his power was not so absolutely gone!

"Good," said the Earl, reining in his horse, as though to turn back at once.

Randolph detained him. "In so far as I have any influence left," he said, "but," he shrugged his shoulders, "how much is that? They have played a very scurvy trick on me, my lord!"

"Yes, yes," replied the other, "it is certainly a bad business for you. So, I can rely on you? Farewell, then, a good journey!" He turned his horse.

★

Well pleased, the Earl of Bothwell rode back to the town. He galloped, as though he were going to some great piece of good fortune. On the morrow his wedding with Jean Gordon was to be celebrated. The bride would bring him no inconsiderable resources in money, estates and important connections. And he loved her.

And Queen Mary herself had brought this marriage about. She thought that it would make the Earl of Bothwell powerful and rich. She was allying the Gordons, now once again proudest of her nobles, with her most faithful servant.

She had asked, almost as a favour, that the bridal pair should celebrate their marriage in her palace. The bride received her magnificent wedding garment from the Queen's hand. Jean Gordon was still a Catholic, although her brother, George, now Earl of Huntly, had gone over to the Protestant religion during his imprisonment. The Queen now desired to have the marriage celebrated by the Holy Office in her royal chapel. The Earl of Atholl, a Catholic, came to the groom, and pressed him earnestly, "But why should you not give this pleasure first to your bride and, above all, to Her Majesty?"

But the Earl replied: "If the Queen needs me, she has but to say so, and I am there. In my private affairs, I cannot allow any one to over-persuade me." Finally, throwing back his head, he said, "All that business of the Holy Office is superstition and idolatry."

So it was only after the bonds had been tied that Queen Mary came to the wedding feast in a room of the palace. She came, however, with all her state, to the most splendid of her rooms.

No sign of royal magnificence was lacking. The walls were glorious with the splendour of tapestries; candles burned in all the candelabra. In the gallery, hung with embroidered silk hangings, the royal band played. Queen Mary could have made no more gorgeous display for her own wedding.

She sat at the narrow end of the hall, beneath the canopy, splendidly attired in white brocade embroidered in golden flowers, with the old Countess of Huntly by her side. The solemn dance, opened by the Earl of Bothwell and his young wife, swayed towards her. Today, the King took the second place in the dance, with Mary Beaton, whom he liked and who could not endure him.

Among the dancers, moving towards the throne in step to the strains of the ceremonial music, were all the men and women who now counted for anything in the ranks of the Scottish nobility. Was there any among these lords and ladies who reflected that a year ago the Gordon family lay under the shadow of poverty and dishonour, given over to the deepest sorrow and irremediable suffering? Or that it had needed high treason and fresh rebellion to bring the despised and rejected back to the light? Through these very rooms, the mighty form of the old Earl of Huntly had often strode. What was his slight, blonde, whitefaced son, now Earl of Huntly, in comparison with him? Here John Gordon had danced as partner opposite to Queen Mary, had knelt before her hundreds of times, had felt the sunshine of her smile play over him. In the meantime, Jean Gordon had had to learn to hate her heart's dearest dreams. Now, young Ogilvy was betrothed to Mary Beaton, the Queen's maid of honour, and danced among the guests at this wedding.

Jean Gordon had beauty, and an air of calm pride. Her husband took her hand, to hold it for a moment in his arm, as he led her past the Queen at the head of the dance. Resplendent in her gown of yellow velvet embroidered all over in flowers in delicate colourings, the gift of the Queen, the young countess sank in deep obeisance before the throne. Her husband swept the ground with the plumes of his hat. When, however, after the Queen's gracious acknowledgment, he led his young wife away, all his movements, generally so passionately hasty, seemed to have been softened by his happiness.

Mary Fleming danced with Lethington, whose chances with her seemed to have improved since he was almost disregarded by the Queen. Mary Fleming said to him: "Her lips are very red today, and her eyes burning. Despite all her splendour, she looks to me tired and overstrained. But it suits her, the whole thing suits her. This is her real life. They all want something of her, if only that she should behave wisely and cautiously. Most of them want a great deal more than that. And she is always giving, and behaving as though she were wise and cautious. Really, however, there she stands like a poor little hare, saying, Who is the least kind to me?"

"Well, I know her letters to the Queen of England," said Lethington.

"Of course, I know them too," replied his lady, "and she is not kind to her."

"Not much use if she were. She wants to be the first everywhere."

"And quite right too. How lovely she is. She is the perfection of beauty."

"I think that Mary Livingstone and Jean Gordon are much more beautiful."

"Yes," replied Mary Fleming, unperturbed. "Every one cannot have good taste. Both of them, Mary Livingstone and the new Countess of Bothwell, have regular features, though there Mary Livingstone has the advantage. The Countess of Bothwell's mouth is too full, and her eyes are too near together. Although that mouth, in her rather austere face, is sometimes very charming, and her eyes, at times, look like a single brilliant light. At others however she simply squints. And she has a lovely figure. But in comparison with *her*, she is nothing. Regularity of feature,—that, with her, one just takes for granted; who thinks about it, with her? She is continually changing and always beautiful, and so there is no one to compare with her; she has a thousand lovelinesses. She is perfectly self-conscious, and plays all her games—and yet, in the end, she is perfectly naïve. She is made for action. As for her face—her brow is broad and gloriously formed, like that of a youthful sage who has, at the same time, the brain of a great general. Then her nose is so well and firmly placed, and withal as delicate as though it were a bridge for every thought to pass, whether into the region of the most tender feeling or of the most passionate.

The curve of her eyebrows is as perfect as though they had been drawn by the greatest painter in the world, after studying in three thousand faces how they should be and how they never are. Her eyes are stars from the gardens of goodness and happiness. The whole thing has a faultless line, that moves in manifold life, and yet never errs, and encloses her countenance, making of it an exquisite whole. But if one is to mention the most wonderful thing of all, that must be her mouth—that little mouth, proud and tender, with the delicate and yet extravagantly generous upper lip resting on the lower lip as though it were a soft little cushion for it: that mouth that contains everything, even a thousand little devils who come out when she gets bored with the angels there. And at the same time, she is no picture; she moves, and speaks, and smiles, and there is a sense, for her, in all the nonsense these dull creatures chatter about graciousness and grace, as they pour out all their old commonplaces. But they do not see how now and then she sanctifies her skilful tongue, and speaks the truth out to them. Oh, and what a Queen she is! No, no one need envy her, for she is a being apart. I never come into her room without being almost frightened by finding how much more beautiful she is than my dreams of her. She turns her head, looks at me, with some question or request, or whatever is in her mind, and her eyes are so eloquent that I almost cry to her—Don't speak, I know far better than you yourself can know what you think or want. Or her mouth burns through the room so that I want just to kiss and kiss her for ever. Or she is like a little child, and I want to take her soft cheeks ever so gently between my hands. I saw her when she was crowned Queen of France. She was sixteen, then; she rode through Paris on a shining white horse, led by reins of gold and precious stones, and looked like the Queen of Flowers who once came down to men on earth. Oh, everything was at her feet then! Ronsard knelt before her, to lay his verses at her enchanting feet; she felt that every one who looked upon her might know what beauty was and understand what was being given to him in that golden moment. Where are we here?

In a kingdom of mists, in the underworld, in the Ultima Thule! And all we can do is to celebrate the wedding of the little Earl of Bothwell, at her expense! Oh, if I were a man, I should love her and never rest till I had won her. But men do not know how to love, and I suppose I should be like the rest of them. And the man she has got—if he were mine, I should long ago have made an end of him! True, I should never have married him. That is the marvel with her; in the end, she thinks quite little of herself. I am waiting for the day, all the same, when her instinct at last lifts its head. Her father had eight illegitimate children—that is to say, eight whom he recognized as his—and he died at thirty. When it wakes in her, then she will be proud. And no longer wise and cautious."

Chapter 7

THE MURDER OF RIZZIO

QUEEN MARY came down from Holyrood to open her second Parliament. But for all the splendours of the occasion, no heart there was glad. As she stood on the steps of the throne, the Queen was no longer the young woman, still almost a girl, who dreamed of leading a world by the sheer radiance of perfect gifts, and for whom no earthly glory seemed unattainable. Now, her figure betrayed signs of her approaching motherhood, and her still youthful features hardly masked a determination to impose her will, no matter what resistance it might encounter.

In the speech from the throne, she said that it would be the duty of Parliament to legalize the punishments imposed on the rebel Lords.

★

Two days later, on the Saturday before the first session of Parliament, which was to take place on the Monday, that is to say on March 9th, 1566, Queen Mary sat at supper about eight o'clock in the evening, with her intimate circle, in the room adjoining her bedchamber. The room was so small that supper for several persons could only be served there with some difficulty; there was only one exit, that giving into the Queen's bedchamber. She had with her her natural sister, the Countess of Argyle, David Rizzio and one or two gentlemen of the court, among them Lord Arthur Erskine and Lord Robert Stuart. The Queen was in no cheerful mood; she complained that she suffered from her deprivation of riding and all other active exercise; also she had a sharp return of the pain in her side which had troubled her since her childhood days. The Countess of Argyle comforted her: all that would pass and afterwards

226

she would have a strong, lovely child, which was sure to be a boy, and then she would have him all her life long.

"Ah!" replied Mary. "Who can say? The child may be still-born or sickly, or I may die, which perhaps would be the least evil."

"Your Majesty, then," said the Countess, "would rather have kept your figure, for exercise sake?"

Mary smiled; but the Countess said that, after supper, David should sing them a couple of songs, really cheerful songs, and then all her sad thoughts would be dispersed.

One of the serving men was just handing round fruit for dessert on silver dishes, when the door opposite to the Queen suddenly opened, at first only a chink, then gradually wider.

The Queen had raised herself, to look what could be coming. Now she smiled, bitterly and a shade contemptuously; it was only the King. She smiled, too, at her fright: of course only her husband could come in that way. Anybody else would have been stopped by the watch in the ante-chamber or at least announced. But there was a narrow concealed winding stair that led from the King's apartments, immediately under those of his wife, directly into her bedchamber.

The Queen looked at her husband. "I had no idea it was you," she said. "I thought you supped likewise about this time?"

Pushing his way between the table and the chimney-piece, he came by the Countess of Argyle and passed behind his wife's chair, placed with its back to the deep embrasure of the wide window. In reply to her remark he said that he had finished rather earlier than usual this evening, and leant over her from behind. Yielding to his apparent access of tenderness, she turned and bent towards him, and he pressed his lips slowly to hers. At that moment the door, which the King had left open behind him, opened again, this time to admit a more unfamiliar figure. Lord Ruthven, the King's elderly supporter, stood on the threshold in complete armour, his helmet on his head. In the draught created by the open door, the candles flickered; under the helmet, his shadowed eyes looked like two deep holes, and his face, haggard and ashen pale, might, in the dim light, have been that of Death himself. All eyes turned to him; the King released his wife. The Queen, like the others, knew that on the afternoon of this very day, Lord Ruthven, who was suffering from a severe nervous inflammation, had been lying sick and feverish in bed in a room in the palace. Thinking that he was now wandering in a nightmare of fever, she collected herself so far as to say, with a gesture indicating to her suite that they too should treat the sick man with the utmost calm, "Have you come to visit us?"

Without closing the door behind him, he came clanking right up to the table with his ironclad stride, and standing stock-still, said, "Will Your Majesty be so good as to order that man David out of your private apartment, where he has already stayed overlong?"

"What has he done?" cried the Queen, clear and tense on the instant.

"He has done the deadliest possible injury to Your Majesty's honour, to the King, your husband, to your nobles and to your realm."

"How so?"

"He has injured Your Majesty's honour," replied the knight. "But I am not so vile as to give details." Clutching at the visor of his helmet, he drew a deep breath. "So far as touches the honour of your husband, the King, he has prevented him from receiving the crown promised him by Your Majesty, and has done him evil in other ways. Moreover, he is to blame for the fact that Your Majesty has banished so large a part of your nobility, simply in order that he may himself become a Lord. He has been harmful to the State, in so far as Your Majesty can do nothing but it goes through his hands, and he has allowed himself to be bribed. And he has made such condemned traitors as the Earl of Huntly and him of Bothwell advisors to Your Majesty."

During this speech, the Queen had looked first at the knight and then at her husband, who, however, had hidden himself

DAVID RIZZIO

(Engraved from an original painted in 1564)

behind her, as if asking, in astonishment, What may all this mean? She was about to order steps to be taken to remove the knight, whom she still thought to be raving, when he signed to the King—"My Lord, take the Queen, your wife and Sovereign, in your charge!" and thereupon made as though to attack David, stretching his hands out towards him. Mary, however, threw herself between them. She stepped, protectingly, in front of David, who clung to the folds of her dress, his limbs shaking and his teeth chattering with fear, as he crouched far back in the embrasure of the window. Lords Stuart and Erskine, with the servants, were about to throw themselves upon Lord Ruthven, and push him out of the room. He drew his dagger; there was a confused shouting—"Watch, ho!—Get out—Dare to attack me?—Traitors!—Rascal!—The King! where is the King?" Then, a noise louder than any in the room came roaring towards them from the Queen's bedchamber, and suddenly there burst in, from there, armed men, with the Earl of Morton and Lord Lindsay at their head, and naked swords in their hands. More and still more came up the little staircase, until the bedchamber was quite full of soldiers, and still the flood came on. Lord Ruthven drew himself up. "Hands off!" he cried, baring his teeth in dreadful madness, and drawing a circle about him with his blade.

Now, under the rush of people who were pouring in to get hold of David, the great, heavy table, behind which the unhappy man was being sheltered by the Queen, was overturned, with all the dishes, and all the candles on it. In the nick of time, the Countess of Argyle saved one of the great branching candlesticks, and held it up, aloft; all the others were extinguished under the table furniture.

Lord Ruthven took hold of the Queen, to hand her over to her husband. No harm would come to her: they would cut their hearts out, rather. "It is all as the King, your husband, wished."

Mary turned on him instantly: "Is that true?"

"No, no," he assured her, in the utmost anxiety.

Meantime, they seized David's hands, which he had enwound tightly in the Queen's dress. Mary struggled to free herself from her husband, who now held her body fast in his arms. There was a confused clash, clang and clamour. Some one stretched over the Queen's shoulder to take the dagger out of her husband's belt, as he still held her, and stab David with it in the side. The Queen's screams rose above the tumult: "He shall go before a court! There he can answer for it, if he has done anything wrong!"

They dragged David, once they had got him clear of her, out of the room, into the Queen's bedchamber. There was talk of dragging him down the King's winding stair and hanging him in the palace yard. But as David cast himself on the Queen's bed, and clung to the curtains there, another dagger stabbed him; and he let go with a roar. Since the press of their own numbers was too great for them to reach the entry to the staircase, they lugged him into the next room, the Queen's antechamber, and there they threw themselves upon him until, pierced by fifty-two wounds, he lay dead. The King's dagger was driven right through his heart, to show who was the author of his murder. The rope with which they had meant to hang him was used to drag his body down to the foot of the stairs, where they left him lying on the entrance floor. When the porter raised the bloody corpse to place it in a chest standing there, he said, as he drew off the clothes—"This chest was his fate. He used to sit on it, in the beginning, when he first came to the palace."

Meantime the Queen was arguing passionately with her assailants. Earl Morton was in command: he would go down with all the men who would be spared hence down into the palace yard, and make use of the new forces that kept streaming in, to guard all the entrances. Soon, he was clanking off, with the Queen shouting after him, above the din, that a black box in David's room must, at once, be rescued, for it contained all the correspondence with the foreign Powers and the key to the ciphers. Morton paused: "Erskine and Lindsay, do you see to it." They obeyed. Gradually, the soldiers withdrew from the room, until only one or two, on guard, were left, with Lord Ruthven, the King and the Queen.

Mary came and stood before her husband. "My Lord, my Lord! and you have done this to me!"

The King, thus addressed in front of witnesses, came out of the corner into which he had crept. "I had reason!" he said, quaking with fear.

Mary gave a strangled laugh. "And I raised you up for this? What were you before?"

He struggled for some show of spirit. "I had good reasons." He attempted to justify himself. "Since that fellow David came upon the scene, Your Majesty has simply ceased to look at me! You have taken no more notice of me, and never confided in me, as you used to do; before, you would come every day after dinner into my room, to pass the time with me, but it is long now since you have done that." He was now well under way. "And when I came into Your Majesty's room, you were never alone, David was always there. After supper, you would sit at cards with David up to one or two o'clock at night, and I have had no other sort of treatment from you, not for ever so long."

"So," said Mary, "it is the duty of a lady to come to her husband? You, you, when have you come to me? So long ago that I cannot remember it."

"But once you used to come to me, and then, afterwards, never. Has anything happened to me? Or what is it that you despise in me?" He was weeping. "What have I done to you? Tell me, have you not always found me willing? But when I came to you, either you did not want me, or you said you were not well."

"Yes," she replied, "because I am with child and, my Lord . . . I have no desire to go shares with the lights o' love to whom you give my gifts to you!"

"I only did that when you began not to want me."

"Oh, no, my dear, that is not so. But why talk about it? It is the same old story. But I have seen it."

"And you always spoke French," he said, "with David and your Maries and Lethington, and every one who understands it."

"Why have you never learned it?" she said. "You have time enough."

"Your Majesty knows that I cannot learn such things."

Shrugging her shoulders coldly, she said nothing.

"You may reproach me with my modest background," he went on, "but I am your husband, all the same, and on the day of our wedding you swore obedience to me and that I should be your equal in all things; but it has turned out quite different, and David is to blame for it."

The Queen stood before him, as he sank down in a chair, lost in pity for his own sufferings; the candelabra, which the Countess of Argyle had placed upon the chimneypiece, cast their quiet light over the devastated scene. "My Lord," she said, "all that you have done to me, which has come within an ace of costing me my life and that of my child, too . . ." Suddenly she interrupted herself: "And after all, it was all directed against me and my child! For if it was David you wanted, you could have got him, any day, in a thousand places!" She went on, more quickly—"And it is you who have brought murderers and traitors here, for if you had not betrayed me to them, they could never have found this way, and could never have got in through any other entrance! So, it is you and you alone who are to blame for it all! And now"—trembling with rage she stood before him—"it is all over between you and me. And I shall have no happiness in my life again until your heart is as heavy as is mine at this moment."

Lord Ruthven, thinking to assist the King, said, "Your Majesty, the King is your husband, to whom you owe duty, as he does you."

Instantly she turned on him. "Indeed, Lord Ruthven, is that your view? If so, why should I not leave my husband, as you left your wife in the lurch?"

Wiping his brow, he replied, "The case is quite different! My wife is legally separated from me!"

"Yes, after she ran away from you!"

He went on speaking, however, appealing to the Queen not to give up hope, but to live in peace with her husband and follow the counsel of her nobles, for then her government would be as blessed as that of any of her forefathers, no matter who. Mary, however, was not listening to him.

"If David is dead, his blood shall cost you dear, that I swear!" she said.

"The more noise Your Majesty makes about it, the worse will the world think," said Lord Ruthven.

"We shall see!"

The knight asked for her indulgence: overcome by weakness, he absolutely must sit down: he asked if a drink of wine might be brought him. One of the French servants, who had pulled himself together and begun clearing the room, filled a cup for him out of a jug that had stood undisturbed throughout all the turmoil in a corner. As he lifted the cup to his lips, and drank in great gulps, the Queen turned her burning gaze upon him.

"You are very ill, are you?" she mocked at him.

"God forbid that Your Majesty should ever have such a sickness as mine," he replied.

The Queen went to the window, and stood there, staring blindly out into the night. With her back turned to him, she said, "If it costs me my life and that of my child, and the ruin of my kingdom, vengeance for this shall be handed on to my friends!" She turned sharply round on him. "And you, Lord Ruthven, shall feel it first of all! You and all your house! And I have mighty friends! The King of Spain and my brother-in-law, the King of France, and my other relations there, and the Pope too—my life is extraordinarily important to all of them!"

"By God!" replied the knight. "Those great princes will hardly concern themselves with a poor wretched man like me!"

"Regicides have always seemed pretty important to them!"

"When Your Majesty says that you or your child or your

kingdom might perish, and that I should bear the responsibility for it, I accept it gladly before God and the whole world. For there is no man in the whole of this palace who honours and loves Your Majesty more than I, or is a more faithful servant, and I would plunge the sword in my own heart rather than have Your Majesty suffer the smallest hurt."

She paused in her restless walk up and down the room to stand in front of him and say, "What have you in mind, when you talk that stuff to me?"

He replied, "If any one here is to blame, it is the King, your husband, and he alone."

Some one knocked at the door; a knight stood without— there was fighting going on in the palace yard: the Earls of Huntly, Bothwell, Caithness, Sutherland, Lords Fleming and Livingstone, the knight of Tullibardine and all the officers and men of the watch were engaged in a hand-to-hand struggle with Earl Morton and his people. Mary moved towards the door: her husband jumped up: "I will go and put it all to rights." Whereupon Lord Ruthven rose. "Do you stay here with Her Majesty. I will go." Mary stood, listening to his heavy footsteps. "Of course they have covered themselves, so that the guard can do nothing."

She sat down exhausted on a seat: the King remarked dryly, "Yes, and the banished Lords will now all be coming back, and I fancy are already in the town."

"What?" she exclaimed. Alarmed, he made no reply, and she repeated, "What did you say? I must hear that again. Speak at once, this minute," she shouted at him.

"I said that the banished Lords would now return, and that it seems they are already in the town," he repeated, in a subdued voice, at the same time making an effort to meet her decisive tone with something of the same kind. She rose, and stood before him. "Have you gone completely mad?" she pressed her brow hard several times. "Why, then, in all the world did I banish them? What, then, in all the world was the whole struggle about? They did me no harm; I was grateful to them. It was simply and solely because they would not tolerate you in the land, simply and solely because they opposed my marrying you, that and only that was the cause of the whole war and strife!" She wrung her hands. "It is only on your account that I did not forgive them long ago! When I showed favour to the Hamiltons, the old Duke, because I had to, since I must have supporters—who was beside himself, almost lunatic? Have you lost every tiniest spark of rational human intelligence? These men are now your friends, you say, these men who were hounded out into misery, simply because they would not tolerate you?" She strode up and down. "This is the end of everything," she said. "Absolute. It is finished." She was silent again: pondered, and said: "From now on it can only be a question of how long."

He sat, numb. The servants left the room, which they had restored to some semblance of order.

Through the silence a confused noise came up to them from the street, and the shrill clanging of the town alarm bell.

A soldier of the guard appeared: citizens of Edinburgh were in the first courtyard, anxious to learn what had been done to the Queen. Mary at once turned to go to the window of the adjoining room. Her husband, trembling with fright, ordered the soldiers of the guard to stay her. He would go and show himself at the open window to the citizens. He went to the window in the Queen's bedchamber. Down below there was a solid mass, shoulder to shoulder, filling the entire space. The King cried: "Good people!" They looked up, recognized him: those who were near to, cried "The King!" He raised his voice: "No harm has come to the Queen! She is quite well!" he cried, exerting himself to shout so that his voice might carry. But no one was listening to him. Down below they began to shout; sharp cries rose above the general confusion of noises. The solid mass began to move forward, like a wall. Then, in the main gateway of the palace, on the threshold, dimly lit by the ruddy glow of torches, there appeared the short stocky figure of Earl Morton, in full armour; he was known to be as strong as an ox. The mighty roar of his voice was so loud that

235

even the Queen, who had pressed her way as far as the open door of her bedchamber, could hear every word distinctly.

"People! The Queen's Frenchmen are collared! Do you want to risk your lives for them?"

The mass stood still.

"And David is dead," Morton continued. "Are you so very sorry? The Queen is weeping for him now, but I fancy she will get over her grief."

The crowd still stood uncertain; suddenly a voice yelled: "Down with the damned foreigners! Long live Earl Morton!"

The crowd echoed it. "Long live Earl Morton! Hurrah for Earl Morton!"

He went on: "If you wish to do me a favour, go now quietly home." For a moment, they still hesitated. Then, amidst shouts of "Long live Morton!" the whole swarm suddenly turned. They literally ran, rushed from the place. Their shouts dwindled to a drone, a mere hum. They rushed to the town, to the house of a preaching monk, whom they dragged out of bed to make away with him. Other monks and priests whom they sought for they failed to find.

The King returned to his wife. At the same moment, Lord Ruthven re-entered likewise. "Everything is in order," he said.

Mary turned on him. "What has happened to David?"

He was silent for a moment; then, flinching, replied: "He will be downstairs, in your husband's room."

"Indeed," said Mary, with a glance at him and at her husband which showed that the whole truth was clear to her. She addressed Lord Ruthven again: "So, I see you have really been working hard for the Earl of Murray, as I have just been told. And I hear now, for the first time, that you and he are good friends! Did you not give me a ring, saying that so long as I wore it, I should be safe against any kind of poison, no matter who were plotting darkly against me? Did you not then plainly intend the Earl of Murray by that?"

"Ah, Your Majesty," replied the Lord, "it was only a little worthless ring. Indeed, I only gave it to Your Majesty because

Your Majesty was so full of the idea that you might be poisoned by the Protestants. So that Your Majesty only required to receive some totally opposite impressions, to be quite clear."

"One learns things, from you!" she replied.

They all sat silent; the candles, which had burned low, flickered.

"What have I done to you?" Mary began, again addressing Lord Ruthven.

Exhausted, he said, "Ask your husband!"

"No," she replied, "I am asking you."

"The nobles," he replied, "have not been able to endure your surrounding yourself exclusively with persons of low rank and foreign origin, who rule the country without so much as consulting the nobles or even the Privy Council. They, too, have particularly incensed Your Majesty against the banished Lords."

"I, reigned without the Privy Council?" said the Queen. "Has something gone wrong with my hearing this evening? You, are you not yourself a member of my Privy Council? And yet you dare to say such a thing!"

"Your Majesty has been constantly away when the Privy Council met, in Glasgow and Aberdeen, and whatever was decided there, in the last resort Your Majesty always acted as pleased you and the handful of people about you."

"I see," said the Queen. "You find me much to blame. Well— I will place my crown before the Estates, and if they find that I have done wrong, I will give it up, to whomsoever it may be."

"Heaven forbid!" exclaimed Lord Ruthven. "Anyhow, who has named the Lords in the Estates?"

"Not I," she replied.

"Pardon, Your Majesty, but you have. And Your Majesty named only those who, you knew, would agree to the outlawry of the banished Lords, although they are guiltless except in so far as perjured testimony has been laid against them."

"Stop!" cried Mary. "I feel very unwell." Deadly pale, she lay back in her chair, her brows beaded with perspiration.

"The King will take you to bed," said the knight.

Mary sat up, with a shudder. "No!" Indicating her husband with a gesture, she groaned, again, "No!"; then, looking about her with a shattered expression: "Where are my women?"

Lord Ruthven said, "Your Majesty will, for the moment, put up with our services, the King's and mine."

The Queen stood up, and moved, dragging her steps, towards her bedchamber. "In my prisons, there are women to wait on the women of the streets!" Leaning on the lintel of the door for support, she went on, "I shall die, and my child too; then, you will have your will. As for you, my Lord," she spoke now to her husband, "you will see, then, what you have done this night."

In her bedchamber she turned shuddering away. "The blood must be washed away first," she said, indicating, with fast-shut eyes, the stains on the floor by her bed, from there right up to the doorway, which none of the servants had yet attended to. "And then one mercy only—leave me alone! I shall not give you the slip," she added, bitterly, "I cannot."

★

The conspirators met in one of the lower rooms of the palace, after they had made peace with the gentlemen of the royal guard, whom, being ten times as numerous, they had easily mastered. The gentlemen were shut up in various rooms in the palace, the Earls of Huntly and Bothwell being confined in a side-wing on the first floor. Earl Morton and Lord Ruthven took advantage of the subsidence of the tumult to go to them and explain that the whole affair had been countersigned by the King, as his signature proved; they displayed a bond with his name attached to it, in which it was written that the Lords pledged themselves, in the first instance, to procure the crown matrimonial for the King, if he would assist the banished Lords to return. It was in every one's interest to get rid of David Rizzio. Earl Morton and Lord Ruthven further declared that the banished Lords had already been sent for and would be in Edinburgh before daybreak. The conspirators offered to abjure all vengeance. In their view, the feuds between the Earls of Bothwell and Huntly on the one side, and Argyle and Murray on the other, could be reconciled. The Earls of Bothwell and Huntly took the paper, to inspect it. After reflection, they gave their hands to the others; everything could be settled. A squire brought a flagon of wine and some beakers. They drank to their good understanding, and Morton and Ruthven then departed, to carry through similar proceedings, with similar results, with the other prisoners. The knight of Tullibardine actually reproached them for having kept him out of so great an adventure. Ruthven replied that in view of the seriousness of the affair they had thought it best to have as few people as possible in their secret.

These transactions took a considerable time. The Lords had but just completed their rounds, and were in the act of communicating the results of their labours to their companions, when a soldier appeared with the news that the Earls of Huntly and Bothwell had escaped by the window. In such a night of confusion, it was obviously quite useless to attempt pursuit. Every one saw at once that this escape smashed the conspirators' undertaking.

"I said at the time," remarked young Ruthven, the son of the old man, "that these two, above all, ought to have been silenced. Now, there will be the mischief to pay, outside."

At first there was general disgust; then, of one accord, they all turned on the King. They told him that everything had been done for his benefit. If he now tried to play the poltroon, and left them in the lurch, they were unanimously resolved to stand together and spare no one. With their hands on their daggers they looked threateningly at him as he sat in their midst, pale, collapsed, silent.

The King had sent for his father, who, already informed of the conspiracy, had returned to Edinburgh, and now came hurrying to congratulate his son on the success of the plot and see what he could get out of it.

First of all, the Lords advised, Parliament must be dissolved.

Next, tomorrow or the day after, the Queen must be brought to Stirling for her lying-in.

"That will keep her busy," said young Lindsay, throwing back his head with a laugh that tore his mouth open from ear to ear and showed all his strong, yellow teeth, his gums, and right down his throat. "She can rock the cradle and sing 'Sleep, baby, sleep,' and play at bow-and-arrow in the garden, as she is so fond of doing, and get on with her sewing, while we men rule the country."

Some one suggested that the whole of the Scottish nobles might not incline to accept such proposals.

"We have got her, though," said young Ruthven, "and if anybody grumbles, she shall pay for it."

They spoke of Mary's approaching motherhood, and young Ruthven asserted—"I will bet my life it will be another girl. If so, it doesn't matter—every one is sick of this woman's ruling."

"She will have another try, then, and get a dozen boys," replied a third.

For a time they talked, and then they fell upon the King again. "Swear that what we have decided shall be, and do what we say! This is life and death for us. This is no joking matter," they declared.

When they at last separated, the King, full of fears, went up the stair from his own apartments to knock at the door of his wife's bedchamber. He found it locked. Although he could hear women with the Queen—the old Countess of Huntly, at the head of one or two others, had forced her way through the guards—nobody opened to him, hard as he begged and prayed to be let in.

During the night a proclamation was issued in the name of the King bidding all members of the Parliament save those expressly mentioned by name by the King, leave the town within three hours, on pain of loss of life, lands and goods.

When morning came, there were no members in Edinburgh.

★

Day was but just breaking when Henry Darnley, after hours of fear and torment, went up again to the Queen and, by dint of endless knocking, got the door opened to him at last. Sobbing, he threw himself on his wife's bed. "Oh, Marie, my Marie! I confess! I repent! But I know it is all too late, and you will never be able to forgive me—my sin against you is altogether too great!" His sobs grew louder. "But the real fault in it all is that I am so very young, and that these accursed traitors shamelessly over-persuaded me. Now, now I see that I have sinned against myself and against my house! And now I know their deceits and all their black proposals, and that you are right and that they seek to destroy us all utterly!" His tears still flowing, he went on, "Before God, I had not the very least idea that they would go to such extremes. I thought they only wanted to kill David, and if I am guilty, God knows it is more out of thoughtlessness than out of ill will to you. I was blinded by ambition—I confess it! . . . But have pity on me," he implored, "have just a little pity on me and on our child and on yourself! God has at least been gracious enough to prevent its coming to the worst!" He handed to his wife the sheet of paper on which the names of all those who had taken part in the conspiracy were written down. In a hasty glance she perceived that more than twenty of her foremost lords were there, among them, heading the list, the name of Lethington, her Secretary of State. Silently, she laid the paper beside her on the pillow, and turned to her husband.

"What possible worth has your repentance now? After you have so sinned against me that nothing can have any meaning more, neither our old friendship, nor any sort of promise for the future!" She broke into tears. "That cannot be made good again; there is nothing to be done: everything must take its course. And whatever happens, everything is lost!" She raised herself into a sitting posture. "You have conspired against me with men who are your declared and most bitter enemies! Truly, I have always been a better friend to you than yourself!" She fell back, again in tears. The King, throwing himself upon her, buried his face in her breast, sobbing the while. She pushed him off. "Thank God, I have no need to reproach myself with anything, not any smallest thing, that I have said or done that could justly have displeased you! Your life has been as dear to me as my own, and I have sworn before God and my conscience to hold you as high as myself." After a moment she added. "Pull yourself together then, and help to get us out of this."

"Only forgive me just this once, dear Marie," he said, somewhat calmed by the gleam of hope there seemed to be for him in her last words. "And believe that this misfortune will make me wiser in the future, and that I shall not rest until I have avenged myself on these shameful traitors. If only we can get out of their hands."

★

In the afternoon of this Sunday, after the murder, it was reported through Holyrood that the Queen was so ill that it seemed her confinement must be imminent. The King came to inform the Lords who were quartered in the palace, that the Queen must be allowed to have her maids of honour, who had been again removed from her, and, above all, a doctor and a midwife. To which they replied, Who would answer for it to them that the Queen was not making up a story in order to escape in disguise with the aid of her women? Anyhow, she was sure to try to use the women as a means of getting into touch with the Lords without, and above all, with the Earls of Huntly and Bothwell, who unfortunately had got well away by now. But the King was firm: in her present condition, there was no question of the Queen's escaping. The Lords could select the midwife themselves, but one the Queen must have. When, after a great deal of to-ing and fro-ing, a woman was at last procured from the neighbourhood and sent in to the Queen, she came down, after a time, to report to the Lords that, as a matter of fact, the Queen's condition was such that delivery must be regarded as imminent. Further, the woman reported that the Queen had put in a pressing appeal to be allowed more fresh air, and, above all, to get out of these dreadful rooms which smelt of David's blood everywhere. This seemed too risky to the Lords, whose apprehensions from without grew and grew. On the contrary, they ordered the King to keep a strict watch over his wife. "Or she will have back at us," said young Ruthven. "She is the most cunning creature."

A further cause of disquietude to the Lords was the fact that during the Sunday considerable bodies of people gathered round the palace, and that their anxiety to know what had happened to the Queen, and why she did not show herself, visibly mounted.

Walking restlessly up and down in the rooms to which she was allowed access, in a state of great pain and disquietude, bodily as well as mental, the Queen came into her reception room, and approached the window. When she saw all the people in the court, she was about to open the window, on a sudden impulse. Down below they recognized her: there was a shout: "There is the Queen herself!"

But Lord Lindsay, in command of the guard in her rooms, pulled her back by the arm. "I'll cut you in pieces, if there is any trouble down there!" Mary, pale with anger, detached her arm from his grip: then, without a word to the boor, walked out of the room. He put a special guard in front of the window, calling to her as he did so, that now they could see that door and window had to be sealed against her.

Yet the feeling of uneasiness among the Lords continued to grow. The very fact of her condition, which seemed to expose her helpless to any violence, made it difficult for them to deal with her without incurring the reproach of brutality.

In spite of their suspicions and their unwillingness, there seemed nothing for it but to utilize the services of the King, hoping that their threats would serve to keep him frightened. Old Ruthven came down with George Douglas, a youth of sixteen, step-brother of the Earl of Murray, to tell the King that he had got to go and spend the night with his wife. They found him already undressed and half asleep in bed. He roused when they shook him, but as he did not appear in the antechamber where they awaited him, George Douglas went back only to find that he had fallen asleep again; he waked him, again with the same result. The King slept till eight o'clock in the morning, when old Ruthven came to rouse him. He woke, sat up, unhappy and confused, in bed, and in answer to the reproaches made him, said he could not help it, he was so sleepy. At last he stood up, and felt for his cloak. He would go now to the Queen.

"She will treat you, in the morning, as you treat her at night," said Lord Ruthven.

Still confused and half asleep, the King, without saying anything more, made for the spiral stair in the corner of his room, and went up it. This time he did not find the door closed above, but his wife lay under her covers apparently asleep. Although he suspected she was shamming, he sat for an hour on the side of her bed, without venturing to touch her. When, at last, the Queen opened her eyes, she asked why he had not come to her in the evening as had been agreed? He replied that he had fallen into so deep a sleep that he was powerless. Now, however, he was here. Now she was going to get up at once, she retorted.

In the afternoon she had discussed with him the possibilities of flight, and he now begged her to take his father into her confidence. This she roundly refused to do. No one in the palace save their two selves must know of this plan. To add another person would ruin the chance of escape. "I am not going to double the danger to myself and above all to my child for the sake of your father, who has repaid all my kindnesses to him by betraying me," she said.

On the previous day, the Sunday, she had had news from without through the old Countess of Huntly, whose activities even Lord Lindsay had not been able to prevent. The Earls of Huntly and Bothwell proposed that she should be let down from the window at night by means of a rope which the Countess had managed to smuggle in, despite the search; they would be near by, with horses. This plan the Queen dismissed as impossible. Even if, as was not the case, she had the physical strength for the effort, it was impracticable on account of the guards in and about the palace. But if the Lords would hold themselves in readiness with their horses, she would manage to get out.

Of these plans the Queen now spoke with her husband. At last even he saw that silence and obedience were obviously in his own best interest. She now turned him out—there was still much to be done. While she was being dressed, she learned that her brother, the Earl of Murray, had entered the town. She stared, then said: "He must come to me at once, then!" Some one must be sent to him: they would let a messenger through. Lord James assented to her request. When, after knocking at the door, he entered the room where his sister was, she rose from her seat. There stood her brother, small, dark, pale; memories of all they had shared, all the work, all the joys, all the dangers endured together, overcame her. What the Earl had suffered seemed to her to mingle with her own experiencs, as though they had but one enemy. Choking with sobs, she hurried towards him and threw herself on his neck, crying, "James, dear brother! If only you had been here, they would not have dared to attack me!" He tried to comfort her, although he was himself so moved that the tears ran down his black beard. He promised that everything should yet be all right, if only she would be quiet and patient. As though his mere presence meant the beginning of happier days, she became more cheerful. So far as she was concerned, she said, the past should be forgotten. "It was not my fault that you had to stay away so long! I should have called you back long ago, if only I could." He promised to do all he could for her. But he had no power against the conspirators, rather depended upon them. Above all, the Queen must not take up a hostile attitude to them. At bottom, they had her welfare and that of the State in mind.

"We will talk of that another time," said the Queen, her manner becoming glacial. She pressed her hands against her brow. "When I begin to think about it, I feel as though all the thoughts in my head were whirling wildly round about and in and out of one another," she said, repeating, "But you will now find in me again the entirely gracious ruler and truest sister, so

soon as you confess yourself once more my loyal subject." Forgiveness, she said, should now further be extended to the other
banished Lords also, the Earls of Argyle and Glencairn, the
Lords Rothes and Ochiltree and the knight Kirkaldy of Grange.
As James Murray left, he renewed his admonishment of rest
and submission.

Mary had forced herself to accept the view that the apprehensions of the conspirators must first be allayed. As arranged
with her, her husband came in the afternoon and said that the
Earls of Murray and Morton, with Lord Ruthven, were in the
ante-room, and asked audience of Her Majesty. Would the
Queen come to them? When Mary, clad in a simple dark cloth
dress, appeared before them, on the arm of her husband, they
knelt down before her, and Morton began, as Chancellor of
the realm, to speak for all of them. He said that the nobility
had, very unwillingly, determined on taking such violent measures against the Queen's Majesty, and contrary to her will.
Now they threw themselves humbly at Her Majesty's feet, to
beg that she might forgive them, in recognition of the fact that
the steps they had taken really were necessary. After Morton
had spoken, Murray took up the word, in the name of all those
who had been banished, and spoke very much to the same effect.
The Queen replied: The Lords knew well that she had never
been bloodthirsty, nor greedy for the goods or monies of her
subjects. Nor would she now begin to be so, but would, on the
contrary, restore to favour all those whom she had been compelled to banish. Even this last deed, and all that she had had
to endure at the time of David's death, she would endeavour
to forget. Earl Morton who, like the others, had soon risen
from his knees, now said: In that case, everything was clear.
"We shall send Your Majesty a treaty to sign, in which are set
out the guarantees that Your Majesty will grant us as a pledge
of our security."

"Send me the treaty," said Mary, after a second's hesitation.
"Your Majesty will sign it?"

Again Mary hesitated for a moment. Then, with a faint smile, she said: "I must, Earl Morton, is it not so?"

He replied, "I think so, at any rate, Your Majesty."

Ruthven and Morton departed. Earl Murray and the King remained for more than an hour with the Queen, who, taking them both by the hands, drew them after her into her bedchamber. Afterwards the King came to the other Lords, who seemed hardly to venture to separate, but went on for ever talking over the matter, this way and that, though the result always seemed to be that their cause was in anything but a brilliant position. "She is cutting into us. Now she is dividing the Earl of Murray from us. In the town, everything is melting like butter. Everything goes after that damn pretty face of hers." So they were talking, when the King came and demanded, with every appearance of determination, that the guards should be removed from the interior of the palace, and above all from the Queen's rooms and the passages. All the Queen's concessions were dependent on the fulfilment of this request.

"Indeed!" said young Ruthven. "I like that! Until we have our guarantees signed in our hands, there can be no talk of anything like that. All this talk of hers, about forgiving us and so on, is mere cheat. She has not been educated in France for naught, where she was taught nothing but black intrigue."

"That is entirely untrue," said the King. "I find that she always says straight out what she thinks."

"So we believe," said Earl Morton, "and, above all, that she is for escaping, tomorrow or the day after, up to the Castle or to Dunbar, and you with her!"

Before his daggerlike glance the King dropped his own eyes while a red flame overspread his cheeks. Still, however, he asserted: "She cannot go! She is physically incapable of it, at present!" Finally he urged upon them: "Even if she signs now, while she is kept so close a prisoner, and then, afterwards, gets back her power, she will be in no wise bound to hold to her word, and her signature will have no value, because her promise will have been given under compulsion, in imprisonment, and such a promise, by the law of Scotland, is invalid. Nor, in such circumstances, will any of the other Lords, our opponents, recognize her pardon."

Earl Morton scratched his cropped, colourless head, and looked angrily at the King. "You get all that from her," he said. "You are not capable of thinking such a thing out by yourself." He smote his brow suddenly with his hand. "Unfortunately, however, you are right." He stumped up and down, on his strong short legs, muttering the while, "A cursed affair! To have to consult stupid boys and cowardly squires of dames in such an undertaking! There can be no success on such terms." He paused, scratching his head again. "I do not trust Murray round the corner," he said, going to the door. "Send up the woman who was with the Queen yesterday—the midwife, I mean!" he shouted.

The other Lords sat, not knowing what to say or think. The King began saying once more, "The guards must be removed, or she . . ."

Morton interrupted him: "Shut your mouth!"

The midwife, a stout little middle-aged woman, at last appeared. Had she seen the Queen again today? asked Morton. "Yes," answered the woman, tartly, casting a look at him out of her squinting eyes that seemed to imply that in all her days she had never despised any one as she did him.

"Well?"

"Her Majesty's life is simply in danger," declared the woman. "Such a lady in such . . ."

"That is not the question," he yelled at her. "You are asked this and this only—Can the Queen run a little way, or can she not? or can she ride?"

The woman raised her eyes to heaven. "Ride? or run? the poor creature . . ."

"Can she or can she not?"

"No."

"Go to Hell!" He turned to the King. "She can have her

way. But may all the bloodshed that will come of this fall on your head and your children's!"

★

Mary escaped from Holyrood about midnight, accompanied by the King, Lord Arthur Erskine (the door of whose room the King unlocked), Darnley's personal servant and three soldiers. Lord Arthur and the others were taken as protection in case of necessity. The Queen had decided that the best way of escape was by the royal vault under the chapel. When they entered the passage leading to it, the first of the party stumbled in the semi-darkness, dimly lit by a single candle, against a new coffin. They all had to pass so close by it that they touched the coffin. Only the King hesitated. His wife turned to him, to spur him on. There he stood, his knees knocking together, and could not make up his mind to proceed, his teeth chattering audibly from fright.

"Quick! quick!" she admonished him: then, as he leaned against the wall, as though unable to move, she said: "What is the matter? What ails you?"

He turned his distracted gaze on her, as though appealing for help.

"In that coffin they have laid David."

Mary looked at the coffin, and then laughed. "There will be many to lie there beside him! . . . Forward!" She drove her husband on. "Do you want the guard on top of us?" This new anxiety behind at last forced him to make speed.

From the vault a small door of which the Queen had the key let them out into the open air, in the vicinity of a little group of shrubs. For a moment they stood, holding breath, behind the open door, until the guard which went round the palace in twos had passed by, round the corner.

"Quickly now," said the Queen, "let one go first into those bushes over there, while the rest wait till the guard has passed again."

Two of the soldiers went first; Lord Erskine's turn was next, but, at the last moment, the Queen said to her husband, "Do you go now." He obeyed at once. Then Mary herself followed, and after her came the others. They made their way to a copse quite near by, where, as had been arranged between the Queen and the Countess of Huntly, a man was waiting with a number of horses, each horse having a sufficiently broad saddle for two persons to ride in it—the usual thing in Scotland for two persons travelling together. The Queen mounted behind Lord Arthur Erskine. The others likewise sat in pairs. Only the King had a horse to himself. At first they rode very carefully: the horses' hooves had been muffled. In a second copse, some half a mile from the palace, they found more horses, and could now remove the wrappings from the hooves of the first set, and each mount a separate steed. Swiftly and silently they rode through the dead dark of the March night, towards the southeast, in the direction of the sea. After a while, they heard, to the side of them, what sounded like the noise of many riders, though, in the thick air, it was impossible to say from what direction the sound was coming.

The King set his charger to a gallop, and smote the Queen's horse many times on the haunches with his crop, to speed it forward too. "Quick! Quick! for God's sake! We are lost! If they take us now they will put us all to death, all!"

Mary's horse bounded until the Queen reined in. "Impossible," she said, "I cannot gallop. I will risk anything except my child. If I have to gallop, I am bound to have a miscarriage by the way."

The King, who was well ahead, turned back in despair. The clatter of hooves grew louder in the distance. He snatched at the reins of Mary's horse. "Hell and Heaven!" he yelled. "If this one goes wrong, we will get six others!"

Her horse made three bounds: then the Queen seized her husband's arm. "Go ahead then," she cried.

Sick with fear, for the clatter was now close upon them, and certainly came from several horsemen, coming hastily, coming as fast as ever they could—but where did it come from? it seemed to come now from in front, now from behind, now from the right, now from the left, now from every side at once—he threw Mary's reins back at her. Grinding an oath between his teeth, he sprang right across the plain. The darkness at once closed behind him. Mary sat groaning aloud in the saddle, sobs breaking from her throat. She felt as though at every moment she were going to die, in the open, in this dead blackness of night.

The riders were quite near now, but it was not from the town they came. So, they must be friends. And they were. Their little troop leaped forward out of the night. Five of them, six, ten. They recognized the others. The group broke up: the Earl of Bothwell drew rein at the Queen's side. "Your Majesty is happily free!" Bothwell's brother-in-law, Huntly, with the Lords Seaton, Livingstone, and Fleming, pressed round Mary. Glancing over the number of those who had escaped, they asked— "But we thought, we had heard . . . where is the King?"

"Ahead," replied Mary.

Bothwell laughed out loud.

Slowly they rode back in the direction from which the lords had come. They assured the Queen that there was no danger near her here. Everything here was safe. No one here would do her any harm. Mary soon recovered her spirits and courage. Her pains, too, intermitted, and she was able to manage the fifteen miles that lay between her and their goal, the Castle of Dunbar, in tolerable comfort. Before the gates of the Castle, which were at once opened for the fugitives, the King once more joined his wife, only to be disregarded by the lords as if he were not there.

★

On dismounting, Mary asked for some refreshment, something that could be got ready at once, an egg or something of the sort. Then, with but half an hour's rest, she called for a clerk to whom she could dictate letters. The Earls of Bothwell and Huntly came to tell her that, by the morning, she would find six hundred men, well trained and armed, at her service.

As day broke, messengers from the Queen were flying to all the four quarters, calling up the Scottish vassals: from all sides, knights or their emissaries came to congratulate the Queen on her escape and offer her all the men she might want. That morning, too, the conspirators sent a knight from Edinburgh, with the paper in which the guarantees of their security were written down.

Mary tore it in two and threw the pieces at the messenger's feet. "Are the Lords mad or do they imagine that I am?"

The messenger, however, took back with him both intelligence of the eager bustle surrounding the Queen and of the royal pardon to the Earls of Glencairn and Murray, Lord Rothes, the Knight of Grange and all those who had previously been banished.

★

On the following Sunday, the Queen rode into Edinburgh at the head of eight thousand men in full war panoply. Up to the town gates she had been carried in a litter. There, however, she got on horseback once more. She rode in in pomp, but did not at first take up her residence in Holyrood, which seemed to her to have a curse upon it, but in the town, in a palace once used by her mother, the Regent, which lay in the upper town, under the shelter of the wall. A great ring of cannon was set round the house.

Soldiers were billeted in all the surrounding houses. The Queen's proclamation was set up at the Toll Cross—she had come to punish treachery. A large number of Edinburgh citizens, charged, after a rapid house-to-house search, with complicity in the recent conspiracy, were imprisoned in the Town Hall. Five of them were executed. Two others were actually standing at the gallows' foot when the Earl of Bothwell appeared bearing the Queen's signet ring, in sign of mercy. Their goods were confiscated and the men themselves banished.

The conspirators had not awaited the Queen's return.

John Knox had joined them.

★

Lord James of Murray was now restored to the head of the Government, supported by a Privy Council in which the most prominent places were filled by the Earls of Bothwell and Huntly, Atholl and Erskine, and the first of all belonged to the Earl of Bothwell. His power was now almost equal to that of the Earl of Murray. The Queen granted him the rich abbey of Haddington, for Lord Lethington was now exiled and a fugitive. Queen Elizabeth, too, took the opportunity to reunite the severed bonds of amity. She had been kept well informed. Mr. Randolph had written to London to say:

"I know from a sure source that the Queen repents her marriage, and hates her husband and everything belonging to him. I know that he is feeling round for supporters so that he may know who is with him and who is not.

"I know that there is a movement afoot, engineered by father and son, to get the crown matrimonial even against her will. I know that if what is planned takes place, David, with the King's agreement, will get his throat cut, and that within the next ten days. Other matters, of graver and worse import, have come to my ears including such as are intended against her own person. But to write in detail of these would be dangerous."

Now, however, Queen Mary was mistress in her own house. Therefore, Queen Elizabeth showed herself in a conciliatory mood and sent hearty congratulations to her neighbour, when Sir James Melville came to justify the action taken by his Government against Mr. Thomas Randolph.

★

The King was no longer a member of the Privy Council. A Proclamation in which he spoke as "I, Henry, King of Scotland," declared that he was guiltless of the murder of David and of the imprisonment of his wife. He had never either advised or encouraged the murderers in their evil deeds. Nor was there any other crime of which he could be accused: he had merely sought to restore the banished Lords, Murray, Glencairn, Rothes and the Knight of Grange, without informing the Queen beforehand.

The King appeared before the Council to swear by his honour, his word as a prince and a knight, that he had never known anything of the conspiracy against Her Majesty, much less had advised or ordered it. The Lords of the Council were astute enough to ask him, first, how he explained his presence in his wife's room on that evening? Henry replied that it was a mere accident: no one could prevent him from going to his wife, when it pleased him. The secret staircase was well known to many, and in particular to his servants and to his wife's. Then they asked: how he explained the fact that it was his active interposition that prevented his wife's coming to the assistance of her threatened servant? quite apart from the fact that he did not make even a pretence of defending him? He swore that, at that moment, he had been blinded by hatred of David, whom he believed to be influencing the Queen, his wife, against him, to such an extent that she no longer troubled about him, as she had used to do, and it was for that reason that he had assisted the enterprise, but throughout without *arrière pensée*. He had known nothing of its ulterior purpose, or that anything was going on.

The people laughed at his proclamation. The Lords of the Council also laughed at his oath, but grimly.

★

The King came to his wife: the lords looked through him, as though he were air. "I have dealt with Livingstone. But this man . . ." From his wild and whirling words, Mary gathered that the knight had reproached him violently, bandying the words ingratitude and treachery, treachery and ingratitude, and also cowardice. Henry said he could not allow this, and they should see what he was. And his wife must put matters to rights. He was prepared to make peace solemnly with the

Lords, and swear close, sincere, and eternal comradeship with them, to which he would be absolutely faithful. "Yes. But I must have people. What sort of state of things is this, what sort of position? It is no position at all. I simply cannot bear it." Suddenly inflamed, he smote the table with his fist. "And I don't need to bear it, either! They must look out, they must!" His wife said that his heart held nothing but a trembling fear. She reflected; she answered in monosyllables. What could be done, should be done. The situation was hard. Well, she would see. By now her husband was almost weeping. He was strangely regarded and treated by all the world. He drew himself up, and began to spread himself in complaints of his misfortunes. Mary bade him go. In these days, she did not feel equal to long and exciting conversations. He went away, growling. She remained, sunk in silent brooding.

On this same day, she sent for the Earl of Mar, one of the ablest and most moderate of her lords, and put the situation before him. It was clear, she said, that the present state of things could not last. Earl Mar, a stately man in the early forties, replied:

"Your Majesty, that certainly depends on him. But what can be done? We did, then, gladly risk our lives in battle for the King in order to make it possible for him to win prizes beyond his deserts, such as the possession of Your Majesty, and his being King of Scotland. We were entirely true to him. But what is our reward? He goes and betrays us to our deadliest enemies, who, simply and solely on account of him, have become foes to us. Is it his merit, that we are still alive? If they had only dared, we should all be dead men together. Including Your Majesty. Indeed, you first of all. Yes, Your Majesty, our legitimate ruler to whom he owes everything he is, without whom even a Jew would advance him not one shilling: and he goes and delivers her to her enemies and his!"

Mary attempted to reply that the King had been over-persuaded, surprised. The traitors had taken advantage of his inexperience, and exploited his limited intelligence in the most cunning way. He was really to be pitied rather than blamed: really had been sacrificed. He had none of the qualities for such a deed as this.

The earl, plainly repressing the severe remarks that were on the tip of his tongue, contented himself with saying: "Your Majesty, on what ground are we to be induced to show consideration for him? We have never sworn allegiance to him. We neither chose nor recognized him as our King."

Tears were falling down slowly over the Queen's cheeks. He went on: "If we are prepared to show him at least the external politeness due to a nobleman—which he has in truth made difficult for us—it is solely for Your Majesty's sake and because Your Highness has chosen him as your husband, and, also, because he is the father of our future ruler."

The Earl of Murray, for whose sake the King alleged that he had allowed himself to be so deeply involved, merely resumed the attitude to him he had taken up in the days before his marriage.

The King came to demand from him the friendly support to which he imagined himself entitled. Lord James replied, icily, that the only course of action open to the King was to endeavour, by a long period of repentance and of the most correct conduct both towards his wife and her lords, to secure the oblivion of his grave transgressions. And Lord James went to his sister to put before her the draft of a document in which her husband had promised the Lords of the conspiracy, as his faithful servants and associates, his utmost favour and grace in the event of the successful execution of his plans.

From this time on, the King nearly always remained in his apartments all day long, going out only at night. He was sick, so he said. Finally, Queen Mary, who hardly saw him, sent a confidential messenger down to his rooms to say that he should not go out of the palace regularly every night. In the first place, it was not without danger to its denizens to have the entrances all kept open. Secondly, he was by no means safe in his nocturnal wanderings, as he must know.

The French Government sent an Ambassador to the Queen

to congratulate her on the happy issue of the great dangers she had passed through, and to suggest that France keenly desired the renewal of the earlier alliance between itself and the Scottish kingdom. Whereupon it occurred to the King that the relations between his wife and her French mother-in-law had always been, whether overtly or covertly, by no means smooth. He desired the French Ambassador to speak with him privily, since he had something important to communicate to him. For the moment, so he instructed his messenger to import, he could only say that he hoped to find an ally in the French Ambassador, in an effort to re-establish his honour, which had been so grievously impugned. His life was in constant danger from his deadly enemies, and above all from the Earl of Murray. He was refused the Crown Matrimonial, which really belonged to him as of right as a Stuart next in the line after the Queen if not absolutely her equal in claim, and had, moreover, been solemnly promised to him both by the Queen, and, subsequently, by the nobles in the most definite fashion, nay actually in writing. The French gentleman, however, informed his messenger, after he had heard his message and had reflected upon it for several minutes, that he could speak with the King only in the presence of the assembled Council, on all these matters. Not long after, he actually appeared. Then, however, he was accompanied by the Scottish nobles, and after the briefest introductory passage, the Frenchman began to overwhelm the King with the severest reproaches, in the name of his master the French King, the close relative of his great and glorious wife, whom he had wronged in such an atrocious and unheard-of fashion. He could never count on the friendship of a ruler who had the keenest pleasure in recognizing all the friends of the Queen of Scotland as his own, but was, at the same time, the irreconcilable enemy of all her enemies.

★

Mary sought to reconcile her other nobles and gather them in peace about herself. She brought about a reconciliation between the Earls of Argyle and Murray and those of Huntly,

Bothwell and Atholl by going to them and adjuring them, in moving terms, for her own sake and that of the child to be born into the world within the next few weeks, to lay aside all personal enmities and simply join with her, the Queen, in working for the welfare of the State, their common country. The Earl of Murray replied that he had never had anything else at heart save care for the country and for the welfare of Her Majesty, and whosoever was concerned to promote these two aims would never find in him anything but a sincere friend. The others, following his example, spoke on similar lines. Afterwards, the lords were on terms of courtesy.

Not long after, however, the Earl of Bothwell came to complain of the Earl of Murray. True, he was now, again, at the head of the Government, presiding in Council, and receiving deputations from vassals throughout the realm, foreign guests, ambassadors from foreign rulers. All the same, he was anything but a loyal servant of his altogether too kindly ruler. On the contrary, he was using his excessive power to concoct secret plans with the lords who had fled to England after their banishment on account of their share in the Rizzio conspiracy.

The Queen, with obvious disquiet, replied to this accusation that, whatever she might, secretly, think on this matter, she simply could not do without her brother, because of his great administrative capacity, and his influence with the nobility and the best men throughout the middle classes.

"But it is just this influence that he is misusing against Your Majesty!" replied the Earl.

"I can do nothing," she replied, in despair. "I can only try to hold things together as best I can. Since I have had to take them back against my will. . . ." She buried her face in her hands. "Whom am I to trust?" she said, dropping her hands, and looking at him in bitter distress.

He drew himself up, offended. "I served Your Majesty well, at a time when there was no question of reward," he said, a dark flush mounting to his brows.

"I know, of course I know," said Mary, anxious to mollify

him, while her heart beat thick and fast. "I know; I know; you
are the only one to whom I can be grateful! . . . But you
must see that my brother has almost the whole country behind
him. I cannot dismiss him. I simply have not got enough power
for that. I have tried. And what was the result? You know
yourself."

Shortly afterwards she received letters from her friends in
England, enclosing copies of other letters, written, quite recently, by the Earls of Murray and Argyle, in which these
gentlemen, with expressions of the deepest devotion, again assured the English Crown that it would find its devoted servants
ready for any service asked of them.

The Queen called the two before her. She was, in these days,
much exhausted; her figure was that of a woman who expects
the birth of her child within a matter of days; her eyes looked
large and fatigued; there were brown circles under them. As
the men stood before her, the one gigantic, the other small,
delicately built, she gave them the copies of the letters to read,
without saying a word. But when she perceived in their embarrassed mien what she had known all along in her heart, she
cried, "Traitors! Thankless men, tear my heart out of my
body, and then perhaps you will be satisfied!" She sobbed aloud.
"I have done you all the good I could. I have forgiven you
black treachery, not once, but twice! When have I ever been
anything but good and gracious to you? Have you ever found
me inaccessible to a sensible suggestion?" She pressed her hands
to her temples. "Gracious God! Only show me the way to deal
with this race!" Then turning again to the two men: "Anyhow, the Queen of England must know it. There she is, greedy,
only yielding what is absolutely necessary. None of her servants gets anything from her except in the very last resort, and
then only what must, at the final extremity, be given, for the
sake of the realm itself. If she is ill-humoured, she throws her
slippers at her lords' heads. And if they cannot wring a stiver
out of her, they yield their own possessions to her. No one has
rest or peace there. And as a result, they are sooner or later

turned out, attacked, maligned, and finally left shamelessly in the lurch. And yet they are all eager to sacrifice themselves for this woman, at whom every one of them is laughing in his sleeve. What is her secret?"

The lords were silent.

"There must be some reason for it," Mary repeated. "Tell it me. I want to know it. I must learn from it."

Murray at last replied, "If Your Majesty would yield to the prayers of your people and cause the offence of the Papist Mass to be removed from the country at last."

Mary threw back her head. "I shall never become a Protestant! That is a religion for tailors."

The lords turned pale.

She added, bitterly, "If the time should ever come when I believe that your religion is other than a mere pretext with every one of you for pursuing his own odious personal advantage, then, perhaps, your faith might begin to look to me like a Christian religion!"

After the Earls had departed the Queen fell into a fit of weeping that was almost beyond her control. She let her hands fall, at last, looked about her, and saw nothing all around save black loneliness.

Whom had she got?

Even now she left her brother in possession of all his offices. As her hour drew near, she committed herself to his protection. She went up to the Castle, in these days under the command of the Earl of Murray, who himself had his apartments quite near to the royal chambers. The Earls of Huntly and Bothwell, who had counted on being commanded to dwell under the same roof with the Queen, had to content themselves with dwelling in the neighbourhood of the palace.

Chapter 8

ON the nineteenth July, in the year 1566, on a Wednesday, Mary Stuart gave birth to her child. The labour was difficult, and her women believed dangerous. At last, after several hours, the child was delivered, a boy, seemingly strong and healthy and well formed in all his limbs.

At noon, the King came up to the Castle to ask after his wife and see his child. Mary caused her little son to be brought to her in bed, and looked sharply at him. Then, indicating to the nurse that she should show the child to his father, she said: "There, see for yourself, my Lord, how like you he is." She laughed: "I will not say he is too like."

★

Queen Elizabeth of England was dancing at Greenwich, at a court ball. She noticed her Secretary of State, Sir William Cecil, coming hurrying through the lines of dancers, holding up his long cloak with both hands, lest it should stay him in his haste. The Queen left her partner standing and stepped out of the ring, looking very uneasily towards her minister. Even he, the imperturbable, seemed perturbed. Breathless, he bent to speak in her ear. "Queen Mary is happily delivered of a son."

The dance stopped: every eye was turned to the Queen, who was staring at the messenger, with a mask-like expression. Then she collapsed on to a seat. Tears ran down her face. "The Queen of Scotland has a fair son. And I, I am a barren stock."

But when she received the Scottish Ambassador, Sir James Melville, she said that her joy in this news had, at a stroke, freed her from all the pains she had been suffering in the last few weeks as the result of a severe illness. Sir James gave a very lively description of the severe sufferings through which his Sovereign had passed, with the idea of frightening the Queen of England, if necessary, from marriage and child-bearing. He then asked the Queen to stand godmother to the little prince, a request amiably acceded to. The most confidential servants of the English Crown should be sent to Scotland for the christening, to represent their Queen.

But Queen Elizabeth knew that Queen Mary of Scotland was, from this time on, a changed being for every one in the British Isles.

In the next few days, there was such a crowd in the dwelling of the Scottish Ambassador, that servants had to be on duty all the time to direct and control the veritable stream coming in and going out. Everybody wanted his name entered in the list of those who sent congratulations. Queen Elizabeth held out the prospect of having the claims of the Queen of Scots examined by her Privy Council. If, as was indubitable, the result was favourable, the Council would proceed to demand the recognition, by the English Parliament, of Queen Mary as successor to the throne, should Queen Elizabeth die without heirs to her body.

★

Queen Mary recovered slowly from the exhaustion of her delivery, with many relapses into fever and weakness. At this time she was overcome with longings for another clime. "How I should like to go back to France once again!" she said. "Now, with my baby. When I think back, it seems to me as though we always had fine weather there, with a lovely sky, and neither heat nor this everlasting fog; here I have never seen a really blue sky; it is always so pallid." She got up and sat in a long chair on her balcony, whence she could gaze right out over her country. But when she lowered her gaze, it fell on the cannon on the walls, standing, charged, trained on to the town below, whose restless and incessant noise and clatter rose up to her ears. Mary sighed, and said it often seemed to her as though all

262

those houses down there were filled with none but her deadly enemies. "Night and day they are working and thinking how, one day, they may bring ruin upon my head after all."

Often, however, the Queen was gay. The young wives and maidens of Edinburgh came with presents and great bunches of roses. Graciously their Queen thanked them and had the little prince shown to them. Was he not a stout and handsome little man? "He is bound to succeed. For he is a true Scot, both by father and mother."

Queen Mary spoke to her lords of her longing for a milder clime. Finally the Earl of Mar came to her. To the south, on the Firth of Forth, there was the castle of Alloa, which belonged to him. Of course, it was not France, but the climate there was really mild and there were woods and great meadows. Would Her Majesty deign to consider whether she could not honour the modest house of her humble servant with a royal visit? Above all, the Castle was easy of access by sea. Her Majesty need not even get into a litter. Perhaps it would be safest for His Highness the Prince to remain in the Castle with his nurse?

This proposition Queen Mary accepted. In the middle of August she departed. The ship that was to convey her was chosen by the Earl of Bothwell, as Lord High Admiral of Scotland, and he provided its crew. The Queen only took her women with her.

The sun shone down on the mighty waters of the Firth, riding softly to and fro under a bluish sky. The Queen felt the load falling from her heart. She walked on deck, on Mary Fleming's arm, and stood by the sailors. They had to explain to her how the sails were set and furled. She inquired about the wind and the current, about the ebb and flow of the tide. At last she smiled: If she were not a woman with a country to govern, she would assuredly be nothing but a sailor. She leaned against the mast, pressing her ear to it, to listen to the singing and twanging high up in air, and said at last: "It has a marvellous sound. As though it reached right up to the sky, among the stars, and tells us about the songs by which they run."

After three days in Alloa Castle, she desired more company. The Earls of Murray, Huntly, Bothwell, and others came. The Queen was in excellent spirits, and talked and laughed much. Some one said that there was an annual market in Stirling, quite near Alloa. Some of the gentlemen had ridden over, and displayed highly coloured purchases.

"I should love to see that!" cried the Queen.

Next day, at noon, a shout suddenly rose amidst all the hubbub of the Stirling market: "Here is the Queen!" And, actually, her suite approached, at its head, between the Provost and the Earl of Murray, the Sovereign herself, all graciousness and, once again, blooming like the loveliest rose. She went through the narrow passages between the booths. There was a rush that way and then, modestly, back: Queen Mary waved greetings to right and left. She paused in front of a cookie-stall. "There"— she gave a sign to buy it all up, and then turned to distribute, with both hands.

She called to the children, and at last won them over; she gave something to each; passed on: finally, indicated to her suite to stand back. There she stood among the children, who pressed round her so that she had difficulty in holding her feet. She waved bright ribbons about her. "Every one gets his bit! But only those who are good. Take your turns nicely, and then you will all get yours." She was as keen as the children themselves.

She stayed till evening, and took part in the dancing under the lime trees.

Next day, however, her host, the Earl of Mar, came to her with a matter of quite another sort. He came with a very urgent request. On behalf of a poor rejected sinner, who had done evil, but whose repentance was even greater than his heavy offence. Could Her Majesty not grant the truest of those of her servants who had been cast out since the late conspiracy, Baron Maitland of Lethington, the favour of allowing him to appear before her here in Alloa Castle? Earl Murray appeared, too, to second this plea. The Queen's face paled. Looking at them, she shook her head, slowly, as if unable to comprehend how men could be for ever coming to her with such requests. Yet they did not give up. Here was a writing of the Laird of Lethington —would Her Majesty not at least consent to cast her eyes over the humble petition of her servant? The Earl of Mar spoke of the great services of this unhappy exile, whose memory could not have been extinguished in the heart of so kindly a ruler. Finally, Mary took the letter. She read it. But when she laid it down, her expression had not softened. She said to the Lords, "This is not the reason, and if there were nothing else in it but this . . . but the Earl of Bothwell has possession of the laird of Lethington's confiscated estates. And, as I think, he has deserved to have them. If Lord Lethington came back, the old trouble between them would all be there again. For that reason alone it is impossible."

Whereupon the Earl of Mar said: "Your Majesty, the laird of Lethington most certainly desires none of the gracious gifts which Your Majesty once so generously showered upon him. He knows only too well that he has lost Your Majesty's favour. All he hopes is to have his ancestral patrimony, to which no one has made any claim, and which would give him all that he absolutely needs. And to have Your Majesty grant him permission again to place his gifts at your service and that of the State."

"In order that he may have the opportunity for fresh treachery! No, no, I will not see him!" She reflected, with a sombre expression; the Lords waited, in tense anxiety. But she merely repeated: "No."

Yet she asked her friend Mary Fleming, "Would you like to have Lethington come back?"

"Yes," replied Mary Fleming. "And now I would even marry him. For he is the only man here with whom it is possible to talk."

"In other ways too he is unfortunately irreplaceable," said her Queen, with a sigh.

On the evening after this conversation the Earl of Mar was informed that he might summon Lethington.

Afterwards, Baron Maitland appeared, spoke with his Sovereign and met with painful coldness from her. She said that in any event he must give her his most solemn undertaking that he would never make trouble with the Earl of Bothwell, but would be sincerely friendly to him. The Earl would leave him in peace, he had promised her that. And she could trust his word.

Wings would soon be sprouting on her, she said jestingly to her ladies that night. She seemed to be exclusively occupied in making peace. "And certainly any one who takes up that occupation, in Scotland, has his time more than adequately filled!"

★

One day, in Alloa, while Mary Seaton was brushing and combing the Queen's hair, she said: "How bad people are, aren't they! It is hardly two months since the Earl of Bothwell was married, to a nice, pretty wife, and he is unfaithful to her already!"

"Is he?" said the Queen, sitting quite still under her maid's hands. After a time, as Mary Seaton seemed inclined to say no more, Queen Mary asked: "With whom then? Do I know her? It is as well to know. If one knows a part . . ."

"It is an awful shame! It is the sort of thing you can hardly imagine—she is a maid from the Abbey, from Haddington," said Mary Seaton. "And he goes on behaving as if he loved his wife ever so! And has so little respect for his young marriage as to do such a thing to his Countess . . . carrying on with a girl of that sort!"

"You talk like a little Protestant," retorted the Queen.

Mary Seaton crossed herself, in amazement. "May the Lord Jesus take me in His blessed protection! With Protestants, marriage is not even a sacrament!"

"Why, then, should one not fall in love with a pretty serving-maid?" asked Mary. "I often look at them, and have often thought that I should be in love with this one or that if I were a man. They are often deliciously tempting, and as attractive as dear, soft, warm little kittens."

"But the Earl of Bothwell has a wife!" cried her friend, breathlessly.

"Ah, my child, if you cannot put up with that sort of thing, you must never get married," replied the Queen. Turning round so that the white hair-dressing cloak fell back from her soft, white elbows as they rested on the arms of the chair, she looked slyly into her friend's face, and laughed as she perceived its injured and distressed expression. "They all do it, without exception," she went on, confidentially, "and the men who attract us certainly do it. There is no help for it. Most women who do not bring their husband a great deal—money, land, connection—can count themselves lucky if he does not exchange them, one fine day, for a more advantageous match. King Henry of England had six legal wives: beheaded two; divorced two; one died of herself, without his aid, another survived him, but only just. When my mother-in-law, Queen Catherine of France, wanted her husband, King Henri, she sent to the Duchess of Valentinois and asked her to lend him to her for the nonce. And Madame Valentinois accepted the position, and bade him go, and so Queen Catherine gradually managed to produce eight children. She was a clever woman, very clever; she made close friends with Madame Valentinois—indeed they really liked one another, and so each had a support in the other against the day when any one of the other ladies upon whom King Henri cast his eyes from time to time, showed signs of becoming dangerous." Queen Mary laughed. "At the time when my pretty governess, Lady Fleming, had to go so hurriedly, my pet, that was the real reason for it. She had a nice little boy by the King—Henri d'Angoulême was her son. And Queen Catherine owed it to Madame Valentinois, and to her alone, that she was not sent packing home again, when ten whole years went by and she had no children."

"I shall never marry," cried the maid of honour, horrified.

"That is certainly the cleverest part to play," said her mistress approvingly. She turned cheerfully back to the table. Then, her mood quickly changing, she sighed deeply. After a while she said: "But let us be just. If one were a man, one would behave, no doubt, just as they do."

"Never!" cried Mary Seaton.

"No, perhaps not you. But you are our little nun."

They were silent, again. The maid arranged the Queen's hair in formal waves and felt for the golden pins with great pierced heads lying ready on the table. "Perhaps, if one loved one's husband desperately, one might not like . . ." said the Queen, thoughtfully; then, breaking off, she continued: "At any rate, in such a case one would be dreadfully cross . . ." She paused again. "And lovely Countess Jean too," she said, as though to herself. "Well, well, well! And she certainly imagined herself passionately loved." Another idea occurred to her, and she said, brightly, "I do not know why you are all so against the Earl of Bothwell. Jean Gordon thought nothing of him. Even when she took him. If she could have got Ogilvy—only he was no longer so much as looking at her—and after all, compared with him, the Earl . . . He is certainly one of the best-looking men here. . . ."

"Oh! my Queen!" cried her friend, indignantly.

"Oh, yes, I have no doubt of that," replied Mary. She went on: "As a matter of fact I know just how Jean was wooed. I went to the Gordons: there was Jean, sitting in the window, I on the sofa opposite to her, on the right, the old Countess on the left; old Huntly told Jean she must be sensible: she was not likely to make a better match; what did she want? and so on. And Jean sat there blank and stiff, her eyes sideways on the ground, her face as pale as chalk. Suddenly from under her drooping eyelids, two big tears rolled down over her cheeks, right down to her chin, and she was too much ashamed of them even to wipe them away. I was so sorry for her as she sat there, trying not to let any one see how wretched she was, that I went up to her and took her in my arms and kissed her and said the

Earl was really a splendid man, so brave, absolutely loyal and able; she really could not possibly have a better husband; he was so good to his mother and was so much attached to herself that she would certainly be happy with him; moreover, she was so young that a feeling that now seemed to her irremediable would nevertheless pass; and anyhow, life was like that. But if, after all, the thing was horrible to her she should not do it. She, however, said no word in reply, but lay in my arms, her face half averted; when I kissed her again, she suddenly sobbed out loud, so loud that it was almost a shriek; then she kissed my hands and was gone out of the room. I said to old Huntly she should leave her alone now, and not use any pressure on her, but let it be as she decided. And next day she said that if the Earl came, he would be welcome. Certainly, she had no passion to give him."

"But she is said now to be very devoted to her husband," insisted the lady-in-waiting.

"That proves that he deserves it! And, come, Jean Gordon ought to be thankful that it is such a little creature as this: she never need be jealous of *her*. And she will get used to it."

Her maid had now finished her hairdressing. The Queen took a gold-mounted hand mirror, and held it up, turning it this way and that, until she got a full view of the back of her head in the great glass above her dressing-table. "You have surpassed yourself once again," she said to her friend, with a smile. Well pleased, she laid down the mirror, and pulled out a lock here and there over her forehead, with her finger-tips, gazing into the big glass as she did so. She smiled to herself, as she looked at her reflection there, and repeated, in a low murmur, "Proud Jean Gordon, too!" Still she smiled, and reflected that many people thought the Countess of Bothwell even more lovely than herself.

★

In the afternoon, the Queen walked in the garden with the Earl of Bothwell. She went right ahead of her suite, while two fair greyhounds leapt about her. She spoke very quickly: her lips moved and her eyes shone with animation, and she often raised her hand to give point to her words. She spoke with her companion of political matters and general principles, talking in French, a language the Earl of Bothwell spoke almost as fluently as his native Scottish, and better than any other of his countrymen at court, better even than Lethington or Sir James Melville.

In the course of this conversation, the Earl remarked: "Certainly a King can only rule with the help of his nobles. How else could he? The nobles stand between him and the people. Your Majesty cannot know them as individuals—that is what we are there for."

Queen Mary replied: "That is so. A ruler cannot do everything himself. But why should he not be permitted to choose for himself the men whom he may place between him and the people? And why should the persons he selects always come from the ranks of the nobles?"

The Earl threw back his head with the defiant gesture peculiar to him, which always seemed to signalize that his pride leapt, panther-like, to action—there was the world before him: there was he: why was not the world at his feet? How could he help gnashing his teeth at such a stupid disposition of things? His eyelids fell half over his eyes, those eyes of such questionable colour that one could never be sure whether the sheen that slept over their brightness were an intensely dark blue or brown. The right hand that held his glove closed more tightly on the hilt of his dagger. He replied, "The nobility represents the power of ancestry. When was a man ennobled? Only when he had proved his possession of noble blood by uncommon services. It is to be assumed that his descendants will not be unworthy of his blood. They have been nobly nurtured, and come, on both sides, of noble stock: they have more to lose both in honour and in possessions than any common Mr. Smith or Robinson."

"Yes," said the Queen, "so it is said. But in reality—poor David, whose father was a mere clerk, was ten thousand times dearer to me than, for example, that rude fellow Lindsay, with all his forefathers and ancestors on both sides. And am I to respect this wretched, barbarous, uneducated, coarse crowd, more than half of them able neither to read nor write, simply because perhaps, once, two hundred years ago, some great-grandfather, in some battle or other, took an Englishman prisoner who, in all probability, was only too glad to yield? They are a pack of traitors, greedy, ambitious, with no thought beyond how, at any cost, they can lay their hands on money and property, and still more money and property, and stuff it in their sacks; they have no shame before God or man; they are ruthless, insolent, crazy—they come of such old family! But they do not know that they are utterly degenerate, because, actually, it has gone so far with them that they do not notice it. And, simply and solely because a great-grandfather was once serviceable—a fact about which there may, really, be a great deal of doubt—is a King for that reason to be obliged to let himself be run by this gang to all eternity? really, to tolerate them on top of him? Although the King is appointed by God, and the nobles only by the King? For God chooses the King and commands the people to obey him. And the King appoints the nobles for his support, not, forsooth, that they should be continually rising against him!"

"Would Your Majesty then destroy the nobles, root and branch?" asked the Earl. "I am afraid you would only have even worse trouble with your beloved people."

"I want to be able to do what I think good," said the Queen, roused, angry, annoyed. She cast an irate glance at the man at her side, who seemed to be looking at her with laughing scorn. "You shall all soon see that I am not to be played with," she said in a tone of desperate defiance. She took one of the greyhounds, which had pressed against her knee, by the collar. Then she turned once again to look into her companion's face. She could not read his expression. She stopped, looked about her. "What is this?" she said, involuntarily, almost breathlessly. "We seem to be losing ourselves in a wilderness. Where

are my people? I want to turn at once, back to the Castle."
With a bow, he obeyed, silently.

★

A great surprise awaited the company at Alloa. Suddenly,
the King appeared among them, at his wife's invitation, and
went about among them with her arm in his. And she would
address remarks to him, to draw him into the conversation, or
compel him to speak, and listen as though his remarks were
worthy of attention. She was noticeably friendly and polite to
him. And he raised his head and looked proudly out of his light
blue eyes over the heads of the company, and behaved as though
everything depended on his good graces. But his wife made as
though she did not notice this behaviour of his.

They remained in Alloa right into September. Then they all
left to go up to the mountains, to pursue the chase with bows
and arrows as the Queen loved to do. This was the first undertaking of the kind since her confinement. Later, after a short
stay in the capital, she planned to go to the southern provinces,
and preside at the days of justice in the town of Jedburgh.

During these mountain days, it chanced that the Queen
tracked down a fine stag side by side with her husband. Her
arrow, recognizable from its feathers, went right through its
heart; his shaft, on the other hand, missed its mark and
whizzed among the trees. Altogether, the King had no luck on
this expedition.

In the evening the company sat at table. They were lodged
in the house of a laird with large estates in the neighbourhood,
who gave himself out as a devoted adherent of the Queen. The
Queen recounted her good fortune in the chase.

Her husband, by her side, occupied himself in drinking. Suddenly, he struck the table. "Well, my Queen, *revanche* tomorrow! We shall ride like the devil."

But his wife shook her head. "Ah, my Lord, to begin with, I
don't like riding like the devil."

He drew himself up. "What of that, my dear? You have been ten weeks on your legs now."

She looked at him, obliquely, with a significant smile. He did not take her meaning. Bending over to him, she said in a low tone, "It may be, though, that I am so far again." He stared at her. Flushing a deep red, but still smiling, she shrugged her shoulders. He smote the table again, so that his cup danced, and going so red that it looked as though the blood were about to burst through his clear complexion, he cried: "Well, what about it? We'll make another if this one goes wrong!" The whole table fell quiet for an instant. Queen Mary sat bolt upright, her eyes shut, pressing the edges of the table with the fingers of both hands. Her lips looked like a thread of scarlet. Then, almost under her breath, and without moving, she said: "You repeat yourself, my lord; I know this turn of yours."

At this, the host interposed, and turning to the King, said: "Pardon, Your Grace. Leaving everything else out, this is no Christian speech."

"So?" the King laughed, with angry contempt: "Mares are better to ride after they are covered."

As if on a flash, the men felt for their daggers, to fall on the man, half drunk as he was.

The Queen rose. "I shall go to rest at once. I am tired," she said. She took her husband's arm. "My Lord, you will accompany me." Her tone compelled obedience.

★

Next day Queen Mary gave orders to depart for Edinburgh, and took her husband with her thither. She rode up with him to the Castle, and brought the little Prince with her thence, since she intended taking him to Stirling. The Earl and Countess of Mar were to guard him there and answer for his life and well-being. Five hundred lances marched with his litter. Behind them rode his two parents. When the drawbridge of Stirling fell down again after the train had passed over it,

Queen Mary gave a deep sigh. "Now at last I can be at rest from all great anxiety about the child."

The King remained in Stirling. His father was to come to him there.

★

Queen Mary rode back to Edinburgh. Holyrood seemed still, to her, to lie under a curse. Extensions were made to her residence in the fortress. The court, therefore, in so far as there was room for it, occupied the house belonging to the royal Exchequer. This was a comfortable and extensive building, distinguished by the possession of a large garden at the back on to which the Queen's rooms looked. The garden appeared larger than it really was, owing to the fact that it was only divided from another by a wicker fence. This second garden belonged to a well-to-do and distinguished savant named David Chalmers, who enjoyed the close friendship of many gentlemen of the court, and in particular of the Earl of Bothwell.

Queen Mary passed two days in the Chequer house, closely occupied with business, visits, deputations, and sittings of the Privy Council.

Early on the third day an extraordinary event took place, of which, however, few were cognizant.

Mistress Mary Fleming, who had accompanied her Queen to Edinburgh, and to the Chequer house, woke up in sudden terror from her sleep, and sitting upright in bed, still under the influence of her fears, asked herself, Was she still dreaming? Her heart beat with painful irregularity. About her all was still dark. But was not something rattling at the door, and crying out, in horrible agony? Suddenly, she was broad awake. She had recognized the voice of the Queen, imploring admission, piteously. She leaped from her bed to push back the bolt and throw open the door. There stood the Queen, in the dark passage, quite alone, barefooted and wrapped in her fur cloak, which she held drawn round her with both hands. "And you bolt yourself in, you bolt yourself in," she stammered, again and again, while her teeth chattered.

The astonished girl drew her mistress into the room. "But I always do that," she said, almost mechanically, her fear passing into horror as the Queen, breaking into cries and sobs, threw herself on her breast. "What is it? what is it?" asked Mary Fleming, again and again. But the Queen hung, as though broken, on her arm. At last, indeed, it seemed as though she were fainting—Mary Fleming only caught her in the nick of time. She bore her to a chair, fetched her fur quilt from her bed and her cloak and wrapped them round the Queen, who was trembling in every limb. But Mary only wept; then, after a while, drew up her knees, bent herself over them, and sobbed drearily. Her hair hung in disorder. Mary Fleming stood, and did not know what to do. She had often seen her mistress weep, with rage, in strong excitement, in helplessness, or even in order to make an impression or get her own way. But this was the crying out of an utterly desperate creature. A thought came to the maid of honour: "Was the King with you?" On this, however, the Queen raised her hand with a gesture of such grim repulsion that her friend relapsed into anxious silence. She thought: "My God, my gracious God, how is this unhappy marriage going to end?" Her question, and the fact that she was aware of the presence of another human being, had however recalled the Queen to consciousness of herself. She sat up, and drawing her friend to her, clung to her, burying her face in her breast. As she did so, her cloak fell off, and Mary Fleming saw that her nightgown was torn in front, and hung in rags.

At last she bore the Queen to her bed, where she lay, her eyes closed, her hands stiffly pressed against her sides, as though she sought to compel herself to immobility. Now and then a bitter sob still broke from her. The maid went up and down, quietly, engaged in dressing herself. Coming near to the bed, in order to fetch something, she looked down at the Queen; as she gazed at the rigidity of that face, frozen in its despair and resolution, her heart turned within her. The Queen felt her eyes and turned her face away as though in pain.

In Mary Fleming's heart a prayer went up—"Turn it to

good, merciful God! Ah, why dost Thou love her so little? Very harshly hast thou always dealt with her!"

At last, the Queen seemed really to have fallen asleep. For a long time, Mary Fleming remained quite quiet. When her mistress at last awaked, her friend brought her breakfast, went to her, sat on her bed, fed her and looked after her. The Queen was much exhausted, nevertheless she ate and drank a little. In a low tone, with her eyes cast down, she said: "It is possible that it was a ghost." Her voice sank still further, and she whispered: "It must have been a ghost." The caresses of her friend she could not endure, and rebuffed every attempt at them. She wanted to get up, she said, and seemed still utterly distraught.

On the morning of this same day, she gave orders that her palace should, at once, be made ready for the transference of the court thither. As reason for so sudden a resolve, she said that it was impossible to stay in the Chequer house with so many people.

With her sister Argyle by her side, she entered Holyrood for the first time since the night of the murder. At every spot which had become so terribly full of meaning for her, she paused. The torn hangings had been replaced by new, the bloody covers had all been taken away. By Mary's bed there was now a carpet, where before there had been bare flooring.

The Queen stood, staring down at it. Then she turned away. "New boards must be put in," she said, tonelessly.

In Mary's sitting-room the sisters sat down side by side in the embrasure of the window. The Queen leaned forward, her head supported on her hand, her elbows on her knees. As time passed, and she still said nothing, still sat without moving, the Countess of Argyle ventured to lay a hand on her, in gentle caress. Mary started, with a look of such astonishment, of such unnatural shock, that her sister's heart ached to see it.

"My darling Marie, what is it?"

The Queen panted in the extremity of her fear. "It is only . . . only . . ." She broke down, sobbing bitterly, and covering her face with her hands. "Everything is lost, for ever lost.

This is the end. I want to die. I want to live not a day longer. I must be dead." She raised her voice in complaint: "Every one, every one has betrayed me and put shame upon me, and there is no setting it right, and everything is now at an end."

The Countess took her in her arms, and sought to comfort her. "But assuredly you will yet triumph over them all, indeed you will."

"No. No one recovers from what I have been through. . . . This is the end, and I know that it is the end. It is the end of all things, and I cannot go on living." Then, after a pause: "When I am here, now, in these rooms—I have been so fond of them, and I had arranged everything here, just as I like, and it all pleased me. But now I feel David's fingers clutching at my dress all the time, tearing at it, as he did in fear of death." She shook all over, with burning anger. "And he, he," she went on, more quickly, "held me with all his strength, and I fought with him, and I wanted to come to David's aid, and I was in my sixth month . . . Never, never can I forget it, never. And everywhere I feel that coarse fellow, that Lindsay, daring to lay his hands on me in his impudence—I feel it wherever I go, wherever I stand here!" She stretched her clenched hands out before her: her upper lip lifted to show her teeth, as she hissed, "God, only let them come into my hands one day!" She went on: "Never shall I forgive them my having had to enter into pacts with them. Their forcing me to that. He! No, I shall never forget it."

Far into the night, she walked restlessly up and down her room, and in the morning rose from her bed as though she were opening her eyes to nothing but torment.

At last she spoke of going, earlier than she had planned, into the provinces, to Jedburgh. Perhaps, she said, she should feel better there, and see more clearly. Then, passionately, she cast this plan aside again. All the time, her mood was dark, irritable. Those about her approached apprehensively.

Then she received a letter from her father-in-law.

For several months now her mind had been hostile to the

old Earl of Lennox. She spoke of him as the arch-coward, the man who breathed only in an air of black treachery to his King and country. She said that, after having utterly destroyed his son by bringing him up to a fawning humility, he was now employing every devilish art to stir him up against his wife and against any kind of rational order. "It is this odious old hypocrite, and he alone, who has filled the King's head with the mad notion that he is the sole legitimate lord not of my land only—oh, no: so wise and modest a cavalier is not satisfied with that —England too is the least that he must have in addition: that is to say, the entire British Isles. Yes, and as for refusing him the Crown Matrimonial—that is not merely an act of wilfulness that cries aloud to Heaven: it is an act of violence. Towards a wife who rejects with scorn so just and reasonable a proposal, there can, of course, be no talk of love. Not even of the simplest sense of duty! Oh, yes, we know it all!"

The Earl of Lennox had fled with the other conspirators after the night of murder. But he had dared to remain in Scotland. The Queen, however, rejected with loathing any proposal that she should allow him to appear before her.

Now a messenger from him, a young man named Robert Cunningham, stood before her. Mary said to him: "I should have thought that your master and I were finished with one another. At least until I had resolved on giving a sign of a changed mind towards him."

The messenger could only look embarrassed and indicate the letter he had brought.

Queen Mary opened and read:

"With the utmost humility I salute Your Majesty and beg earnestly for forgiveness if I permit myself, in the great trouble of my heart, to intrude upon Your Majesty with a very grave and evil matter. But it has seemed to me as though the King, my son, in pursuit of all sorts of unhappy notions in his mind, were reaching singular determinations—for example, a plan of leaving Scotland: and the ship is already there in the harbour of Glasgow, and I think that he intends, in the first instance, to visit the courts of Paris and Rome. Inasmuch as it was impossible for me to make sure whether Your Majesty were fully informed of such plans, which, in another event, such as, however, is quite impossible, would represent a very heavy misfortune for the realm of Scotland—for the King, my unhappy son, himself; for me, as his father; and, in the end, also for Your Majesty—I felt that it was necessary to my own peace of mind that I should convey this intelligence, earnestly begging Your Majesty, at the same time, to forgive me if in so doing I have ventured to communicate something for whose prevention Your Majesty has already long ago taken the best possible measures."

Mary felt, as she read this letter, as though all the blows of fate that had fallen upon her hitherto were but vain imaginations. Now came the truth, stood before her and said—Here I am. And from now on, you have got to live with me. And something within her said: I knew it, and yet, in spite of all, I know now that I had nevertheless not believed in it. And for a moment, she felt as though she must recoil in horror from herself, as from a creature chosen out by God for such misery that, if the world knew the depths of her wretchedness, it must, centuries hence, still shudder at it. And her thought went on: and I have never believed it, and yet I know what I have lived through already!

She rose from the seat in the window, where she had received the messenger, and moved as though aimlessly to the table, where she stood, lost in thought and at the same time like a person broken from within.

★

Half an hour later, royal messengers were hastening through the town summoning all the members of the Privy Council who could be reached to come to a meeting. There came the Earls of Murray, Argyle, Atholl, Caithness and Huntly; the Archbishop of St. Andrews, who was a Hamilton; the Bishop of Galloway, a Gordon; John Leslie, the Bishop of Ross; the Protestant Bishop Adam Bothwell, of Orkney; Lord Rothes; Lord Lethington, whom the Queen, she had forgiven him, had reinstated in his previous offices, for good or ill, since she had no other of his capacity. The French King's Ambassador, M. du Croc, was also called. The only missing member of the Council was the Earl of Bothwell. Five days ago he had marched to the southern provinces, to Jedburgh.

Queen Mary laid her father-in-law's letter before the Council. At first, the Lords were inclined to doubt. The Earl of Lennox' exasperation against the Queen and her counsellors was only too well known: might he not have sought to create disturbance by news that at least was exaggerated? Queen Mary, however, replied: That she now recalled certain dark hints of her husband's, to which, at the time, she had paid no particular heed. Now they left no room for doubt that the letter spoke truth. She brought a note from her husband to herself, in which it was written that he was going, and going very far, and the Queen as well as her counsellors would yet hear enough of him.

Embarrassed, the Lords looked in each other's pale faces. This certainly was very bad. The Queen reported what she had decided to do. They sat long, deliberating. Hours passed before they dispersed.

On the evening of the same day, a page came to the palace, to the Queen. She recognized him at once: he came from her husband. The youth announced: His Majesty was before the palace. But he would not enter in any circumstances so long as his deadly enemies, from whose murderous attacks he was not safe for a moment, were there—Murray, Argyle, Rothes, and Maitland of Lethington.

Queen Mary reflected for a moment. Then, accompanied only by the page, she went down into the court of the palace. On this side of the gate, but only just by the first barricade, stood her husband. Dismounted, he was leaning by his horse, near the wall, striking regularly with his riding whip against the leggings of his riding boots, and whistling the while: near him were several squires, still on horseback. Queen Mary looked out over the square in front of the palace; on the far side, one or two women were passing, otherwise it was quite empty; then she looked at her husband, at his would-be bored, but really uneasily nervous and defiant demeanour; and controlled herself so far as to step up to him, saying gently: "Will you not come into the palace with me, my Lord." With his back turned to the entrance to the palace, he had not seen his wife's approach; now he swung round, and, utterly taken aback, stared at her with popping eyes. Inwardly trembling, she had enough control over herself to go quite close up to him, with an encouraging and complaisant smile, and, taking him by the hand, say: "Come, my Lord!" Dumbfounded, he followed her into the palace, and so up to her own apartments. There were hardly any servants there, and none of her intimate suite. The Queen asked her husband, as he was divesting himself of his cloak, whether he had already had supper? On his confused reply, that he did not know, she ordered it to be sent up for him and her alone, and then served him with her own hands. It was late when the meal was over, for they did not hurry at all. Rising, Mary took her husband's arm, as though, as a matter of course, to lead him into her bedchamber with her. In the silence of the night, when she thought that he was calmer and more approachable, she said to him softly, Why had he thought of going away from Scotland? What could have been his reason for so gross an injury? Although, hitherto, he had dully let everything be as his wife found good, at this question he seemed to go suddenly rigid with anger.

Mary sat up in bed: "Tell me what offends you so much."

He lay stiff as a doorpost, and merely laughed aloud.

"If you speak, it may perhaps be altered," she said, in despair.

"Tell me another!" he replied, scornfully. She wanted to go on speaking, but he turned away.

"I want to rest! I want to sleep! I don't want to hear any more! Tomorrow, I go back to Stirling."

He pretended to be asleep. Mary listened to the hours striking: first the delicate beat of the clock in her dressing-room: then the heavy boom of the towers in the town, among which she could distinguish the different tones of the various churches —most distinct being that of St. Giles, the Cathedral. When she saw that her husband was really asleep, she gave way to her tears. It was towards morning before sleep came to her, and when, in the early hours, she awoke, she was alone.

The King had gone down the winding stair to his own apartments. There he began rummaging among his things. His servants and pages were, he said, to make ready to ride back to Stirling with him forthwith. He had hardly finished his breakfast when the door was thrown open: "Her Majesty the Queen!"

Mary came in, but not alone: she was accompanied by all the Lords of the Council who had been present at yesterday's session, and the French Ambassador was likewise with them. Henry Darnley, who had sprung to his feet, stood beside his table, his face puckered, his eyes drooping, as though rooted to the ground. The others ranged themselves in a semicircle about him. The least embarrassed among them was Leslie, Bishop of Ross, since he had practically never had to do with the King. To him, therefore, the word was assigned on this occasion. He began by saying that the reason for this visit on the part of the Lords of the Privy Council was that, with all due humility and respect, they desired to be informed as to the truth of the news conveyed to Her Majesty by the Earl of Lennox, to the effect that His Majesty the King had formed a determination to leave the kingdom by sea: and, if so, what reasons had induced the King to come to such a decision? The Bishop paused: every one looked at the King. Clutching with his fist at the dagger he had buckled on in readiness for departure, he remained silent, his eyes still on the ground. The Bishop resumed, Were such a determination on the King's part

due to any dissatisfaction on his side, they were all here, to ask
with deep concern, who could have given him grounds for dissatisfaction? "If Your Majesty can complain of any of your
subjects, then, no matter who he may be, the fault shall be
unconditionally repaired." The King made no reply. "Your
Majesty's honour, the honour of Her Highness the Queen,
your exalted Sovereign and consort, are involved in this! Let
Your Majesty reflect: You desire to depart from here, you
desire to leave your exalted consort, to whom you owe a debt
of gratitude so great that it can never be repaid, who, your
Sovereign, has nevertheless condescended to be your wife! Believe us, you will, if you execute your plans, accomplish nothing save that you will be stigmatized by the whole world as
thankless and undeserving of the place to which you have been
raised by the goodness of Her Majesty. Once again, however—
if you have been given any just ground of complaint—and it
must be some grave matter which can have caused such a
thought to form as that of leaving so lovely and exalted a wife,
and such a flourishing kingdom! And it must be to be sought
either in Her Majesty the Queen herself, or in us, faithful
servants of the State! We are entirely ready to do all that may
be in our power to grant Your Majesty satisfaction. Her
Majesty, assuredly, is so far from having afforded any opportunity for dissatisfaction that, on the contrary, the man whom
her goodness raised to the rank of her consort has every reason
in the world to thank God for such a virtuous and affectionate
wife as Her Majesty has proved herself in all her dealings."

The King remained obstinately silent. The Queen then, coming close up to him, appealed to him:

"My Lord, you were not willing to open your heart to me
when we were alone. Therefore I must beg you, in the presence
of these lords, to say to me—How have I ever injured you?"
She went on, more quickly, with a voice that shook, scarlet
patches appearing on her cheeks, and her eyes sparkling: "My
Lord, my conscience is entirely clear! Never in my whole life
have I done anything that could be contrary to your honour

or to mine! And if, unintentionally—God in His truth is my witness, and may He stand by me in truth—if, contrary to my intention, I have injured you, I will do whatever you may wish to make good! If only you will not conceal from me what has made you turn from me so completely! Pray do not spare me in any way." She tried to take his hand, but he clutched the hilt of his dagger with it the more firmly, to keep her off. Shaking, glowing, threatening, Mary stood before him: "Think, my Lord, think! You know not what you do!" Her gaze compelled him to turn: under its magnetic power, he raised his eyes to her for the first time, only to drop them again immediately. In those eyes there was nothing but an immovable vanity and a hint of something like triumph—he would show them, these sapient, tongue-twisting lords, who imagined that they could put everything on earth to rights by their words, he would show them that all their pains and cleverness was wasted on him. "Can I not desire to travel?" he produced, at last, his voice brittle, as though his throat were parched. "I am young: I wish to see foreign countries."

"True, but not secretly, without Her Majesty's knowledge," said Bishop Leslie. The King shrugged his shoulders contemptuously. "Your Majesty must understand," the Bishop went on, now seriously perturbed—the urgency of the Queen's manner had shown them all that she was in earnest: this was no question of a mere demonstration designed to put the King to shame—"Your Majesty must understand—here are we all, Her Highness, your exalted consort, we, her servants, the most important and noblest of the State, and we are all ready to meet any reasonable demand of Your Majesty in the most generous spirit."

M. du Croc, the French Ambassador, intervened at this point, representing to the King that if he were to present his complaints at the foreign courts, his reception would be by no means so distinguished as he seemed to expect.

Maitland of Lethington desired to speak, to set out the position of the Privy Council more fully, and half turning to the

French Ambassador, he began, in the French language: "Such an opportunity . . ." when the King interrupted him.

"My Lord of Lethington, your French is too good for me!"

When Maitland sought to continue in Scots, the King again interrupted. He had no time, he must be off, he said peevishly. Turning to his wife, "Madame, you will not have to bear with me much longer!" He bowed to the French Ambassador, waved his beret to the others, "Adieu, sirs!" and was gone out of the room.

That evening he sent a letter to the Queen, from a village near Edinburgh, in which he said that, if she really had no suspicion as to why he felt himself injured, where was the position she had promised him, which was to make him honoured above all others in the realm, as she had begun to make him at the beginning? and, second, nobody took the least heed of him: the nobles positively avoided him: it was unendurable.

Mary replied to these lines in a letter which she sent to Stirling, whither the King had gone. If she had not raised him higher, he had himself, not her, to thank. In the beginning, she had heaped so many honours upon him that she began to be anxious herself about it, while the lofty station in which she had set him had merely served as a shelter under whose cover others could carry on their scandalous designs. She would not blame him on that account, but excuse him and assume an attitude of disbelief, were it not that the others perpetually cited him as the head of the whole conspiracy. As for not receiving honourable attendance—had she not put her own servants at his disposition?

"When the nobles come to court, either on business, or to show their respect, they turn to him who shows them a friendly face. Have you, my Lord, ever taken the trouble to do that? On the contrary, you forbade your room to the nobles whom I nominated to wait upon you! Meet them with good will, make an effort at least to be sociable and amiable, I beg of you. Otherwise it will remain beyond human power, and certainly beyond mine, to settle this point to your satisfaction, and the nobles will never be disposed to place the conduct of any sort of business in your hands."

To which the King replied that he saw how superfluous he was; he should certainly leave Scotland; if the French rejected him, there must, somewhere, be a little place for him. As for the conspiracy against David, he was not guilty, but only Lethington, who envied David, and, with him, the Earl of Murray, who had bound himself by oath to the Queen of England to compass the death of him, Henry Darnley. If his consort had the smallest real concern for him and his welfare, those men would long ago have been beheaded, as the Pope expected them to be, instead of which they were first in favour and grace —a favour and a grace which they enjoyed at his, the King's expense.

★

The Queen rode with James Murray to Jedburgh. After a state entry into the town, which brought children, men, women and old folk out into the streets to see the Queen, Mary dismounted before an old, fortified dwelling-house, where she was to lodge for the duration of the Courts of Justice. As she was about to take up her quarters, she asked for news of the Earl of Bothwell's campaign in the mountains. She was informed that numerous bodies of prisoners had already been sent up for judgment by the Earl, and further detachments of them were daily expected. While the Provost of Jedburgh was making report to this effect to his Sovereign, James Murray entered the room, bringing with him a man apparently of low degree. The dust and dirt with which he was caked, and the obvious exhaustion of his bearing, showed plainly that he had ridden long and far through wild country.

"What is this?" asked the Queen, with no great concern.

"Your Majesty, this man comes from the Earl of Bothwell."

"Yes?" Her tone was quite indifferent: then, suddenly, an uncontrollable impatience seemed to master her. "What is the matter? what is it? what is it? Speak, speak!"

At last the man managed to get some words out. "Yes," he said, "and his lordship, the Earl of Bothwell, sends me, and I am to say to Your Majesty, and the Earl sends his humble duty, and I am to report that he has been killed by the robber Elliot."

"But it is not true!" cried the Queen, instantly. She gripped hard on to the pocket hanging at her belt, while her eyes darted like lightning between her brother and the man, and her face went as white as a peeled wand. "But it is not true?" she repeated, with a sort of laugh, again looking first at her brother, and then at the man. Then, suddenly, springing up from her seat, she shrieked at the fellow: "Speak, speak! Are you daft?"

"In any event, the Earl has been wounded, eh?" interposed Lord James, addressing the dazed messenger.

"Yes," replied the man, relieved.

"Who is this robber Elliot?" asked the Queen. "I never heard of a robber Elliot."

"He hacked the Earl thrice on his body, on his head, and on his breast and on his hand, and my Lord the Earl says by now he is probably dead."

Impatiently shrugging her shoulders, Mary looked over to her brother again. "I can make no sense of this clown's chatter," she said.

Murray again took a hand. "So, his lordship has been attacked by this robber, Elliot, and, anyhow, severely wounded. He himself thought his wound was mortal, and he gave you instructions to come here to Jedburgh to Her Majesty and report—my Lord lays his humble duty before Her Majesty, and believes that, by the time you have got here, he will be no longer alive? Is that right?"

"Yes," replied the man.

"I managed to gather so much, at the last," said the Queen, very irritably. "But is the Earl dead, or no?" she asked the messenger.

"I do not know," he replied awkwardly.

Lord James seemed to have lost interest in the affair. The Queen moved towards the window; the man stood, in the centre of the room, turning his cap about in his hands. Lord James busied himself with the papers on the table. The Provost of Jedburgh had been summoned away, some time back. The messenger looked helplessly at the Earl of Murray, as though to ask whether he ought to go, or no. "Her Majesty will have all sorts of questions to put you," said Lord James, in an undertone.

The Queen came back from the window. "Where did the attack take place?" she asked, in a calmer voice. "Not in the Hermitage?"

"Oh, no," said the man. "On the heath, or near by."

"What on earth does he mean?" said the Queen, wrinkling her brows again.

"By the heath he probably means the woods. You mean, it was in the woods?"

"Yes."

"Were you there?" asked Mary.

"Yes."

"My God, speak then, speak!"

The man started to narrate, and, at last, something like the outline of a story began to emerge from his vague and discursive circumlocutions, though the Earl of Murray had again and again to interpose, to disentangle the thread, bring him back to the point, and explain expressions unintelligible to the Queen. Its gist was as follows: The Earl of Bothwell had been engaged in daily expeditions against the lost and dangerous characters lurking in the woods, heaths and marshes of the Debatable Land, fugitives from Scotland and from England. Those who were not slain in the course of the hunt were captured and sent to Jedburgh for trial. Finally, on a last round-up, the Earl had ridden out after one of the chiefs of these robbers, a man named Elliot. He pursued him right over the marshy heath. Both the Earl and his quarry rode at such a headlong

288

pace that the Earl left his small body of followers far behind. At last the robber, seeing that he could no longer hope to escape his pursuer, turned on his horse, still galloping forward, to shout to the Earl that he would give himself up if he were promised his life. The Earl shouted back: "Right gladly, my friend, and freedom to boot. But unfortunately you must come before the Queen's Court first." By now, they were on the verge of a copse, and the robber slid, swift as a streak of lightning, off his horse, to take to the trees; if he could reach the thickets, he would be practically safe against pursuit. Aware of this risk, Bothwell fired his pistols after him, then, overtaking him with a few bounds of his horse, he too leapt off and was stretching out his arms to seize the man when he stumbled over a fallen tree-stump. He raised his arms to save his balance, but in vain: he came crashing down with such force that he lost consciousness for an instant. Immediately the robber was on top of him: struck at him, as he lay, thrice, as the messenger reported, with his short sword, wounding him in the chest, hand and head. The shock of the blows brought the Earl to his senses again; gathering himself together with a mighty effort, he drew his dagger and drove it with fearful force into the robber's breast, once, and again; the man sank back, dying. Then the Earl again lost consciousness. When his people came up, they washed his wounds and bandaged them as best they could. He roused himself to command them to bury the dead robber at once, on the spot where he lay, and bring himself to his own castle, the Hermitage, that he might die there—he was done for. He had sent the messenger to the Queen from the field where he lay. Beyond this, the man knew nothing, save that the Earl's men had carried him off on a bier.

Next morning, Mary opened the Courts, and sat like a blanched goddess among the men, with an expression that did not promise any amplitude of mercy. The French Ambassador had accompanied her, that he might survey these wild and singular regions on an occasion which promised him a profound insight into the nature of their inhabitants; he came to express his sympathy with her in the accident that had befallen the Earl of Bothwell. He understood perfectly what the loss of so brave and resolute a leader must mean for Her Majesty, but hoped that the worst might yet be happily averted. The Queen replied in monosyllables, though politely. At midday, a second messenger came from the Earl of Bothwell. He was still alive, though still in danger. The man reported that the Earl had not been able to go direct to his own Castle. During his absence, the vagrants, who were held in the castle until enough of them were assembled for an armed train, had broken their prison. The messenger said that it was the Earl's own fault that this had happened, since he had always refused to have the fellows strung up singly. Now, however, when the squires approached, bringing their wounded lord, they found the castle in the hands of the prison-breakers, who yelled out of the windows that there was no admission, the castle now belonged to them, and they were only to be driven out by force. While the men stood about the bier on which their lord lay, not knowing what to do, he roused himself, although he fell from one fainting fit into another, and every breath he drew was anguish, and said: The squires were to say to the vagrants, in his name, that he must come into the castle, there was nothing else for it. Those within should not be such fools as to try force against him: they knew perfectly well that there could be no talk of holding the place; if they were reasonable now, he would let them go free; it was to their own interest to have and keep him as their friend. So the men actually went through the outer gate, and the Earl was able to be brought under a roof and put to bed. He was fevered and wandering when the messenger left him.

For seven days the Queen presided over the Assize in Jedburgh. She did not use extreme measures, but imposed fines in most cases. News came daily from the Earl of Bothwell, reporting his gradual recovery. After the close of the Assize, the Queen intended going to other towns, where judgments were to be pronounced. Everything was ready for the move when, on

the evening of the day fixed for departure, the Queen came to
her brother, and said to him she wanted to give her suite a rest
after the heavy fatigues of the sessions.

"We do not need to start till the day after tomorrow," she
said, "I have worked it out." Earl Murray stood in doubt.
"And I should like to use this day," she went on, "to ride to the
Hermitage. I must speak personally with the Earl of Bothwell
—that has become clear to me in these last few days. Without
his reports and findings, our hands are tied. He is the only
person who knows, in the sense in which it concerns us, I mean.
Everybody in the town thinks in terms of his own pocket only.
The Earl cannot come to us; so there is nothing for it but for
us to visit him."

Lord James was intensely astonished. "Your Majesty, it is
an immense ride; the Hermitage is a very long way off."

"I know it is a pretty long way," she replied, "but the Earl's
messengers always manage it in half a day. We ride as well as
they do." She had worked it all out. "We need only take a
very small party. You will come with me. You would not let
me ride alone, would you?" she said, with a rather painful
smile, looking straight at her brother. The slight, almost imperceptible twitching of her fine dark eyebrows, and the constant change of her colour, the red patches on her cheeks, high
up, under the ears, showed him that she would never be moved
from her purpose. "Certainly not," he said; "but, Your Majesty, it is my duty to draw your attention to the fact that this
ride lies through the most dangerous territory!"

"Yes, yes, but no one knows about it. So, tomorrow morning
early," she said, indifferently: once she had got her way, she
seemed suddenly to have gone limp. "We must start before
daybreak," she added, "for the days are already all too short,
and if we don't, we shall not get back by evening." She was
gone.

Her brother looked after her. They would have to start in
the dark and return in the dark: they would have to follow a
fearful and uncertain track, through a wilderness, through

virgin forests and morasses, through a region swarming with
fugitives from both countries, in which hundreds of violent men
had been roused to a passionate lust for revenge by the recent
Assize sentences; there was no saying what might not befall,
were the slightest rumour of the Queen's intentions to get
about. The Earl shuddered at the prospect. He went to his
sister's room, only to be informed by the waiting woman that
he could not possibly be announced. Her Majesty was already
alseep; she had given the strictest orders that she was not to
be disturbed, since tonight she was certainly going to sleep,
whereas in the previous nights she had hardly closed an eye.
The Earl, much perturbed, returned to his own room. His
sister's mood seemed to him to be such that she would think
nothing of dismissing him with scornful laughter, if he ventured
to oppose her. He asked himself what the meaning of this ride
might be? Was it no more than a wild humour? For weeks, now,
the Queen had grown steadily more difficult to deal with. James
Murray sighed and thought, as he had thought so many times
before in this unhappy time, "This ill-starred marriage with
that creature—what is to come of it all?"

They rode. James Murray knew that his sister was a superb
horsewoman. She had chosen Stella, a bay mare, accounted the
best horse in the kingdom. Murray knew that, if it came to it,
Mary could beat any man. In an advanced state of pregnancy,
after the most appalling experiences, she had ridden half the
night from Edinburgh to Dunbar, and when her male companions, who had suffered none of the shocks she had gone
through, fell exhausted from their horses, she had at once called
for messengers to be ready to take the letters she was that
moment going to write. The Earl therefore knew that he would
need all his strength for this ride. But this wild chase right
across the moors seemed to him sheer madness. The Queen said
nothing; she pushed right ahead of them all; her black habit,
very plainly cut, clung close to the lines of her slender figure;
she wore a small black beret on her golden hair, closely plaited

round her head. Every line of her form and of her proud head seemed rigid with inflexible will. She rode on and on, never pausing, only now and then, as though unconsciously, taking her handkerchief to remove the spots of mud that splashed from Stella's hooves right up into her face. At last James Murray ventured to draw near her. It was impossible to keep up such a mad pace. She turned to him, at the sound of his voice, when he had drawn close up beside her, and her face wore a smile that positively frightened him, as he met those dark eyes looking at him, half unaware, half contemptuous, out of her dead white face. He did not know whether she had understood what he had said. "Your Majesty must ride more slowly," he commanded in a decided tone, pointing, as he did so, to the others, panting after them. She nodded dully, but the Earl had to speak again, and more pressingly, before she came out of her remoteness and replied: "Very well—let us ride more slowly."

A flight of crows flew screaming in front of them, going sideways across the landscape. Otherwise, there was nothing: only the shaggy heath and the sky overhead, and, far in the distance, a dark line of wood. The way ran, almost invisible, through the uniform grey of the dead grass. Murray thought how they would have to return this way, in the evening, when at best it would be all half dark, and muttered to himself, "God's will be done." And he thought that were the Queen to be attacked here—and there was no protection against that save the secrecy of her ride—every one in Scotland would say that her brother had led her into this adventure. She was riding again as fast as before, but this time he did not attempt to stay her.

At midday they reached the Earl's moorland fortress, which lay before them, greyish brown, like some natural monster that had grown out of the barren land about it, uniform in its colouring and its wretchedness with everything that here surrounded it. At the windows—hardly windows, merely cracks for shooting out of—faces appeared: as the little train approached, the drawbridge was drawn up with a rattle; some squires, all of whom knew the Queen, rushed out to the entrance. Before any one could help her, Mary was out of the saddle and throwing her reins to a boy.

"Give her a good feed and rub her well down," she said. Then, gathering up her habit for walking, she asked: "Where is the Earl?"

A boy led her up the winding stair and through a narrow passage. "His lordship is going on well?"

"Yes, quite well," the man replied, "though he is still in his bed, the Earl. It was a bad affair. At first, we thought we should never manage it, I mean with his lordship."

The Queen smiled. "Is the Earl very impatient?"

"No," said the squire, "he was always very reasonable."

A door opened. "Here, Your Majesty." They stood alone by the door: Earl James was some way behind. The Queen hesitated before entering, and said at last, "His lordship knows . . . ?"

"Yes, Your Majesty."

Then, all at once, she crossed the threshold; at the first step, the train of her habit fell over her feet: she took a firmer hold of it with her left hand, which also held her riding whip. So, she slowly approached the sick-bed. She had recovered her self-possession; in an easy, upright pose, her cheeks slightly flushed, she stood beside the couch, on which he raised himself. His head, his breast and his arm were closely bandaged; but his demeanour, and all that could be seen of his face below the broad bandage over his forehead, showed that his breath was almost taken away by such a mark of distinction as this visit.

"Your Majesty!" he stammered: and seemed unable to get any further than a repetition of the words—"Your Majesty!"

"Yes, my Lord," said the Queen, holding his free hand in hers, and bending down as though to look at the wounded man. Then, straightening herself, "You may well be astonished. I can well believe that you did not expect us here. Yes, really, I have come the whole way, in one ride, and we have flown as though the Evil One were at Stella's heels. But, my Lord, what can one do?" She gave a rather bitter little smile. "I had to see after you, my most, most loyal servant, the one and only on whom I can always rely." Her mouth quivered as though with pain. She looked about her, for a seat: the squire, who waited at the door, attended to her at once. The Queen sat down.

"Yes, that is how it is," she repeated. She was silent; he too was silent, in wretched embarrassment. Without turning her head, her eyes indicated the man at the door; the Earl, comprehending, dismissed him to see that the best there was in the place was made ready for a meal for Her Majesty.

When they were alone, Mary said: "My Lord, it can neither be altered now, or undone. Now, there is nothing left but to accept it and make the best of it. That is the only thing that I can see. Torment—yes, that assuredly I have been through. I cannot have you beheaded. I cannot drive you away again: after all, I have nobody but you." She raised her eyes, and looked away from him, up at a little wood-cut, representing an armed man on horseback, fastened on to the wall opposite to her with four little nails. Drearily, she added: "For my own sake, too, I have got to be silent. You thought it all well out. But that you would do this atrocious thing to me—that I should never have believed, nor did I deserve it at your hands."

The man felt that the earth ought to open and swallow him. Sweat poured from him, from every pore. "Your Majesty!" he groaned. "Oh, God, my God!" Anguish wrung him; he could only repeat, "For God's sake!" and bring out, in a broken voice, "Truly, it has haunted me: I have thought, all this time, when I seemed to be dying, that this was why, and I could not get any word to you to tell you how I felt, but I thought that you would think so too—and so, in truth, it is . . . Your Majesty!" His voice broke, as he appealed to her, hoarsely, "Your Majesty! . . ."

She raised her hand, to stay him. "Silence, silence, silence! . . . There is nothing to be said. Silence!" In a different tone, she added, "My brother Murray is with me. He will be coming in, now."

"But Your Majesty will pass the night here? True it is not very . . ."

"Impossible. Many thanks. I have come in the midst of my journey. Tomorrow, I must go on with it: the day after tomorrow, I must be on the heights of Berwick." She turned again to him, pressingly: "You are not going to die?"

"I think not, for the moment anyhow," he replied.

Again, they were both silent. Mary sat, bending her riding whip backwards and forwards across her knees. He lay rigid, staring straight in front of him.

"I think you are still very ill," said the Queen, in a strangely brittle voice, revealing what it was meant to conceal, the furious beating of her heart.

"No, no," he replied, without looking at her. "Really, I am quite all right again." With a smile, he glanced at her. "I am consumed with eagerness to put myself entirely at Your Majesty's service again."

It was her turn to smile. "That is most unpractical of you! To consume yourself, I mean. What use would you be then? And it will not help you to get well quickly. Nor would it suit you. I advise you to leave that."

He laughed. "Well, we shall see what can be done, madame."

"Yes, we shall see."

In the midst of this jesting, her fear came back upon her.

"My Lord," she said, bending over him, her folded hands held out towards him, "and now you will despise me, for not sending you to judgment! But I cannot do it, I cannot. Oh, my Lord, my Lord, why did you do it to me? How could you, how was it possible for you, how did it so much as enter your head to do it to me!"

He raised himself in strong excitement. "Your Majesty, I cannot stand this! I do not know! But this I cannot endure."

She covered her face with her hands. "Oh, my God!" As though for help, she felt for his hand. "Every one is not like that . . . But I will not torment you. . . ." She drew herself up. "Here is my brother." She had heard his step outside.

296

Lord James came in. "Well, my Lord, I hear you are going on splendidly. Her Majesty will be truly glad . . ."

They sat by the bedside, and partook, there, of a light repast.

The Queen, who was not to be moved from her purpose of remaining only for an hour or so, got the Earl to give her a report of his chase after the human monster. His adventures with the robbers who would not let him into his own castle she found comic, so she said. "You were not afraid, for a moment, although you seemed to be wounded to death, were you?" she said. She was very restless, hardly touched the food, soon rose to her feet. "We must be going; the days are very short; you know what the roads are like here. You will soon come after us?" she asked, "to Edinburgh, to the court, to us—won't you?"

She held out her hand to him in leave-taking. "You see, my Lord, I came, after all," she said again. They were alone: Lord James was busy arranging for their departure. "I really thought you were going to die. That was the first news that met me in Jedburgh, your man saying you were dead." She smiled again. "What a clown that was you sent me! He kept on saying, you sent your humble duty but you were already dead." She imitated the man's fashion of speech. "And I screamed at him, awfully. Did he tell you about it?"

He took hold of her hand to kiss it devoutly; she bent and kissed his.

The Queen's party rode back. By afternoon, great clouds had gathered, and then the rain came down in heavy streams. The moor stretched for miles without a house, and the riders were wet to the skin, through all their clothes. A cold wind followed on the rain. The return journey seemed hours longer. At last the Queen rode as though her exhaustion had reached such a pitch that she was a mere dead creature, a thing whose movements were automatic.

Her habit was stiff with mud up to her hips; her face, her

hair stained with the mud that spurted up from the horse's hooves.

Murray, who rode sometimes a little behind his sister, and sometimes close to her side, thought, when in the darkness of the evening there was nothing clearly to be seen, that, every now and then, he heard her heaving a sigh, such a heavy sigh, that he asked her at last whether she were feeling sick. She made no reply. They reached Jedburgh at night. Torches were burning in front of the house in which Mary was to sleep this one night more. All her servants, knights and officers were waiting her in the court.

Stella halted. A knight came forward to assist Mary from the saddle. She fell into his arms, as stiff as though she were frozen: she felt ice cold: her head sank on his shoulder: he did not know whether she was unconscious as he lifted her down or lost consciousness only when she tried to stand.

★

In the October days immediately after her ride to the Hermitage, Queen Mary fell so sick that every one thought she was dying. She sent for the King, but he did not come. The English Government was informed of her state.

Queen Mary was seized by convulsions; there was a green mucus about her mouth; she came out of one fainting fit only to relapse into another. By the fourth day, she was so weak that she lay in bed like one already dead, so shrunk, immobile and waxen white was her aspect. She wished to receive Supreme Unction and prepare herself for her end, she whispered.

All her lords should come to her. They had gathered in the course of the previous day, and all were there, save only the King. Mary looked over them, as they stood before her, as though she were counting them: then turned away her head, without a word. Of her husband she made no mention. Her lips moved incessantly, and she prayed without ceasing, the rosary between her closely folded hands. She said more than once that she was dying in the Catholic faith; they must convey her duty to the Holy Father; if she had had to resist him for the sake of her subjects, nevertheless she was dying his obedient daughter. Then anxiety seized her again; she clasped her rosary, murmuring, "Mary, Blessed Mother of God, All merciful one, have mercy on me, have mercy on me!" she said: "All my fathers and forefathers have died in the Catholic faith; I have not been faithless, oh, no, no." She had the prayers for the dying read to her, and the candles lit at her head, and said to the lords who had gathered about her bed: "I have erred, I have of a surety not troubled as much about my realm as I ought to have done. But God in His mercy will forgive me all my sins." Rising a little as though it hurt her to lie flat, she sighed: "Oh God, oh God, it has never gone very well with me!" Then a faint gleam of happiness crossing her face, "Ah, but once, when I was in France, then it was often good." She turned her eyes to the others: "My husband in France, King François, he really loved me. . . . And my uncles in France are glorious people!" Her eyes began to fail her: "James, my brother," she called to the Earl of Murray, "come here to me."

He approached: she felt for his hand. "Come nearer!" she said, with a touch of the old impatience. He put his hand in hers. "You must swear to me that you will watch over the Prince as though he were your own son. Swear that to me. And swear too that you will let him remain Catholic." She said that she specially commended her son to the Queen of England. "She will be good to him, especially when I am dead: for she really knows perfectly well that he must inherit her kingdom. You must give her my best greetings." And she said to the Ambassador that the French King must not leave her son in the lurch.

Lord James, like every one else, thought that his sister's end was imminent, and gave orders that they should pray in the churches for an easy passing for her. The changes that must follow on the Queen's death were prepared for; Lord James issued exceptional decrees for the preservation of order, in any eventuality. With Lethington, he took a little walk, before the house. The Secretary of State recalled an expression he had himself used years ago, at the time when the Queen's return from France was expected. He had said, then, that he foresaw singular and terrible tragedies, if the young Queen really did come home. He looked out, into the distance. "Truly she has had experience enough," he said, "and now it is all over." And he added: "And she has brought the child into the world."

On the evening which they had all decided was to be that of her death, the Queen recovered, only to fall, a few days later, back into an even more terrible condition; she lay quite unconscious, while coldness and insensibility mounted steadily up to her breast. Then the French physician determined, as a last resort, to rub and shake her all over her body, with the utmost violence. After that, she recovered again, only, again, to relapse as though into death; her eyes closed. But the physician who stood beside her bed, his hand on her pulse, would not abandon his efforts to revive her, even so. Mary's maids of honour declared that he was tormenting their unhappy mistress uselessly: she might at least be allowed to die in peace. He replied that he knew what he was about. At length he told Mary Seaton and Mary Fleming, who, doing all in their power to carry out his instructions, were incessantly, one on either side, kneading the fragile body of the Queen, that her pulse was not as low as might have been expected from her apparent state of collapse; every now and then, it seemed to be making a determined effort to restart; certainly, the struggle between life and death was not yet over. The Queen might be delicate, but in the last resort her constitution was of an amazing toughness. For hours, the women, never sparing themselves, went on with their efforts; when one set were worn out, another took their places; and, at last, it seemed to them as though the almost petrified body were answering to their efforts; the awful cold yielded; and, at long last, the Queen lay there, bathed in sweat, warm, rosy-red, damp all over her body; her unconsciousness passed over into sleep, a sleep out of which she awoke, very weak, but in such a condition that every one realized that, if there were no further change, she would live. She, however, wept when she realized how things stood, and said to Mary Fleming: "Ah, but I think I should have been so glad to die."

★

Meantime, the Earl of Bothwell had arrived in Jedburgh. Although he had still to be carried in a litter, he had, nevertheless, presided at an Assize on the day after the Queen's visit, as was his duty in the case of all but major offences committed in his district. Now, in order once more to offer his services to his Sovereign, he came and stood upright beside the Queen's bed. He had got so far: tomorrow, he said, he would be on horseback again.

"We seem to pay visits to one another in turn," she jested, "finding first one, then the other, lying only just this side of death."

Several days after the decisive turn in her illness, the King too, came to Jedburgh. But as he stood, in a state of defiant helplessness, by his wife's bedside, she could find no friendly word to say to him. "So you have managed to come, my Lord?" —"I could not come before!"—"You have chosen a good moment, for I am still alive!"—For a few minutes, the empty interchange of words went on; then the King remarked that he could see Her Majesty was now better; he had been told that she was nigh death, yet here she was, marvellously recovered, and surrounded by every tenderness—"Not one of your many faithful lords lacking!" It seemed to him that there was nothing for him here; he was, at best, superfluous.

"You ought to know, my Lord," said Mary, looking away from him.

He departed. His wife heard that his horse was brought to him outside, and he had ridden off with a few companions. She knew that he would go to Stirling, or perhaps come to Edinburgh; he would be out at the chase all day long, spend his evenings drinking with young men of low degree, and his nights with his women. Although his rooms were right under

301

hers, weeks would pass without her seeing anything of him.

When her physician came at night, he said, in astonishment, "If Your Highness does not absolutely avoid every kind of excitement, all my pains will be thrown away."—"Ah, my dear master," she moaned, "if you only knew all the things I have got to avoid!"—"Your Majesty must do it. Do you realize how ill you were?"—"Yes, I think so," she said, slyly. It was so pleasant to her to be spoken to so sternly by any one, that she actually found pleasure in thinking of herself.

"Now I am going to live," she said. To spare herself, she stayed another fourteen days in Jedburgh.

★

She had barely recovered her strength when she resumed her tour through the southern provinces. She was accompanied by the Earls of Murray and Huntly, and by Lethington, as well as by the Earl of Bothwell, now quite recovered. They came so far south as to touch English territory. Over there lay the fortress of Berwick, which had originally belonged to Scotland, and then, for many decades, been an apple of grim discord between the two countries, only to be at last for ever lost to England. Its cannon greeted the Queen as she approached the town, and the second in command, representing the chief, the Earl of Bedford, who was at the moment in London, came out of Berwick to bid the Queen of Scotland welcome in his name, in the name of his town and of his whole country and nation. He asked Would not the Queen come nearer, across the border—it was but a step? Together with the first citizens of Berwick, he conducted the Queen round about the town, which she, however, declined to enter; finally, the whole company of Scots and Englishmen stood about the Queen on a hillock, whence the whole town, with all its walls and towers, and the broad stretches of the fertile land beyond, could be discerned. After the Queen had looked and admired sufficiently, the Englishmen conducted her back to the border, with many expressions of the most profound respect, to which she replied with the assurance that, whereas, in the past, the welfare of these two neighbouring countries had been, again and again, nearly destroyed by fearsome wars, she, of a surety, would never, so long as she had any power to impose her will, permit any revival of that horrible conflict.

Slowly, she made her way in the direction of her capital. Wherever she came, there were scenes of overpowering enthusiasm, as though the people did not know how sufficiently to express their sense of what it meant to them that their Queen, who shone above them all like a friendly star in the skies, had not died, had not been snatched from her country. Never had Mary seemed to be so passionately loved by her subjects.

Encouraged by the notably courteous, nay hearty, reception she had had on English soil, Mary's audacity ventured an unheard-of step, an attempt such as had hardly ever been made by any prince. She arrived in Dunbar, her own border fortress-town, and, having already written to Queen Elizabeth, and to her minister Cecil, addressed herself, this time, directly to the Privy Council of the English Crown. In her letter, she said she felt she must personally express to the esteemed lords and dear friends, the nobles of the realm of her good sister, her deep sense of gratitude for the sympathy they had shown her in her severe illness.

She on her part could not have demonstrated the attachment which bound her personally to her neighbour State more clearly than by the fact that, at a time when she believed that she had not more than twelve hours to live, she had confided her son to the protection of the English Queen.

"We believe that you, dear sirs and much esteemed friends, have always been such good servants of the realm and of the Queen, your exalted ruler, as to incline her to show us all just favour and assist us in all that is our right. For, as you well know, we must hold ourselves to be the nearest kinswoman to the Queen, your Sovereign, so near, indeed, that we have the greatest interest in any discussion of such questions in the parliament of our neighbour State, such as has recently taken place. Of a surety it is not our wish to press our good sister; yet, should it come to a new treaty on such an issue, we would fain have asked you, in all friendliness, to approach our cause, which we would wish settled wholly in accordance with the laws of England, with a just kindliness. We should, further, like to take this opportunity of conveying our most earnest assurances that our whole future life is intended to be spent altogether in peace and friendship with the Queen, your Sovereign, and with her realm, and that, should any prince on earth think to injure her, our whole strength shall be directed to opposing him. You cannot advise our dearest sister to show favour to a truer friend than ourselves."

Chapter 9

THE CRAIGMILLAR PACT

FROM Dunbar, Queen Mary went to Craigmillar, the charming castle among the hills near Edinburgh, where she loved to live. Hither, under pressure from the French Ambassador, M. du Croc, came her husband—only to depart again almost at once. After that, the Queen's depression mounted almost to illness. For a time after her recovery, she had been more cheerful, especially so long as, while she was on English soil, she seemed to hold happiness and grace between her two white hands, like a flowery bouquet. But now, she wept daily, became restless, went from one room to the other; she was for ever asking for something new, and then, as soon as she had got it, dropping it again as worthless. Symptoms of the illness from which she had barely recovered reappeared; she grew thinner, and yet obviously sought to hold herself all the more proudly erect. She sat at table, at the midday and evening meal, without enjoying more than a mere mouthful. When her friends implored her to take a little more care of herself, she would reply, "I would that I were dead."

Those about her understood her trouble. One day, State Secretary Lethington appeared in the room of the Earl of Argyle, where he found the other lords also—Murray, sitting with Argyle in the window, in front of the chess-board: and Bothwell, who was explaining the illustrations of a French book on the science of war, which lay on a table in the centre of the room, to his brother-in-law, Huntly. Lethington, taking a place beside the two men in the window, began at once—This thing must be settled, once for all. There were those unfortunates, the Earl of Morton, Lords Lindsay and Ruthven, and all the rest, far away, in exile, under the ban, in bitter need and continual danger. "And are they not suffering all these evils, because they once took risks for other people?" He said that their friends, who had, meantime, gathered the fruits of their sacrifices, would deserve to be branded guilty of the blackest ingratitude, if they did not put their whole strength into the effort to get the exiles restored to favour and bring them home again, to the enjoyment of their property.

The others, who had desisted from their occupations, sat silent, waiting to see what the Secretary of State was really driving at. At last the Earl of Huntly encouraged him with a "Well, what are we to do?"—"Those of our party must really desire it," said Lethington.—"Well, what next?" asked the Earl of Bothwell. He continued, "We, Huntly and I, have, as a matter of fact, no interest in the return of the absent. That they have not done the smallest thing for us they would, I fancy, themselves admit. . . . All the same . . . well, what next?"—"We must begin by getting Morton pardoned." Lethington proposed. "The rest would then settle itself."—"Hm, hm. Well, let us assume we all want that—how are you going to get the Queen to do it? to take him back into favour? when, as it is, she goes into convulsions if his name is so much as mentioned?"—"We shall offer to get her a divorce, if she will do it." At the sound of this word they all fell silent. Then, the Earl of Bothwell, with a laugh, said: "This is pretty! We get her a divorce, by way of return! The simplest thing in the world! Except that she happens to be a Papist . . ."—"That is no insuperable obstacle." The State Secretary abounded in examples of Catholic princes who had separated from their wives. They all sank again into silent thought. Lethington added: "If we were sure of each other . . ."—"Come, there need not be any question of that with us, with Huntly and me," replied Earl Bothwell. His brother-in-law agreed: "For anything that is in order . . . we shall be no spoil-sports. And if the Queen really will. . . ."

The lords went that afternoon to the Queen, Lethington

again acting as spokesman. Her Majesty must forgive them, if he, in the name and at the commission of all these gentlemen, ventured to touch upon matters that were painful and even evil. But what was the use? there were times when the knife had to be employed. Certainly things could not go on as they were. Her Majesty would recognize, in them, loyal servants, who had, before this, not been found wholly unworthy of the confidence of their gracious Sovereign in matters, like that, of a quite intimate kind. Queen Mary, whose face had gone as white and still as marble, said: "Speak!" Lethington then said that, painful as it was, he felt compelled to recall to Her Majesty the quite intolerable insults, to which, unfortunately not on one occasion only, she had been subjected by the King her husband, so publicly, so without any shame before any and every command of God and man, that no one, however much he wished to do so, could overlook them. Moreover—unmindful of all the honours heaped upon him by the Queen in her excessive kindness, the ungrateful man was daily going on, adding worse to bad. Of a surety, this could not continue. But where was the way out? "We see Your Majesty fading away," he continued, "and must ask ourselves, how long can it go on without our losing our stay and protection, the defence of all of us against heedless, boyish folly? Think, Your Majesty, of the anxiety with which the events of the last weeks have filled our hearts! If only Your Majesty would permit us to gather all our strength, bringing those who are scattered into association with us again! Then, indeed, it would be easy for us, Your Majesty's most faithful nobles, to find some way of help." For the moment, he was at an end. . . . They all looked at the Queen. She sat, without moving, still with that marble pallor, her hands pressed together in her lap, her head bent down and her gaze fixed on her lap. The Secretary's last words seemed to hang in the air, and echo through the room, reverberating, soundlessly, from the walls.

"I see none," Queen Mary replied at last, very softly, and without looking up.

"A divorce could be effected without difficulty," Lethington
began, cautiously, "if Your Majesty only . . ."

Mary looked up, sharply: her eyes, now, were like flames:
"What?"

They all understood that she thought an adherence to the
Protestant Church was being suggested to her.

"If only Your Majesty would unite our forces," the Secretary hastened to put her right. "I mean, to put it quite bluntly,
if you would permit the Earl of Morton, and young Lords
Ruthven and Lindsay, and all the others, to return!"

Queen Mary looked into his face; he did not blench: she
then looked at the others, in turn; when she came to Earl Bothwell, her gaze averted itself, quickly. "So, that, too . . ."

"It is for your own sake, Your Majesty!"

She sank, sighing, into reflection. At last she said slowly,
"It would have all to be done quite legally. . . . But, no, no!
It is quite impossible!"

"Why?" asked Lethington, softly, knowing full well what
his Sovereign meant.

"The Church can annul a marriage, but not dissolve it. No
doubt an annulment, a declaration of invalidity, could be secured. The Holy Father's dispensation for a marriage within
the prohibited degree of relationship came too late, not till
after the betrothal. But that is all impossible."

"On account of His Royal Highness, the Prince?"

"Yes, also for that. It is impossible, quite impossible."

"Pardon me, Madame, but on that point," the Earl of Bothwell intervened, "my parents were divorced, that is to say, their
marriage was declared invalid, according to Papal law, without my being in any way injured. I entered into my inheritance
of all my father's possessions, without any sort of let or hindrance, and all his dignities too."

"Yes, yes," interrupted Queen Mary, hastily, "that may
have happened."

"It happens in Scotland every day," added Lethington.

"Yes, yes. But it will not do for my son." She drew herself

up. "I would rather go to one part of the country and let the King remain in the other."

"That is impracticable, from the very nature of the King's character," said Lethington. "Are we to have two kingdoms in Scotland?"

"He will come to his senses, yet! He is still so very young!"

"By the time he has grown old enough, we shall all be ruined. One is always waiting, in the case of every fault of youth, for growing older. But in many points—if they are not there in youth, when are they going to come?"

"Or I can go to France!" said Mary, in an agony.

Then Lethington said: "Madame, care you not. We are here the principal of Your Majesty's nobility and council; who shall find the means that Your Majesty shall be quit of him without prejudice to your son; and albeit my lord of Murray here present be little less scrupulous for a Protestant than Your Grace is for a Papist, I am sure he will look through his fingers thereat, and will behold all our doings, saying nothing to the same."

Queen Mary rose suddenly, and stood drawn to her full height and dignity before them. "I will have you do nothing whereby any spot may be laid to my honour and conscience," she said, impressively. "I shall endure what I have to; that is my affair only. I shall be at more pains than ever to secure that no one beyond myself has to suffer for all this. No one else must meddle in the matter. Let it be in the state it is, abiding till God in His goodness puts a remedy thereto." She looked about the group, at the faces of the men, whose brows were dark with determined hatred. "Things might happen, that might turn to my hurt and disservice."

"Madame," said Lethington, "leave it to us to attend to this matter which, say what one will, is now an affair of State. Your Grace shall see nothing but what is good and the Parliament will approve of."

★

Mary came to Edinburgh, to Holyrood, to make preparations for the solemn christening of her son. Queen Elizabeth, invited as principal sponsor, sent the Earl of Bedford as her representative. Since the Earl neither would, nor by his mistress's instructions, might, enter the chapel, the Countess of Argyle, at Elizabeth's request, held the infant at the font, she being selected for this office because, so the Queen of England wrote, she was so dear to her good sister of Scotland. The King of France, the second sponsor, sent gifts by his envoys, as did the Duke of Savoy, who was also invited by Queen Mary. Queen Elizabeth's principal gift was a font of heavy gold in which, according to the custom of the Catholic Church, the little Prince should be totally immersed. The Queen of England wrote, however, that, since the gold font was put in hand immediately on the receipt in London of the news of the little Prince's birth, it might, though large at that time, now prove to be too small, in view of the splendid development of the little gentleman, of which the Queen of England heard with such delight. In that case, it might serve for the christening of the next baby.

Queen Mary received her guests with charming grace. Great festivities had been prepared; there were masked processions and performances in honour of the foreign guests. At all these junketings, however, the child's father was absent, although he was residing in the palace at the time.

Some people said that this very noticeable absence on the part of the King was due to a new and most serious breach between him and the Queen. For the King, as for the other lords of her court, the Queen had caused costly state garments to be prepared; especially magnificent ones for him. A few days before the christening, however, when the foreign guests were already beginning to arrive, a letter came to the Queen from her French uncle, the Cardinal, from which she had to learn that Henry Darnley had written to the King of France and likewise to his Holiness the Pope, violently denouncing the lukewarmness of his wife in matters touching the Catholic religion; he, the King, by the greatest exertions, and at the cost of the most extreme hostility, was alone to thank for the fact that the cause had not, long since, been completely lost in Scotland. None stood in such favour with the Queen as the declared enemies of the Catholic faith, the heads of the Protestant Party, the Earl of Murray and the laird of Lethington, whose execution had frequently, but always in vain, been urged upon the Queen both by his Holiness and by her French relations.

At this time, Queen Mary was expecting subsidies from the Pope; a nuncio for Scotland had already got as far as Paris, where he was tarrying only until a message from the Queen should report the moment as favourable for his advent.

It was, therefore, in blazing anger that Mary went to her husband with this letter in her hand. What was the meaning of this fresh imbecility? He retorted that he took no one's orders as to what he should, or should not, write to foreign powers: he was King of Scotland. His wife, in tones of contemptuous coldness, drew his attention to the fact that there might be some limits to his authority. He replied, "Yes, so far; but not for long now." The Murrays and the Lethingtons had better be on their guard, he raged. He would stick a knife into them! He was visibly bursting with anger. Mary looked at him, as though the sight turned her sick. "How red you are, my Lord! A bleeding, such as the poor Earl of Bothwell had to endure the other day, would do you a world of good!" With that, she left him.

Others gave other reasons for the King's absence from his son's christening. In spite of his quarrels with his wife, he had, it was said, come, at the last moment. Only to learn from his wife that the Queen of England had given express instructions to her ambassadors that Lord Henry Darnley was on no condition to be given the title of King. He was not so much as to address him. The Englishman was, in fact, so it was said, given strict orders to behave as though he were not present. But neither the Queen nor he were prepared to have so public a slight put upon her husband. At the same time it was even more impossible to protest to its author.

In all other matters, the English Government was more accommodating than it had ever been before. The Earl of Bedford was the bearer of a letter from his Sovereign, which comprised his instructions, but was also directed to Queen Mary and her Council. In this declaration it was stated that the Earl of Bedford was commissioned to express everything friendly to the Scottish Majesty in the name of his Government. It continued:

"Further, at a convenient time, you should inform the Queen that we are tired of saying certain things over and over and always causing unfriendliness thereby, but expect that she will accept the proof of our readiness to make an end of all the unpleasant matters of the past and now and later in ever increasing measure to show her great friendliness.

"Touching the matter last treated between us, that her claim should be publicly examined and declared here, we are disposed to assume that she is, in this, in nowise intending to injure us. We think that she will be satisfied with the answer which we herewith transmit—that we shall never do or permit anything that, whether overtly or covertly, may prejudice her rights, and that she may rely altogether on our friendship. In order to make an end of this matter, we shall send envoys for the ratification of the Treaty of Edinburgh, as of right, but in such fashion that, in order to remove all grounds for the questions arising therefrom and continually causing disquiets in both our kingdoms, a mutual alliance of friendship be concluded. She to assure us, in accordance with the Treaty of Edinburgh, to do nothing that may ever injure our rights and those of our children. In return, she to receive from us the assurance that we shall in the future neither make nor allow any attempt so much as to question her claim to be after ourselves the next in succession to the Throne. You shall lay these points both before the Queen herself and before her Council, so that it, too, is satisfied and realizes that, in this fashion alone, of a mutual Alliance of friendship, concluded before all the world, can the means be found for ending all jealousy and tension and substituting a genuine and sound relation."

★

But Queen Mary was never glad again.

She was pressed, on every side, to pardon the banished lords. She still rejected all these appeals, bitterly. But her melancholy increased; she almost refused to eat, and would say, with a groan, "I feel as though a pall were hanging over the future."

One day Sir James Melville, coming to her, met the Earl of Bothwell just going. To Sir James's distress, he was, of all persons, the one most with her in these days.

No good could possibly come of the immense power now exercised by this wild and enigmatic creature. What might he have been telling the Queen, today? Sir James found her in a state of considerable excitement. She began, almost at once, speaking in passionate terms: she was surrounded by treachery and faithlessness; where was she to find honest devotion?

"I have been five years in this country," she said. "I have done everything in my power, God knows, and more. I have only got to go to my window. There is Saint Anthony's Chapel, in ruins, utterly destroyed by these incendiaries! And every stone of it cries out to me reproachfully—'You have not avenged us!'" Her passion mounted. "But I will do it yet! What are they without me? I have been far too good to them. That, and that alone, has made them strong enough to treat me so ruthlessly."

Sir James admitted the justice of her complaint. "Certainly," he said. "No one can resist the view, no one above all, who has lived in foreign countries and had the opportunity there to study foreign matters and especially those of the nobility—no one, I say, can resist the view that the Scottish nobility is quite extraordinarily addicted to brawling and revolt. But, for the very reason that it has always been proved impossible to exercise force effectively against these wild spirits, ought not the attempt to be made to tame brutality by gentleness, and even to accustom it, so, to order?"

"Let them make a puppet of me, to do just as they please?" exclaimed Mary.

"Remember, Your Majesty," said her counsellor, "that the country has been endowed, in you, with an extraordinarily kind and wise ruler, whose mission it remains to unite the whole island some day under your beneficent sceptre. If Your Grace sought to remove every opportunity for strife! You would then make a fair development possible!"

The Queen was silent, gloomy.

"What Your Majesty does freely, no one can compel you to do," said Sir James, significantly.

"I know," Mary replied, with bitterness, "that they are for ever threatening me in secret. Once they have done it—why should they not do it again, with more success in the second attempt? Well, if I have to let them have their way. . . . Let them look to it lest I one day set a rule over them that will be able to pay them out!"

Another afternoon, when Sir James came, he reported that there were musicians from the Highlands without—two youngish men who played the pipes, and an older one who sang and knew all the popular songs and ballads. Would the Queen not care to hear this music? It might not please her ears, but it was something quite characteristic. And the poor fellows might afford her a little distraction.

The Queen followed him. In the hall of the palace, where a considerable number of people had already assembled, since they were allowed entrance there, stood the musicians, two robust young men with their bagpipes, and an old man. All three wore Highland garb, kilts in scarlet, blue or yellow tartan.

"The old man is the singer," said Sir James Melville.

"Does he know Scots?" asked the Queen. "I understand Gaelic no better than the barking of dogs."

"He knows Scots. He is a Stuart, of Your Majesty's own clan. For these poor fellows Your Majesty is not only the Queen of Scotland, but also the head of the clan, which, for a Highlander, means pretty well the divinity to whom he says his prayers. He knows all the songs of Your Majesty's royal forbears."

The Queen took her place in the seat prepared for her. Her Court ranged itself behind her, in a semicircle; the elegant ladies and gentlemen stared at the Highlanders who, on their part, looked about them quite unmoved. The old man was short and stocky, with a mighty white beard and red-rimmed eyes, bleached by extreme age. The Queen said that she had once heard a song about all the kings of Scotland, or least about all the Stuarts. A long song. She had heard it once, but forgotten it again. They were to ask the man whether he knew it. He said, Yes, he did. "Sing it, then," commanded the Queen.

The pipers on either side of the old man raised their blow pipes to their lips and began their singular shrill and penetrating drone, beating time continually, as if, although they stood still, they were on the march. The old man then struck up, singing loud and clear, like a man singing in a language which he knows quite well, but which is not his own. Every one could catch every word, while the pipes screamed out the accompaniment. He sang:

> "Then spake the good King, Robert Bruce,
> Come Stuart, here to me,
> My Kingdom hast thou guarded well,
> My daughter I give to thee!
>
> Whom do they crown at royal Scone?
> King Robert must it be.
> Twelve stalwart sons stand by his side:
> Twelve daughters, fair to see.

Aye, Robert of thy race the third,
Thou hast a splendid son:
Yet look about, King Robert, for
Thy brother seeks the throne!

And where, King Robert, is the Prince?
The Prince lies stark and cold.
Earl March leads on the Englishmen,
King Robert is weak and old.

They kneel before the little King:
King James, but twelve years old:
As on the sea to France he sails,
The English seize and hold.

For eighteen years they hold him fast:
King Henry gives his hand.
See how he comes a-riding in,
Whom finds he true in his land?

King James, a hero, mighty, bold,
King James fresh laws will say:
And if my lord has burned my house,
His head for that shall pay!

King James, he gathers in the heads,
As one who berries picks:
His daughter fair is France's Queen,
But others play their tricks.

Eight knights come softly riding by:
There the good king lies dead.
Earl Atholl, art thou now a king?
How thy blood dyes thee red!

Again they kneel before the king,
King James with his six years.
The Douglas is his dear friend,
Douglas, with golden hairs.

THE CRAIGMILLAR PACT

Where is my friend, my comrade true?
What is this bloody day?
Another Douglas holds the land,
A Douglas strange and fey.

Thou art my foe, wilt snatch my crown?—
Let the old feud now sleep—
Let go, King James, thy word was pledged—
Go, bury the rebel deep.

You break all pledges, seize our land,
In the dust lies our power;
And the king falls by Roxburgh,
In thirty summers' flower.

They kneel again before the king,
King James is nine years old.
Poor Henry of England, what seekest here?
Shall Scottish faith not hold?

In the castle there is singing,
And fiddling and fluting beside,
The king loves not his knights
Who sit in dismal pride.

An you bring the English against us,
And bring your fiddlers too,
We shall string them up on the bridges!
If your brother's tread you knew . . . !

The king sits bound i' the castle;
The king again is free!
Ah, king, if thou dream of vengeance,
Thy son thinks not with thee!

At Sauchieburn, nigh Bannockburn,
The fight is joined and fought;
Alas, poor king, who saves thee now?
Thy life is but a thought!

King James is fifteen years,
He grieves his father's doom;
The Englishman sends ships:
The Scots at once strike home.

Ope wide the doors and cry for joy!
England's child to us they lend!
Fair Margaret comes, a queenly bride,
What crowns does Heaven send?

O'er Flodden rises black the sun,
Goes down in bloody night,
King James has died upon the field,
And ten thousand of his might.

They crown the king again at Scone,
A babe in mother's arms:
His mother's man's the Douglas black,
God keep the king from harms!

King James has many sentinels,
The Douglas sets them there;
His mother finds another man:
King James sets out for war.

King James lies before Douglas' keep,
But he's to England flown;
Step off, ye knights, the king he says,
Too near ye stand the throne!

Who is the finest man of all?
Will England's Henry say,
Come here and see my daughter fair!
King James he says him Nay.

Like lovely blooming flowers,
The ladies are in France;
Mary is Queen in Scotland,
King Henry's cheeks they blanch.

THE CRAIGMILLAR PACT

The battle now is lost—
The English army's won—
The King's true heart it breaks,
His joy in life is done.

Then our fair Queen is born,
As lovely as the day;
God send her length of life,
And all the joys he may!"

The minstrel fell silent, the pipers likewise, on the stroke. The Queen sat stiff against the high back of her chair, her hands folded in her lap, her eyes sunk, her expression as rigid as though there were a dark veil before her inward eyes. As she looked about her, opening her eyes, her face shocked those who knew her—she looked suddenly old.

"Enough," she said, rising. She left the hall, in silence. On the way, however, she turned to the knight at her side, "Sir James, go to the men and tell them that I thank them, very much. And give them each a gold piece in my name, and two for the minstrel."

★

Now, there was no one in the whole country who did not know that the Queen could not live with her husband. He followed her about like a dog, scorned as if he had mange.

The King invariably supped in his own room, alone. In the daytime he did nothing but go out hunting with his dogs and two or three squires. He would come home, at evening, through the grey rain, wet through to the skin, and look up to the Queen's windows, all brilliantly lit, and realize that, in the end, she was now further away from him, more unattainable, than the Queen of England or of France would be, were he staying at their courts as a guest from abroad. He went into his own rooms, sat there, did not know what to do, and heard steps and often the murmur of voices in his wife's rooms, over his head. At last, he could no longer control the shame and anger that filled his heart; repeating an attempt which he

319

knew was bound to fail, he went upstairs to his wife's apart ments, where he found the light of many candles, and warmth and beauty. The walls were gay with rare tapestries, the floor covered all over with richly coloured carpets, so soft that the step sank into them; there was handsome, French furniture, elaborately carved, everywhere, and the sheen of sumptuous velvet. And the Queen sat among her lovely, high-bred young women and listened as they gossiped, easily and carelessly, about everything in heaven and earth; and there were gentle men, too, the Secretary of State, the Earls of Murray, Both well and Huntly. They all talked French; the Maries often sang French songs; but nobody so much as turned his head towards the King. He stood about; his wife's arrogant steward approached him. He spoke Scots, but spoke it as though, in so doing, he did an irreparable injury and severe damage to his tongue, as he asked what was he to do; did His Highness pro pose to be at table this evening? He had had no orders to that effect. Then the King, his heart bursting with rage and wrath, would bolt past him to the door, go down, and invite anybody who was still friendly with him, among the lackeys, or the people of the town, or anywhere. And with them he would sit drinking the evening through, and then, night after night, betake himself to his women, of whom he maintained three or four in Edinburgh alone. When the morning came, his mood would be dark and dreary again, and he would again try to make his way to his wife, generally only to be turned back at the door by her servants. Her Majesty slept still, or Her Maj esty had given strict instruction to admit no one. When, either in his rage or in his misery, he wrote to her, she would inform him by word of mouth, through her lackeys, that she really had no time for such correspondence, either to read or to reply to it.

There were other stories going about the town. The Queen knew what she was about when she withdrew from her husband and permitted him no access to herself, such as every wife owes to her husband. For the King had entered into a new conspiracy with his father, with the object of seizing the Queen's person, and then carrying on the government entirely by himself. Old Lennox was busy, day and night, spinning a web of plots over Scotland and England. His son had involved himself with the Pope, who had turned against the Queen because she had, once and for all, refused to execute her loyal servants and subjects on account of religion. The King had promised the Pope, that, so soon as he was master of the land, he would chop off the heads of all the Lords of the Council, and first and foremost of the Secretary of State, whom he hated because he had betrayed him after David's murder, then, those of the Earls of Murray, Bothwell, Huntly and Argyle. The only question now was, who would strike first, they or he? Certainly, frightful deeds were being prepared by both parties.

★

Shortly before Christmas, in the year 1566, the King received a warning from one of the nobles about the court. Was he aware that Joseph Rizzio, David's younger brother, whom the Queen had sent for, to Italy, to come and take the place of his murdered brother, was due to arrive immediately?

Further, and still more important for the King, the Queen had granted pardons to all the exiled lords and their adherents, some sixty or seventy persons in all. Immediately after Christmas they would reappear in Scotland, in Edinburgh, and at court. What had the King to say to this piece of news?

Horror at the entirely unexpected intelligence made him stand, his mouth open. If these lords, whose cause had been ruined by his treachery, came back, they must be his deadly enemies. And his wife must know that he could not occupy the same ground with the men with whom he had first entered into a conspiracy for her destruction and then betrayed to her later. The man who warned him referred him, for fuller details, to an individual of inferior rank, a magistrate's clerk named Hiegate. The King knew the man. He had even drunk with him. For him Henry Darnley at once sent. He came, stood, astonished, before the King—a wretched creature, in every respect. In reply to the King's singular and unskilfully eager queries, he seemed at first to be unwilling to say anything; he knew nothing. At last, as much embarrassed as excited by the King's threats, complaints, and promises, he said, with all the importance proper to a first warning, that certainly he had learned this and that. He said that the banished lords, the whole body of them, would really be in Scotland again for Christmas. Their return was a warning to the King to be prepared for the very worst. "Some time ago," he said, "it was a settled plan to take you prisoner. At the time when it was said that you wanted to go to France. The Privy Council decided on that, unanimously. After that you would have been indicted. Then, however, matters did not reach that point. For they did not, at that time, venture to lay hands on you. Mainly because the Queen refused to know anything about all that. By themselves, and without the exiles, the lords could not risk any action. But the fact that they have now got the Queen to pardon all the conspirators, even those who killed David, whereas she always said she would die rather, is the very worst sign, for it shows that Her Majesty has now withdrawn her hands from you." The man, continuing, said: "At the moment, they are still discussing methods. They have thought out four or five ways of making away with you. Either they will poison you, or stab you in bed, or get up a quarrel and then kill you in a duel, or perhaps they may blow you up. But, as I have said, at the moment they are still not clear as to how it is to be done. But that they will do it soon, that is quite decided."

"Who? who?" screamed the King, who, at the moment, comprehended nothing beyond the fact that some outrage against him was going on. His folly brought the other up sharply. He tried to withdraw: "For God's sake, you are not going to betray me?"

"Who?"

"I do not know."

"I shall make mince-meat of you!"

"I know nothing more!"

While the King stormed up and down, the man made off.

The King threw himself on his bed. He was booted and spurred. When his servant took the cover off at night, it was all torn in pieces at the lower end.

As if stung by a tarantula the King rushed into his wife's room. He did not go by the little winding stair from his rooms to hers, since it had long since been closed up and bolted. As he tore, clanking, through the ante-chamber, the pages there sought to stay him—"Your Majesty cannot . . ."—but he saw and heard nothing. He seized the door-handle, rattled it violently: the door flew open. In the centre of the room stood the Queen, with the Earl of Bothwell a few paces away. She moved to the carved oaken table, resting both her hands upon it: blazing with anger, she looked at her husband. "How dare you?"

He fell back. "Madame!"

She collected herself. "The guard is to blame. I gave express orders . . . I have important business with the Earl. . . . You were not in my mind . . ."

The Earl approached, pride in his glance. "Madame . . ."

"Yes, go, go," she said sharply, turning away from him.

He bowed courteously, calmly, made the barest inclination towards the King, and marched coolly out of the room.

The Queen turned at once to her husband, with no very friendly air. "Well, my Lord?"

He stood, absent, pallid.

She asked again, "What has caused me the honour of this visit?"

Her tone enabled him to recapture his former rage. "Yes, yes," he cried: he heard that a creature, a certain Joseph, a brother of David's, had been sent for by her all the way to Italy, his home, to come here. "And you have planned all that, diligently, simply and solely in order to cause me pain and torture, and to injure and insult me." Helplessly he sobbed, struggling to express himself. And the exiled lords were to come back, too! But they were all making a great mistake. Not for one hour would he remain under the same roof as these traitors.

Queen Mary flinched, as he came close to her in his excitement. "Please, sir!" She raised her hand, to keep him off.

His wild declaration that he would be gone within an hour only made her say, in icy tones, "Who is keeping you, sir?"

"I shall, I shall . . ." He raised his clenched fists against her. Words failed him.

"Should you be thinking of going to Stirling to seize possession of the Prince, I may assure you that you will find that precautions have been taken." As though he were no longer there, she turned to the table, took up letters there and read them.

He stood in the centre of the room, struggling to find words. She raised her eyes from the page—"Anything more, my Lord?"

Next morning he received a letter from his father in Glasgow, in which it was stated that his death was planned. Was he going to put off his flight for ever?

On this, he departed to his father. He informed his wife of his departure in a letter to which he received no reply.

★

At court, the Earl of Bothwell was now supreme. The Queen hung on his glances. His wife was sometimes in the Bothwell town house, more often at Crichton with her mother. She no longer came to court. But Earl Bothwell's sister, the wife of Lord Robert Stuart, was often summoned thither by the Queen, the more that Mary Fleming was at last on the point of marrying the Secretary of State, Lethington.

★

One day, after her husband's departure, the Queen actually signed the decree permitting the banished lords to return. The Earl of Morton, young Ruthven, Lord Lindsay and all others, were pardoned. Old Lord Ruthven was no longer living. His illness had carried him off, a few weeks after the attack on the

Queen and the murder of David. The people in England in whose house he had died declared that the white angels and the black had visibly contended for his soul. He had passed as a great adept in the black arts, but, so they said, before his death he had accomplished his reconciliation with God.

Excluded from the Queen's pardon were only one or two soldiers, who had, so she said, personally turned their weapons against her. And John Knox did not venture, as yet, to lift the decree of banishment he had voluntarily passed upon himself.

After Christmas, all the pardoned men appeared in the palace, in order to pay their due respects to the Queen and to her little son, whom she had fetched from Stirling and held in her arms when she appeared before them. The King passed Christmas with his father. Of his wife he heard nothing.

★

Henry Darnley fell sick in his father's house. At first, poison was spoken of, but later his illness proved to be the small-pox, which had appeared here and there in Scotland at times, and which he was said to have contracted during a visit to a house of ill-fame. His attack was not a very severe one, and there was hardly any danger of his life, at any stage in it. His wife sent her own physician to him, whose skill was renowned: he was said to be able to treat this disease so effectively that no scars were left after it. Further, the Queen sent a messenger from Stirling, whither she had gone for one or two days, to inquire whether her husband would care to have a visit from her? If so, she was ready to come to him. The messenger returned. He believed His Majesty did not desire it. "Very well. What did he say, then, Joachim?" asked Queen Mary. The man looked her straight in the face. "His Majesty said he wished that Stirling were Jedburgh, Glasgow the Hermitage, and he himself the Earl of Bothwell, for in that case Your Majesty would have been with him without waiting to be asked."

Whereat the Queen laughed.

★

She received various persons, among them Mr. William Drury, the new Ambassador of the English Government, come to initiate negotiations for a fresh alliance between the two States, as Queen Elizabeth had proposed at the time of the christening of the little Prince.

Late in the evening, Queen Mary gave orders for preparations to be made for a small suite to accompany her on a journey on which she proposed to start next morning very early. Her litter was to be made ready and the quietest horses in her stable attached to it. For she was going to Glasgow to visit the King and bring him back with her to Edinburgh.

Early in the morning she rode forth, accompanied by one or two gentlemen, ladies and servants. As Dame of Honour, Lady Reres was commanded to attend her. Like her sister, Lady Buccleuch, it was reported of her that she was a dangerous adept in the black arts, and that, again like her sister, she had once been a love of the Earl of Bothwell's. Whatever the relations of the two sisters to him may have been, they had not clouded their friendship: he was constantly in their company.

Lady Reres was the younger of the two and at this time in her early forties. Her quick wit amused the Queen immensely: she used, indeed, to say that her repartee was quite un-Scottish, almost French in its lightness and freedom. Lady Reres was small and stout: her face was broad, with full cheeks and narrow, sparkling eyes. Proof of her secret arts seemed to be afforded by the fact that, despite her ugliness, she had a success with men surpassing that of many a beauty of twenty summers.

Among the Queen's servants were the Frenchmen, Joachim and Nicholas Hubert, the latter known as French Paris, after the place of his birth. Paris had been taken over by the Queen from the Earl of Bothwell's service. Among her gentlemen, the Earl of Bothwell was far the most distinguished.

On the way from Stirling to Glasgow, the first halt was made in Callender, where Lord Livingstone entertained the party in his castle. At this point, the Earl of Bothwell turned back.

The Queen employed the day's pause to write a letter to her faithful emissary in Paris, the Archbishop of Glasgow, a Beaton, in which she complained bitterly of the mad notions of her husband, who believed himself to be surrounded on all sides by would-be murderers. She, the Queen, had been compelled to summon before her a quite common fellow, a magistrate's clerk in Edinburgh, Hiegate by name, because she had been informed that this wight had actually strengthened the King in his dark fantasies by foolish chatter about dangers and plans of murder by which, according to him, the King was encompassed on every side. When called upon to produce any sort of evidence for the wild and scandalous stories with which he had frightened the King and attempted to sow discord between him and his wife and the entire nobility, the wretched creature had naturally produced nothing but the flimsiest talk. No one, however, could imagine how unspeakably difficult life was made for her, the Queen, by such goings-on. Often, she was so utterly heart sick, that she would prefer to live no longer. The Lennoxes had set a regular spy service about her. She mentioned a certain Valcar, one of the hangers-on of their party, as having given her definite information on this. Yet, in spite of all this, apart from the insult contained in such suspicion itself, she regarded every such rumour with contempt. For nothing could ever be discovered against her. She was now hastening to withdraw her husband, with all possible celerity, from the disastrous influence of his treacherous and hypocritical father.

Two days later, towards evening, Queen Mary entered Glasgow, where she at once sought her husband out. She did not see his father, who shut himself up in his own room. The Queen remained in the town for two days, and went often to her husband, though she did not choose to dwell under the same roof with him.

The world, however, understood this reunion of the royal pair to imply a complete reconciliation, the more so that when the Queen had to return to Edinburgh, her husband agreed to travel with her, despite his still sickly condition. By slow stages, the train reached the town, the Queen on horseback, her husband on a litter. On account of possible infection, which might be dangerous to the little Prince, who was still in Holyrood, the King might not be brought to the palace. His wife proposed Craigmillar as a good place to recover in. He replied, however, that Craigmillar was so far from Holyrood that he might just as well have stayed in Glasgow as be there. Finally, Kirk-o'-Field was selected, a small building, once an abbey, lying isolated near the town wall, with one side to the open fields, the other surrounded by poor gardens. There was nothing near it save the allotments of poorish folk; the single largish house in its neighbourhood was that of Archbishop Hamilton of St. Andrews. The church of St. Mary-in-the-Fields (which was also the full name of the little abbey) now belonged to a Balfour, brother to Sir James Balfour, who passed as a specially devoted supporter of the Queen's and an intimate friend of the Earl of Bothwell's. Only the portion of it that served for dwelling purposes was now employed, a wing built on to the side of the church itself, consisting of two stories, each containing one large room and one or two smaller ones. Its remote location, removing any dangers of a spread of infection, made it suitable for the purpose for which it was now used. At the same time, it was so near to the palace that the Queen could be with her husband within ten minutes.

★

It was on the last day of January that Queen Mary entered Edinburgh, alone in the first instance, in order to make preparations for her husband's reception. She had sent messengers on in advance, to see that the appropriate rooms were suitably arranged for her sick husband. In the large room on the first floor a carved bedstead was set up; costly hangings were arranged over it; tapestries were hung upon the walls; the Queen's green brocade-covered furniture was brought from Holyrood. Since Queen Mary thought she might herself sometimes pass the night in the room on the ground floor, it, too,

was got ready. The other rooms were for the servants. The
Queen inspected everything, ordered alterations to be made in
this and that, and then departed to fetch her husband from
Linlithgow, where he had remained. On February 1st the King
himself arrived, saw how things had been prepared for him,
and was satisfied with everything. In Kirk-o'-Field he took
baths; every day, he was better. True, he still lay for hours
in bed, but generally with his clothes on. His wife came, as she
had promised, every day from the palace, and always stayed
for a long time. She seemed to the King so friendly disposed
towards him that he wrote to his father in Glasgow that he
was now free from all trouble, nay, well content in spirits. For
Mary, his dear love, did everything for him a wife could do for
her husband. Almost every other night she remained in the little
house, in order to be able to have a good long time with him.

★

In spite of the King's sickness, many visitors came to see
him, now that he again shone in the splendours of his wife's
favour. On Friday, the seventh of February, Lord Robert
Stuart visited him. In the course of a conversation ranging
confidentially over the period at which Henry Darnley and
Robert Stuart had brawled together in Edinburgh and entered
into all possible pranks there, the latter remarked that the
King had really not treated him fairly, for not once but countless times had he met him with insufferable arrogance and had,
moreover, often tried to anger the Queen against her brother,
and this although that brother had never been other than the
King's devoted friend. However, for the sake of old times together, he was not now going to think of his justified reasons
for anger, but only of how he could behave as a thoroughly
good comrade. That being so, there was one question he wanted
to put: did the King really feel quite safe in this remote hole?
The preamble had made the King uncomfortable; he now exclaimed, What could happen to him? He was the Queen's consort!

"Just so!" replied Lord Robert.

"Explain yourself—speak plainly!"

"Catch me! You know that you have enemies. I do not need to mention names."

The King pondered, wrinkling his brows. Then he began pressing the other: he must say more, for Christ's sake. But Robert was not to be persuaded. "No, no, you cannot keep what is told you to yourself," he said, getting up from his chair beside the bed. "But be upon your guard. You have been warned. If anything happens to you, it is your own look-out." The latch in his hand, he added: "If I were you, I should be clean away first thing in the morning."

Next day, about noon, Lord Robert received a message bidding him come to the King at once. The message was couched in such urgent terms, that Lord Robert obeyed on the spot. But when he entered the room, he saw to his great and painful astonishment that the King was not alone: the Queen herself sat there in the arm-chair by the window, with Lord James beside her. Lord Robert knew from the faces of his sister and brother that they were fully informed of all that he had said on the previous day. As for the King, he was crouching in the deep shadows of the curtains of his bed.

Almost before Lord Robert had closed the door behind him, Queen Mary began: "Sir, you have said, so the King maintains, that his life is in jeopardy here. And you are said to have named Lord James, your brother, as the promoter of the attack upon him."

Lord Robert, casting a glance of angry contempt towards the obscurity in which Henry Darnley was hiding, merely laughed. "His Majesty has bad dreams! That comes of his illness. Obviously, there is not one word of truth in the whole of this grotesque affair. Not a mortal syllable can I have so much as hinted of any of it. For I know nothing."

"But it is true," the King now raised his voice from his corner. "And you went on to say that I was to say nothing

330

about it, and if I were clever. . . . You did . . . you did. . . ."

"Has Your Grace suddenly gone mad?"

"You did say it, and you meant the Queen herself and not only Lord James, though about him it was quite clear, and you said, just because I . . ."

"Your Majesty is lying," Lord Robert interrupted, loud and quick.

"Sir! . . ."

The King had leaped up; he felt for his dagger, which he still carried at his side; Lord Robert pulled his out—but, at the critical moment, the Queen flung herself, with a cry, in front of her husband: Lord James pulled his brother back.

"No bloodshed! In Her Majesty's presence!"

Lord Robert thrust his dagger back into its sheath. "Elsewhere then," he said, as he went out.

On the same day, Lord James Murray departed to his castle, to be with his wife, who was expecting her confinement. State Secretary Lethington, on the other hand, when his mistress wished to send him to London with detailed answers to the inquiries of the English Government, asked whether he might not be allowed to remain for a day or two. He gave his young wife as his reason for the request: he did not wish to be parted from her so soon after their wedding. He had married Mary Fleming but a short time previously.

At court there were bets laid as to whether the King would be dead before or after Wednesday of next week.

★

On Sunday, February 9th, various visitors, in addition to the Queen herself, were still with her husband at a late hour in the evening, among them the Earls of Huntly and Bothwell, who sat dicing together. Earl Bothwell was in the act of raising the leathern cup to throw the dice, when Paris, formerly his servant, now the Queen's lackey, came in. Leaving everything as it was, the Earl rose and went out of the room with the man, as though on some business. When, after a while, he came back again, his brother-in-law was preparing to be off. He too must go now, said Bothwell. Speaking to the Queen, he said, "Does Your Grace not come with us?"

"No, you stay with me: you promised to: you came so late today!" implored her husband.

"Naturally, Your Majesty remains: of course," said the Earl.

"I shall soon follow you," she said. Turning to her husband, she explained that she could not sleep here tonight, as she had promised to appear, later, at a ball in honour of one of her French servants, her chamberlain Bastian, even if only for a short time.

"But the weather is so bad," her husband objected, shyly.

"All the same, I must go."

Earl Bothwell interrupted, impatiently, to take his leave. With curt abruptness, he made his bows to the royal pair. He was at the door, when Queen Mary took a step after him.

"My Lord!" Whether he did not hear, or did not take the remark as addressed to him, he was gone, without turning round.

His departing steps echoed down the stairs; the Queen was alone with her husband. Only one of his servants stood dreamily in a corner. Queen Mary sat silent in an arm-chair by her husband's bedside. Outside, a storm was now raging, making the walls of the little house rattle: somewhere a tile fell to the ground with a clatter: the gutter of the roof, which had come loose, apparently, at one end, kept knocking against the wall. Queen Mary sat on, immobile, bending forward, her hands folded in her lap, sunk in a brown study. Her husband looked at her, uncertainly: the light of the candles on the table flickered over her face with alternating light and shade. At last, with a heavy sigh, he began to talk across a silence made all the more palpable by the raging of the wind, now howling in the chimney. He asked whether Mary had noticed how, the whole

332

way from Glasgow here, a raven had flown with them: when they halted, it halted too. Here, they had begun to think that it had gone, but, lo! there it was, sitting on the tree outside of the window and screeching the whole day long.

"That must be a different raven," said Mary, indifferently.

Her coldness depressed her husband. "No, no," he repeated, in small, suddenly tragic tone. "It was certainly meant for me." He sighed, heavily. "I have so often thought that, for Your Majesty, it would be far better if I were dead."

Mary cast a glance at him, sideways: then relapsed into her former position.

"You would never take me again, if you had the choice again!" he insisted, desperately, as if itching to be contradicted.

"The raven might be for me," was all she replied, leaning further forward, so as to sink her forehead on her right hand. She was lost in dark brooding. She let her hand fall, and in her eyes was a lightless melancholy. "A month today it will be a year since David was murdered," she said, in a dull, cold voice: it sounded like a warning. Horrified, her husband fell silent.

She rose. "Why are you always so nervous?" she said, standing close by her husband's bed. He looked up at her, large tears in his eyes. Unable to bear his gaze longer, she bent over him and kissed him lightly on the forehead. His tears poured down his cheeks. "Yes, poor little Harry," she said, stroking his hair while he hid his face on her breast, and hung on to her with both his arms. A shudder passed over her: she looked about her, as though in fear: carefully releasing herself from him, she laid him back on the pillows.

"Take this ring," she said, drawing one from her finger. "It will keep you company, for I must go now."

She left him.

Outside the pages were waiting with the horses. In their hands were great, guttering torches, to light her through the darkness. By now the wind had fallen a little. As the Queen's horse was led out, Paris joined the others as they came out of the house. He sought to pass behind the Queen, so as not to be observed. But as Mary swung herself up into the saddle, she turned directly to him. "Jesu! Paris," she said, bending forward, "how begrimed you are!"

At first they rode along an alley-way beside the town wall, then turned into Blackfriars Lane, leading into the High Street. There the Queen's train crossed the Cowgate and entered the Canongate area, in which the palace itself lay. After a rapid change of dress, Mary at once betook herself to the ball-room. Here the marriage mirth was at its height. The whole court was there, and gaiety and jollity reigned supreme. From the gallery, music was blaring. Masked figures, some splendid, others comical, ran in and out, with loud laughter and shouting.

The Queen only remained for half an hour, talking with the wedding guests; she had insisted that no special notice was to be taken of her presence, and had consented to come only on that condition.

When she withdrew to her own apartments, she asked a page of her suite for the Earl of Bothwell, whom, contrary to her expectation, she had not seen at the feast. She had urgently to speak with his lordship. The page was to go and look for the Earl, and bring him at once, to her sitting-room, late as it was. The page came back to the Queen with one of the Earl's servants: almost at the moment when the Queen entered the ball-room for the wedding feast, the Earl had left it and, soon afterwards, the palace. Where he might now be, no one knew.

Queen Mary pondered. "Say to the Earl . . ." Then, breaking off, "I will write to him." But at her table, she sat before a blank sheet, and, at last, laid down the pen. She turned to the page, who stood waiting, near to the door. "Say to his lordship that I must speak with him as early as may be tomorrow."

"Very good, Your Majesty."

While the Queen was being disrobed in her bedchamber, she said nothing. Only as she lay in bed, and her tiring-woman was in the act of leaving the room, she remarked: "The Prince is quite well?"

"I think so, Your Majesty," replied the tiring-woman.

★

Henry Darnley had called his page Alexander Taylor to him. He asked where his other servants were. Only one, Nelson, was, so he heard, in the house, and he was already asleep; the others had gone to the wedding. The King, accustomed to have his servants do whatever they liked, without any regard for him, sighed heavily when he heard this. "Do you stay with me," he said to the page. He lay still in his bed: his companion sat in the arm-chair by his side, given over to a dull nothing-doing, nothing-thinking state.

"Let us sing a psalm," said the King. The page fetched a psalter for himself and for the King: they struck up, and, in the stillness of the deserted house, began to sing the psalm which the King had chosen:

"Give ear to my prayer, O God, and hide not thyself from my supplication.

Attend unto me and hear me: I mourn in my complaint, and make a noise.

Because of the voice of the enemy, because of the oppression of the wicked, for they cast iniquity upon me, and in wrath they hate me.

My heart is sore pained within me: and the terrors of death are fallen upon me.

And I said, Oh that I had wings like a dove! for then I would fly away and be at rest. Lo, then would I wander far off and remain in the wilderness.

I would hasten my escape from the windy storm and tempest.

Cast thy burden upon the Lord, and he shall sustain thee: he shall never suffer the righteous to be moved.

But thou, O God, shalt bring them down into the pit of destruction: bloody and deceitful men shall not live out half their days. But I will trust in thee."

Chapter 10

"THE GOOD KING IS DEAD"

HENRY DARNLEY was blown up about two o'clock in the morning of February tenth, in the year 1567. The effect of the explosion was to send a vast column of flame rising out of house of Kirk-o'-Field with a shock as of thunder that made every window in Edinburgh shake. Far and wide flew the hail of stones, large and small, of pieces of wood and other stuff. For an instant, the naked walls stood up in the harsh light of the flames; at the next, they collapsed upon themselves in a ruin which soon extinguished the flames of the burning wood of the house. Then all was still again, with the wintry night sky sparkling above it.

From the poor hovels of the neighbourhood, men and women came rushing out, shrieking, half naked, with their poor coats and shawls cast over them. As soon as they saw that the horror that had caused them to rush out of their beds did not mean the end of the world, and really had nothing to do with them, they began to cry out, all the louder, "The King! The King! The good King is dead!" At first, no one dared to come near. A thick, evil-smelling smoke was now curling up out of the heaped-up ruins, so dense that it obscured the outline of the ruins themselves and made the whole scene look strange and unfamiliar. "Ah, the King, the good King!" the men and women went on muttering.

Gradually, as the crowd was continually increased by newcomers, curiosity overcame fear, and they pressed closer and closer to the place of catastrophe. "Who can have done it? The poor, good King! He must be quite dead!" Then a clanking noise was heard—the royal guard, with its commander, the

336

Earl of Bothwell at the head, marched up, with heavy determined tread.

The Earl had hardly got home and laid down in his bed when a squire came rushing in, crying out that Kirk-o'-Field had been blown up! Leaping up and snatching at his clothes, the Earl cried: "Ho! Treachery!" He hastened out of his room, and found a sort of confused life beginning to stir in the passages. His brother-in-law, Huntly, came to meet him out of the semi-darkness of the dimly lighted corridor. "Go to the Queen!" cried Bothwell. "She must not be alarmed, whatever she hears. I must go thither." Then he bethought himself: "No, I shall come with you."

When the two lords came to the Queen, she was sitting upright in bed; her long thick hair hung in two plaits on either side of her face: there was no one in the room but her French tiring-woman, moving, weeping, to and fro about her mistress's bed. A single candle was burning disconsolately.

"Madame!" said Bothwell, hastening towards Mary. Huntly remained by the door; the tiring-woman withdrew into the darkness. Bothwell, standing close to the bed, spoke to Mary quickly, in a whisper; his knee supported against the edge of the bed, his right arm, along its head, was almost round the Queen's neck; she, clasping his left hand with both of hers, looked wide-eyed up into his face. He went on, speaking in a low tone, ending with:

"But you will be good and brave, won't you, so that I can rely on you?"

"Of course, of course."

He smiled. "I must be gone with all speed. Who knows what they may have done in all this time!" Bending to kiss her hand, he almost touched her cheek. "I shall soon be back." She followed him with her eyes.

The Earl found the antechamber full of persons, talking to one another in undertones. Among them was Sir James Melville, who made as though to go in to his Sovereign. Brusquely, the Earl stopped him. "The Queen is beside herself! She can see no one! She wishes to be quite alone. Nobody is to go in to her until she calls. Huntly!"

"I will see to that," his brother-in-law reassured him.

The Earl dashed off, down the staircase. The soldiers of the guard, of which he had for some time now been in command, were standing to in the courtyard, with torches lit, waiting his advent.

The Earl threw himself on horseback. Arrived at the place with his men, he first proceeded to disperse the crowd, which surged towards him, yelling: "Here, here is the good King, done in and lying quite dead!" The soldiers, with flaring torches in their hands, made a ring round the devastated area, while their captain, accompanied by a couple of torch-bearers, went about inspecting the ruins. At a distance of a few yards from the house, they found the corpse of Henry Darnley, lying under a tree, and quite close by that of his page, Alexander Taylor. Both were in their shirts; near to the King lay the fur-lined night-robe in which he was wont to protect himself against the cold when in bed. A soldier raised up the two bodies. Swiftly, the Earl looked them over. At a sign from him the man laid them down again. Bothwell looked about him. There, into that deserted house, they should convey the corpses for the moment. Some soldiers brought up a third body, which they had found. But, so they said, the man was not really dead, indeed he was already more or less conscious: apparently he had merely broken his arm. Bothwell ordered guards to be placed before the house in which the bodies were bestowed, so that no one, absolutely no one, should be admitted save on the order of their captain. Then, in the dark morning light, round about six o'clock, he went back to the Queen.

He found Mary up and surrounded by her women. Dressed in black, she was sitting in an arm-chair. Her women were busy hanging the windows and walls of the apartment with black. The light of a single candelabrum was still burning. The Earl came nearer to make his announcement—the King and one of his pages were dead, a third man, however, saved. In the Queen's face, but dimly illuminated by the pale light of the candles, there was no sign of expression, beyond the lowering of her eyes.

In the course of the morning, she went to look upon the dead body of her husband, which had, meantime, been brought in from outside, and lay in a side wing of the palace. Silently, she stood before the bier, almost as motionless as the dead man at whom she stood staring. He lay, his hands folded on his breast: on his face, mainly no doubt due to the open mouth that now could never be closed, was imprinted a look of helpless, awful terror. On his hand the ring still sparkled, which his wife had given him in parting on the previous night. At last, the Queen turned away. Drawing over her face the heavy black veil that covered her from head to foot, she went quietly out. Returning to her apartments, she gave orders that the body should be embalmed and laid out in the royal chapel. There it lay for four days behind closed doors, and then, at night, was interred in the vault under the palace, close to David's grave. Two officials of the royal household supervised the interment. Queen Mary had removed to the castle, for her own security's sake. The disaster that had overtaken the King was, so she said, designed against her also. Only the accident of her attending the wedding festival that night and so being, contrary to custom, away from Kirk-o'-Field, had saved her from sharing his death.

In this sense, too, she wrote to the Archbishop of Glasgow, her emissary in Paris, from whom she received a letter, on the day after the King's death, warning her of a conspiracy against his life, and saying that reliable information to that effect had reached him, the Bishop. The English Ambassador, Mr. Drury, and the representative of the Duke of Savoy, who, while occupied with preparations for their departure, were still in Edinburgh on the night of the murder, endeavoured to see the King's body during the time when it was still lying in the house near to the scene of the crime. In this they did not succeed: the soldiers of the guard firmly denied them access. On every hand, and especially through their servants, rumours came to them to the effect that it had been definitely observed that the King's body bore no signs of burning or of any other wound: in fact, the King had not, so it was said, been killed by the explosion of the powder-mine, but strangled in advance, perhaps as he was trying to escape through the garden with his pages from the murderers whose steps he had heard approaching. Many old wives in the neighbouring hovels, who, by their own account, never slept sound, maintained that they had heard, all through the night, right up to the moment when the explosion took place, an uninterrupted coming and going of men's footsteps, with whispering and muttering. One old wife, whose house was the nearest to the ruins, said that she had heard a man screaming quite distinctly in the garden of Kirk-o'-Field, and made out, quite plainly, the words: "Mercy, mercy, brothers! Have pity on me, for the sake of God who has pity for the whole world!"

A black velvet shoe, with high sides and sharp toe-point, was found by the crowd which stuck near the tree under which the King lay when he was found, until the guard drove them off. No one wore such shoes, they said, but Sir Archibald Douglas. Sir Archibald Douglas, held to be the most learned man in all Scotland in the law, was a close friend of all the great lords, and most intimate with the Queen herself. Again, soldiers and servants were said to have sought admittance continually through the gates of the palace and the Canongate, and when asked by the Watch "Who goes there?" the answer always was "Friends of the Earl of Bothwell."

★

While the Queen remained invisible to the world at large up in the castle, announcement was made, by herald and proclamation, at the Market Cross and all the other important centres in Edinburgh, to the following effect:—

"THE GOOD KING IS DEAD"

"Every one is aware that on the ninth of February, at two hours after midnight, the house in which the King's Highness had taken up his abode was blown up into the air, within the space of a minute, at a time when His Highness lay asleep in bed, and with such violence that nothing remained intact of the entire building, walls and all, but the whole structure was utterly destroyed and lies in ruins, while the corpse of His Grace and of a servant were found at some little distance from the said house. In order to avenge this hideous and treacherous deed, the Queen's Majesty, on whom in the first instance the cruel blow has fallen and who would rather lose all she has than allow such a crime to go unpunished, commands, in agreement with her nobles and Council, that no inquiry be neglected which may lead to the capture and rigorous punishment of the authors of so godless and unheard-of an act. Therefore, Her Majesty commands, in accordance with the resolution of her Privy Council, that whosoever first gives information leading to discovery of the originators, advisers or actual perpetrators of this appalling and most treasonable murder, shall, even if this first informer be himself an accessory to the crime, be assured not only of his life and liberty but also of a reward of two thousand pounds in Scots gold, together with a yearly allowance to be paid to him and his dependants."

The crowd pressed round these announcements, murmuring comments. On the morning after the posting of this notice and three days after the murder, there was pasted up on the door of the Town Hall underneath it a second placard which ran as follows:

"Whosoever can give information about the murder of the King, is told to present himself and receive two thousand pounds and an income for himself and his dependants. Well— the doers of the deed are: the Earl of Bothwell is one, the pastor of Flisk, Master David Chalmers is another, and black John Spens another. But the main doer is Sir James Balfour.

341

Sir Archibald Douglas also helped. And the Queen knew about it all, for she has been bewitched by Lady Buccleuch."

On the same morning another notice was officially affixed below this one, in which the writer of the placard was called upon to give his name in order that he might receive his reward and be led before the Queen and her Privy Council. Whereupon he replied:

"If the money be placed in the hands of one trusty individual, I will come next Sunday, with one or two witnesses, to sign my name to my first communication. Further, the lackeys François and Bastian, and Joseph, David's brother, and the Queen's goldsmith ought to be arrested. Then I will set out what each man has done himself and what with his accomplices."

Whereupon the Earl of Bothwell rode through the town at the head of fifty horsemen. At the Town Hall he halted and ran the placard through with his bare blade. "Tear up that nonsense!" A squire obeyed at once. The Earl raised his hand with the sword in it towards the door where the notice had stood. "If I can lay hands on you, I will wash my hands in your blood!"

★

Queen Mary came down from the castle to go into the country on the invitation of one of her most devoted Lords, a Seaton, the father of her Mary. While she was still in the fortress, she had made some important appointments. Thus, the Earl of Mar, who had hitherto been commandant of the fortress of Edinburgh, was removed from this post, in order that he might devote himself entirely to his task as guardian of the little Prince, in favour of Bothwell's friend, Sir James Balfour. Bothwell himself was given command over Dunbar, which counted as the strongest fortress in Scotland. Further he was given absolute control over Blackness and the Inch, the fortress which guarded Leith harbour. Already he had the

Palace Guard and royal police of Edinburgh under him. He
had long held the little fortress of Borthwick.

After the Queen had thus, as she thought, ensured her safety,
which, so she said, was continually threatened by conspiracies,
she was no longer sad. True, a powerful detachment of sol-
diery surrounded Lord Seaton's castle day and night. This,
however, may have been intended to protect the Queen from
mannerless curiosity. Certainly her conduct was calculated to
disappoint any one who expected that her attachment to all
French customs would cause her to observe the ceremonial
court ritual of thirty days of solitude in black-hung rooms,
shut off from light and air, as mourning for her dead husband.
She took her court state with her to Seaton, more than a hundred persons, including the Earls of Bothwell and Huntly,
Archbishop Hamilton of St. Andrews, Lords Fleming and Livingstone, and State Secretary Lethington and his youthful
wife. She rode out daily with her suite; they sat at table to
all hours of the night, music alone being lacking; there was more
gaiety than for long, far more than in recent days. One day
the conversation at table turned upon archery, in which Queen
Mary believed herself past mistress. "We are the best at it!"
she cried, indicating herself and the Earl of Bothwell. In jest,
Earl Huntly, and Lord Seaton contested this claim. "Let us
see, this very day!" cried the Queen. And that very afternoon
they did shoot in the park, in an open space, protected from
the wind. Drawing herself up, Mary stretched the bow with
all her old power. Had she ever been languid, suffering, down-
cast in body and mind? Her whole person glowed with joy.
When, after her, the Earl of Bothwell took up his bow, and
drew it slowly, as though tasting the pleasures of victory in
advance, she stood leaning on her bow, with bliss shining in
her eyes: recklessly, her eyes caressed the face of the man before
her as though they closed him in rapturous embrace. He raised
his arm, and took careful aim. The arrow shrilled on its way.
"Bull's eye!" Mary rejoiced openly. She turned to the others.
"Beaten, beaten, you two, from the very start! Is any one

going to try, after that?" They stood their ground; at least
they were going to try their luck. "Brave fellows! My best
wishes!" All the time she kept teasing the marksmen uninter-
ruptedly, as though she were determined to leave them no
chance of a quiet aim. Anyhow, whether out of want of skill
or abundance of kindness, they both shot very ill indeed. "Of
course!" said Queen Mary. "I told you so. But if people will
not heed . . . It is really hard on us, to win so easily! The
inequality was too great, all the time." She seized Bothwell's
arm. "But you two gentlemen will have to give some sort of
jollification for us!" she remarked, to the others. "We insist
on that, this evening." Till long past midnight the company
remained in the great hall of the castle, lit by countless candles.
Queen Mary laughed and talked. She picked off a twig from
the ivy wreaths with which the table was decorated, and hung
it playfully about her neck. "What a pity there are no flowers
now!" she said. "But when the time of roses comes we shall be
ever so beautifully adorned!" She rose. "Ah, if only I were
not a Queen!" Her eyes shining, she looked at the Earl of
Huntly, by whom she was standing at the moment, who knew,
as did they all, that her radiance was for another. She laid
both hands on his shoulders. "No! I am glad that I am a
Queen! For I want to give, give, to be always giving! I should
like to give all of you so much that you would all be richer than
any man on earth yet. But for that, even as a Queen, I am far
too poor!" Half embarrassed, the men looked at her, for melting in her own transcendent glow, she seemed utterly to have
forgotten how a human heart may shake with fear and with
remembrance.

★

None of the Scottish officials had so much as attempted to
inquire into the deed but recently accomplished. The very
nature of the crime implied complicity on the part of dozens,
nay of hundreds. In a hundred other ways the King might have
been quietly put away, secretly, so that no one could say, after
the event, Well, did he not meet his death by accident or by

some carelessness on his own part? His house blew up with a report that made every window in Edinburgh rattle. If the murderers, as was universally said, really had found it necessary to make sure of the King's death before the mine was set, they could hardly have thought that their plan was an efficient one. The deed had been carried through as though it were an object with its doers to say to all the world, with laughing openness, There! That is how the nobility of Scotland deals with the insolence of a silly ass who presumed to push into their circle.

The people? What did Henry Darnley matter to the people?

★

But the Powers, whose concern had been so often and so earnestly invited by Scotland, thought they were therefore now entitled to make their views heard.

From France, Mary's loyal servant, the Archbishop of Glasgow, thought fit to write:

"Talk here of the murder goes so far as to calumniate Your Majesty yourself as prime mover in the whole deed and to suggest that everything was done by your orders. I can draw no inference from the news of Your Majesty but that it has pleased God to preserve you in order that you may exact merciless vengeance. If this be omitted, it seems to me that, so far as this world goes, it would have been better that you should have lost your life and all else. Only the extremest determination can be adequate here; the obligation of doing what is due to God must take precedence of every worldly interest. Otherwise, I am gravely apprehensive lest this prove but the opening and first act of a tragedy which I can but pray to God in His endless mercy to avert."

Queen Catherine of France also wrote to her daughter-in-law that, if she did not fulfil her duty by avenging the blood of her husband, her honour would be lost and friends no longer to be looked for by her in France.

Elizabeth of England expressed herself without reserve:

"Madame, My ears are so deafened, my mind so darkened, my heart so oppressed by the news of the accursed murder of your late husband, my dead cousin, that I hardly yet have the power to write about it. And although nature impels me irresistibly to express my sympathy for the death of a man so near kin to myself, yet if I am to speak my thought plainly to you I cannot conceal the fact that I think you more to be pitied than he. Madame, I should but poorly fulfil the duty of a faithful cousin and affectionate friend if I thought more of pleasing your ears than of urging you to the preservation of your honour: and therefore I shall not conceal from you what is the talk of most people here. It is that so far as the execution of this deed you look through your fingers and take no pains not to be too near to those who have done you so much pleasure—as though the murderers would not have carried through the deed before they knew themselves assured. I beg you most earnestly not to conceive that I could ever permit so atrocious a thought to find entry into my heart! Never, for all the wealth of the world! But I do exhort and advise and implore you to lay this matter so to heart, without any regard for the fact that it may affect a person who is very near to you, that no eloquence may have the power to dissuade you from giving to the world an example of the great princess and true wife that you are. I write thus vehemently not because I myself harbour a shadow of doubt of you, but out of the special affection in which I hold you."

Mary's blood rushed to her heart, as she read this letter. She let the hot tide subside, and sat still while a smile of bitter scorn crossed her blanched face. She imagined to herself what sort of attitude the Queen of England would assume, were she to write to her: Madame, You are perfectly well aware that the man with whom you have for years preferred to spend the night, in England, Scotland and France, is looked upon wherever your name and his are known, as the murderer of his wife, and that you are believed to have promoted or, at best, connived at and afterwards condoned his deed. And this self-same man you, for years, recommended to me, in his capacity of pearl of created beings, as the sole suitable husband for me, so much so that you threatened me with war and roused my subjects to rebellion against me, on no other ground than that I could not bring myself to be, in this matter, entirely of your mind. Cousinship you rejected with scorn, so long as Henry Darnley was alive as my husband. Now it seems to you that anger for the death of such a dear relative has become a useful instrument for you to use.

Queen Mary knew that she would write nothing of this sort, and that she had no need to do so. Queen Elizabeth, at her own good time, knew this better than any one could tell her.

★

Soon, indeed, Queen Elizabeth had her second thoughts. Her ambassador appeared to convey to the ruler of Scotland the sympathy of his Government in the heavy blow that had fallen upon her. Queen Mary came from Seaton to her capital in order to receive this envoy, and he found her in black-hung apartments, dimly lit by the light of a few candles. She spoke, in a low and languid voice, a few words only, to the effect that she thanked her good sister of England most sincerely for her friendly and genuine concern.

Queen Elizabeth, however, had apparently sent this ambassador because Queen Catherine of France had already done so. Mary knew that her mother-in-law had said, confidentially: At bottom her daughter-in-law was bound to be glad to be so quickly free of the tiresome man. "Had the young fool had more sense, he would be alive today."

★

Yet another person wrote to her.

Earl Matthew of Lennox sent the following letter:

"Your Majesty, I have by the hands of my servant who brings you this, received Your Majesty's gracious and comforting letter, for which I give you my humble thanks, confident as I am that I shall never deserve anything other of Your Majesty than what you there offer me. Since Your Majesty has deigned to receive my simple counsel in good part, I find courage to continue it, notably as follows: Since, in spite of the pains and trouble which, so I understand, Your Majesty has devoted to a thorough investigation of this last hideous deed, the criminals have not yet been detected, I find myself to my own great distress compelled, in nature and in my duty of being so bold as to proffer to Your Majesty my poor and simple counsel, in the clearing up of this matter, humbly to urge Your Majesty to summon with all due speed the entire nobility and estates of the realm and so make such provision for a complete investigation of the matter as may, as I do not doubt, through the working of the Holy Spirit of Almighty God in the hearts of Your Majesty and of all Your Majesty's faithful subjects, cause the bloody and horrible doers of this deed to be discovered. I know that Your Majesty does not need to be reminded in this matter, and beg you humbly to forgive my troubling Your Majesty with it, as the father of him who is now no more.

"And so I confide Your Majesty to the protection of the Almighty, trusting that He may grant you a long life and a most happy reign.

"HOUSTON. 20th February, 1567."

Queen Mary replied:

"Most honoured cousin and counsellor of our Crown, greetings.

"We have received your letter of the 20th of this month, from

Houston, in which you express your thanks for the fact that your good-will and counsel have met with so friendly a reception from us. We have done but what was right: and in showing you all kindness and good-will that we can, we do but do our duty and what our natural inclination suggests to us, on which you may count now, and hereafter, so long as God grants us life, and which we have shown to you at all times since our first acquaintance with you. As touching the summoning of the nobles and the estates, as you recommend, with a view to making a full investigation of the horrible murder of the King, our husband, it is admissible that such may take place. For that reason shortly before the receipt of your letter, we had commanded the calling of a Parliament, where, we do not doubt, all the members will appear and where first and foremost this matter which lies most on our heart may be taken up and not abandoned before everything has been investigated that may serve in any way to clear it up. We ourselves, and, we doubt not, all our nobles, will most gladly do all in our power to this end, as, with God's grace, the event may prove to all the world.

"Your faithful daughter, M. R.

"SEATON, 21st February, 1567."

Earl Matthew replied swiftly:

"Humbly do I thank Your Majesty for a most gracious and comforting letter, which I received on the 23rd, and from which I perceive that it is Your Majesty's pleasure to postpone the investigation of the ruthless deed until a Parliament can assemble. Although I am well assured that the time will seem as long to Your Majesty as to me, before this matter is ordered and the criminals justly punished, I do nevertheless beg Your Majesty humbly to forgive me for troubling you as often as I do, but the matter lies too near my heart, and for that reason I implore Your Majesty to accept my humble advice, viz. that the time that must elapse before a Parliament is too long: further, that this matter is not one for Parliament, but is of such weight and of such significance that it must be followed up with all speed and celerity so that the punishment may serve to the entire world as an example. I know that Your Majesty's wisdom sees all these things, and sees them far better than my poor brain can do. As I hear that certain placards have been fixed to the door of the Town Hall in Edinburgh, by way of reply to Your Majesty's proclamation, and that in these placards the names of certain persons are cited as the originators of the horrible murder, I therefore beg Your Majesty most humbly to be pleased to order first, that the persons named in the aforesaid placard be seized and brought under safe custody; second that the whole nobility be then assembled; third that public proclamation be made compelling the writers of these declarations to appear and prove their declarations.

"If the said persons fail to appear, it will then be open to Your Majesty, on the advice of your nobles and your Privy Council, to set the individuals so named at liberty again. Your Majesty would thus do a good and honourable act in so far as either the doers of this deed would be punished in accordance with justice, or the declarations proved to be vain breath, in which case the persons charged in them could appear before all men cleared and relieved of all suspicion.

"*26th February*, 1567."

Queen Mary replied:

"We have received your letter and perceive therefrom that you have misunderstood our last letter, in so far as you imagine that we intended putting off investigation of this atrocious deed until Parliament met. We had not such intent but before God rather desired that it might be investigated swiftly and without delay, the sooner the better and the more comfortable for us. But when you advised that we should summon the entire nobility for this purpose, we replied that we had already summoned a Parliament. It does not seem to us possible either that a second Parliament should assemble earlier or that it should assemble twice in succession. We have not intended that this matter was a matter for Parliament, nor to postpone it till then, but to call the nobles together for this specific purpose. As for your demand for the arrest of the persons named in the placards on the Town Hall door, there are so many placards there and all so eagerly engaged in naming so many different names that we do not know at all with which we should proceed. Should any names be set therein which seem promising, we shall certainly proceed so far with your suggestion as the laws of the land permit, and, in the event of the guilty persons being discovered shall proceed against them with all the severity that the gravity of the crime deserves. Whatever else you think serviceable for us to do, you will doubtless inform us of; we, on our part, shall neglect no opportunity of clearing up this matter, and so Farewell.

"Your good Daughter, M R.
"SEATON, *first of March*, 1567."

To which the Earl replied:

". . . May it please Your Majesty: my humble request to you was that it might please Your Grace to arrest and place in safe custody those persons named in notices posted in response to Your Majesty's proclamation; as for the names of these persons, I am astonished that they have not reached Your Majesty's ears, in view of the stir made by this notice, and the open talk caused by it. The first notice concerns the Earl of Bothwell, Sir James Balfour, Master David Chalmers, and black James Spens; the second, the Frenchman, Bastian, Jean of Bordeaux, and Joseph, the brother of David. These persons, I assure Your Majesty, are highly suspect, and now that Your Majesty knows the names and as you are so deeply concerned in this, even more so than I am myself, although I am the father, I have no doubt that Your Majesty will cause the

proper steps to be taken in view of the gravity of the matter, about which I humbly and earnestly entreat you.
"*17th March, 1567.*"

Queen Mary, who had, meantime, returned from Seaton to Edinburgh, replied in her last letter:

"We have received your letter, with the names of the persons cited in the placards, and whom you suspect. So far as concerns the assembly of our nobility, we have done what you desired in your letters, and have ordered it to take place in the coming week in Edinburgh, when the persons named in your letter shall be subjected to such examination as the laws of the State prescribe. If their guilt in this appalling crime should in any way appear, we shall, in accordance with our earlier letters, apply the punishment of the law with the rigour and stringency deserved by the gravity of the crime, the more so that, as you say in your letter, we are ourselves involved in the suffering thereof. Therefore we ask you to prepare to appear in Edinburgh in the coming week, in order to inform yourself about everything involved in this matter, and you will then have proof of the serious purpose and earnest mind with which we have regarded this matter from the beginning and shall always continue to do. Farewell.

"Your good daughter

"M. R.

"*28th March 1567.*"

★

Before Queen Mary despatched this letter she knew that the writer of the placards, accusing her closest friends, her most personal servants, and not least herself (as the Earl of Lennox must well know) would not present himself, nay, that he was, in fact, no longer in Scotland.

The inquiries made by the Privy Council had established the identity of the writer of these placards as one, James Murray by name, a former servant of the Earl of Bothwell: a man who

352

had once seemed utterly devoted to his master, so much so that he had probably shared many a dangerous secret, but who, attracted by the prospect of reward, had attempted exposure. Before the inquiries were well under way, the man, roused to consciousness of what he had done, and the powers he had set in motion against him, fled from the country. There was nothing to be done but charge him with slander in his absence. This was done at a session attended by the Earls of Murray, Huntly, Bothwell, Caithness, and some other lords. According to Scottish law, the greater offence includes the lesser, and also extinguishes it; therefore the man was charged with slandering the Queen. On this charge, he was condemned to death as a traitor. The judgment was made known all over Scotland, together with the warrant for, and personal description of, the fugitive from justice.

★

The task of avenging the murder of the King was now left to Earl Matthew.

Chapter 11

IN AINSLIE'S TAVERN

VERY early on the morning of the thirteenth of April, William Drury, Mayor of the English town of Berwick, rode out to Edinburgh as an extraordinary ambassador from his Queen. He came to transmit to the Queen of Scotland a holograph letter from his Sovereign, which he absolutely must deliver into her hands before the day of law on the Earl of Bothwell, fixed to take place on this very morning. As he rode, Mr. Drury shook his head slowly, more than once. For it seemed amazing to him that his Queen should still harbour misapprehensions so complete as to imagine that the punctual receipt of a letter from her could in any way affect the course of such an affair. Probably all that she wanted was to cover her retreat, no matter what turn things might take, by having sent the warning contained in her letter.

As the English gentleman approached the town, he found himself joined by many troops, large and small, on horseback and on foot, whose number grew whenever a by-road entered the general main road. The Englishman rode through the town gate, and found all Edinburgh seething with excitement. It seemed as though there were no work being done today, in any house or workshop, and but one idea occupied every mind, that of going to the palace to see, to stare, to get excited and to gossip. Drury knew that he would find almost the entire Scottish nobility assembled in Edinburgh. Every younger branch of the Hamiltons was present—that family whose deadly enmity to the Lennoxes was known to every child in Edinburgh and to every one throughout the world who knew anything of Scottish conditions. Among the great lords of the realm the only one missing would be the Earl of Murray. On the previous day, indeed, Drury had seen him in Berwick, when he, in passing through, had told Drury that, with his Queen's permit in his pocket, he was, at his own wish, about to spend some months abroad, in France or Italy. Lord James had spoken with disquiet of the turn everything seemed now to be taking in Scotland. No patriot could possibly reconcile himself to it. He, therefore, wished to utilize this opportunity to fulfil his long-felt desire to see how matters were conducted in other parts of the world. He had only spoken in general terms of all the events that had driven him from home. But he knew well enough that Drury understood his mind. His Queen had been very reluctant to give him leave of absence, he added. There had actually been tears in her eyes when she let him go. Again and again had she earnestly appealed to him, could he not stay? no one had any other feelings for him than those of appreciation and affection. Resolutely rejecting all such appeals, he had come away.

Drury thought of him, and of what he had said and hinted at. He also thought of the reputation enjoyed by Earl Murray, that impeccable Christian and patriot, of an astounding prescience which invariably enabled him to disappear on the eve of momentous and difficult events.

Busy with his own thoughts, the English gentleman pursued his way amid the thick stream of traffic, every step of his horse hindered by the throng. While he now gave way, now pressed through, now drew in his reins and now spurred on, adjusting his motion to the movements of the crowd, he reflected: They rush as if to a theatre! The issue doesn't interest them.

He reached the stockade of the palace. It was closed, save one small entry. On the farther side Mr. Drury saw that the place was full of a press of knights. At the gate a big detachment of spears stood ready to march out. As he tried to push his horse through the narrow entry, the guard stopped him with lifted halberd—"No admittance!" Intent to avoid further delay, Drury explained that he was an emissary of the Queen of England bearing a holograph letter from his Sovereign to the Queen of Scotland, which he must place in Her Majesty's hands at once. Every minute, nay every second, of delay was intolerable. The guards would have to answer for the evil that would result. The men considered. That was very well, they said at last, but they could not allow any one to come through on any pretext. They called to one of their officers; he came and informed the Englishman, No, he could not go into the palace. But an official of the court should be called out, who would give him definite information. Soon after a middle-aged man appeared, who introduced himself as the Chamberlain of the royal household. He was very sorry, he said, but it was impossible for any one, no matter who he might be or on what business, to have admittance to Her Majesty. Her Highness was so exhausted by the events and excitements of these last days—which touched her so very nearly—that she was in the most urgent need of rest. It was after midnight before she had been able to retire. Now, she was sleeping and had given strict orders that she was not to be waked. Such a statement, uttered amid the surge of such a roaring sea of noise and clangour, could not but strike Drury as ironical, but face to face with this dry, discreet, supercilious, courtly Frenchman, he could only accept it. With a proud shrug of the shoulders, the Chamberlain refused even to present the letter, as Drury, at some cost to his own feelings, suggested. Finding it more and more disagreeable to have to stand on the far side of the gate like a beggar, Drury finally said that he would return in an hour, when the Queen would surely have awakened.

He sat down in a tavern near by, and his excitement cooled off as he watched the bustling life around him and listened to the talk of the people who filled every seat at the neighbouring tables to his. Experiences in his own country, resembling what had happened and might be about to happen here, occurred to him: his uncle had been a member of the Court which had condemned Queen Katharine Howard to death; another had taken part in the divorce proceedings of Queen Katharine of Aragon.

IN AINSLIE'S TAVERN

When, at the appointed hour, Drury again approached the palace gate, the knights in the court were mounted; some one came to throw back the gates for a whole troop to march out; the spearmen drew their lines close. All the cavaliers, hitherto moving noisily about the courtyard, were now decked out as for a tourney, except that they all carried gleaming weapons. He tried to count them. Including the spearmen, there must be at least three thousand armed men there.

Two horses were just being led out before the inner entry to the palace, one, a glorious steed, hardly to be held quiet, with a tail that swept the earth. Out of the door came the Earl of Bothwell and Maitland of Lethington. The squires sprang forward to the horses' heads: loud hurrahs, resounding thunderously round the yard, greeted the gentlemen. They were just about to place their feet in the stirrups when Lethington, looking round, recognized the English envoy, who was still standing outside, before the gate. He turned to the Earl and said a word or two to him. Stepping back from his horse, he too looked in the Englishman's direction. Maitland walked across the court to Drury. He was extremely sorry, he said, amiably. "I know, I know—it is most annoying, but Her Majesty is still sleeping.—You will understand. . . . It is quite impossible, absolutely impossible. . . . Give me the letter," he added. "I will answer for its coming into the right hands, and will myself see to that." Drury, despairing of any success for his own efforts, and thoroughly sick of his humiliating position at the gate, in full view of the populace, handed over the document. Lethington, with it in his hand, turned back into the palace, accompanied by the Earl of Bothwell. Half an hour had passed, seeming to Drury like half a day, before they reappeared. Lethington approached the English gentleman. "It was impossible, after all; we have done what we could, but it was not possible to get in to Her Majesty. It may well prove to be impossible until this day of law is over. Well . . . all I can say is that I am most extraordinarily sorry about it. But you will understand. . . ." He turned back to his horse.

Bothwell, who hitherto had stood in conversation with a knight in the court, now joined him. They mounted, and followed by the proud array that closed clanking round them, rode out of the gate, past the envoy. The Earl of Bothwell was a superb figure on his splendid horse. The Englishman knew his bearing—that of a proud man, utterly sure of himself, facing a world of weaklings. Before the troop was clear of the courtyard, the Earl turned round in the saddle: Drury saw two tall women at one of the windows of the palace, one of whom raised a white hand in greeting. There at the window was the Queen with her friend, Mary Lethington. The quick colour sprang up in Bothwell's face; he smiled, showing his white teeth brilliant between his scarlet lips; he just raised his hand in an almost imperceptible motion of returning greeting; then, spurring his horse, he turned to the gate. The whole troop trotted past Drury, all laughing and talking, all insolent in bearing. In a thick cloud of dust, they disappeared into the narrow streets of the Canongate, which led straight up from Holyrood to the Town Hall in the High Street, where the day of law was to be held. The people, hitherto pressed back so tight behind the iron barriers of the ranked soldiers that they threatened to storm the way that was being held clear for the train of knights, now poured out and pressed up after them.

In the town, new swarms kept adding themselves to the train of the Earl's adherents. When he reached the Town Hall, he had over nine thousand men behind him. At the gate, he was met by Earl Morton, of whom it was said that in a secret nocturnal conversation with the Queen he had had to swear inviolable faith and alliance to the Earl of Bothwell as the price of his own reinstatement in the lands he had been deprived of after the late rebellion. In any event, he had been reinstated. Now, accompanied by Earl Morton, the Earl of Bothwell entered the Town Hall, to ascend the steps to the hall of judgment; a young relation of his, Hob Ormiston, placed himself on his other side. Immediately after the doors of the hall had been opened to admit the Earl, for whose appearance the court was waiting, the entrance was barred by soldiers. Admission to this session was confined to the nobles, and, among them, to those who possessed immemorial right to attend. In the great hall, filled by a level grey light from small but numerous windows set rather high up in its walls, the judges were seated in the railed-off upper portion, behind an immense table: the Earl of Argyle, magnificent in stature, with his singularly insolent robber-baron's countenance, with all the dignity of a lord of Supreme Justice, and the right of presiding at all meetings of the tribunal of peers: two Marshals, chosen for their age: and four assessors, one of them being Lord Lindsay. At the narrow side of the table two clerks were in readiness, dressed in sober civilian clothes, whereas all the knights wore dark but costly garments of French fashion. On the table before the judges lay a skull and a great sword, the Sword of Justice of Scotland; between the two, a crucifix. On either side were the benches on which the jury sat, in three ranks, each raised a little above the others. Among them sat the Earls of Cassilis, Crawford and Sutherland, Lord Rothes, Lord John Hamilton, second son of the Duke of Châtelherault; James, Lord Ross; Robert, Lord Semple, the husband of Mary Livingstone; Lord John of Maxwell; Lord Ogilvy of Deskford and Findlater, the one-time enemy of the Gordons and lover of Jean Gordon, now married to Mary Beaton; and many other adherents of the Royal party. The whole of the rest of the space in the hall, up to a wide passage in the centre which ran from the door to the barriers, was filled with benches occupied by those knights whose rank gave them admittance to hear though not to participate in the proceedings.

While the Earl of Bothwell, accompanied by his cousin, Hob Ormiston, approached the barriers before the judges, the latter whispered to him, "Do you know that you are as white as chalk? You are not going to go flop at the last moment?"

The Earl, with a sombre glance at him, merely muttered, "Be quiet!"

His brows knitted, pale, yet erect in bearing and with

measured tread, the Earl marched right through the hall.

He knew, as did all those present, that his opponent, to whom the direction of the affair, as a purely personal matter, had been assigned, would not appear. Earl Matthew Lennox had written to the Queen to say that he could not come to the day of law, since he had fallen sick on the way between Glasgow and Edinburgh. He earnestly implored Her Majesty to postpone the day till he should have gathered first enough strength and then enough adherents, to meet so fearful a power as the Earl of Bothwell had developed. The time allowed him was too short. He was in the depths of despair.

The Earl of Bothwell stood at the bar, his hand on his dagger hilt. He was magnificently attired in dark purple silk, with a short velvet cloak about his shoulders: feathers waved proudly in the beret on his head. He stood straight as a dart: above the snow-white folds of his ruff his face was of an earthen hue, and the glance of his eyes was as dark as the unreflecting mirror of a pool deep in the woods.

The secretary, at the narrow end of the table, began to read the accusation in a monotonous voice. He began: "James Hepburn, Earl of Bothwell, Lord of Crichton and Hails"—all the titles and dignities of the Earl were set out, that he was hereditary High Admiral of Scotland, commander of the fortresses of Dunbar, Blackness, the Inch and Borthwick, Generalissimo over the forces in the Southern and Western Provinces—then, the accusation went on: "You, therefore, James Hepburn, Earl of Bothwell, are accused of having taken part, in plan and action, in the horrible, treacherous and cruel murder and death of the late exalted, mighty and most noble prince, His Grace the King, the beloved husband of our ruler, Her Majesty the Queen, and moreover that you have done in deed in such fashion that, in the silence of the night, when the King's Highness had given himself up to rest within his own dwelling, Kirk-o'-Field, within the precincts of Edinburgh, and the peace of the city, you have treacherously set fire to the said house, and with the force of a great supply of gunpowder, have caused the whole dwelling to be exploded in the air and so the said late King has been treacherously murdered, slain and destroyed by you, through your intention and by your design. This you did on the ninth of February of this year in the silence of night, as is universally known and cannot be denied by you."

The Earl of Argyle took up the word—"James Earl of Bothwell, appear as defender in this case, and you, Matthew Stuart, Earl of Lennox and all other of the Queen lieges who maintain that they can bring forward any evidence in this matter. Appear before this court, to accuse and to defend, as the law prescribes."

Earl Bothwell approached nearer to the bar so that he stood directly facing the judge. By his side were the two advocates who had undertaken his defence.

Lord Argyle put the question: "James, Earl of Bothwell, do you declare yourself guilty of the crime of which you are accused in this charge and which is known to all this assembly?"

In a level voice the Earl replied: "Not guilty."

Argyle once more summoned the Earl of Lennox to appear and represent his cause; and a third time. At last, with clanging step, there approached the table, through the gangway between the benches, a young, robust, blond man, in simple clothes, his cap in his hand. He halted there, to announce that he was Robert Cunningham, a liegeman of the Earl of Lennox, and carried credentials signed by his lordship himself with his own hand. The youth drew the document from his wallet and handed it to a servant who passed it up to the judges, who, in their turn, passed it on to the jurors after they had examined it. Drawing himself up, the young man waited to be allowed to address the assembly, which he did in a loud and penetrating voice:

"My Lords! I come from my lord, the Earl of Lennox, to explain the reasons for his absence on this day and am clothed with full authority to speak for him. The cause of his absence is the shortness of the time and the fact that he has been deprived of his following, of his friends and servants, who would never have left him for the protection of his honour and his life. In view of the strength of the opposing party, while no one stands for him but himself, he has commanded me to ask for a day more suited to the importance of this matter, in order that he may then attend. If, however, your lordships will proceed today, I enter my protest, as is alone open to me, without seeking to particularize my charge. I give notice that, should those presiding over this day of law today acquit any persons whomsoever who may appear on this day at the bar of complicity in the murder of the King, such an acquittal will not represent ignorance but malicious error. For it is universally known that those who are presiding at this court are the murderers of the King, as my liege, the Earl, asserts. I desire that my protest be entered and recorded."

Since there was no one in the hall who had not known beforehand every word that was to come, no face showed the smallest sign of astonishment. The men sat there calmly, looking almost without interest at the youth, whose bold, lively voice and manner seemed to seek to offset his impotence.

A clerk had written down the protest, in accordance with the proper formalities. In a dull, monotonous voice he now proceeded to read out the words which the young squire had just spoken. He in his turn, half-dazed by the official calm of the entire proceedings, took up the pen to confirm the fact that his words were correctly transcribed by affixing his signature to them. That done, he withdrew to the side.

The letters were next read out which the Earl of Lennox had written to the Queen, together with copies of her answers.

Then the Earl of Argyle took up the word again: There would now be an interval, in which the court and the jurors might withdraw to consider their verdict. He rose to go out with the other presiding judges through a door in the wall at the back; the jurors went out likewise. There was a general movement, among the others, towards the Earl of Bothwell. Every one was in the best of spirits, and turned this way and that, in loud conversation. The Earl of Huntly clapped his

362

brother-in-law on the shoulder, with a laugh: "Excellent! We
are on velvet, so far!" A page squeezed through the press to
Bothwell, to hand him a packet wrapped in a silken kerchief.
Flushing a deep red, he turned aside a little to unwrap the
little wallet. It contained a ring and a paper, folded over and
fastened with a seal, which he broke open hastily: then, after
quickly perusing the few lines it contained, thrust it with the
ring and the silk wrapping into the front of his doublet. Red
and white passed in rapid alternation over his face. His eyes
met those of his brother-in-law, still standing by him, almost
shamefacedly. Huntly smiled.

Bothwell said quickly: "If I could only get out into the open
air for a moment: I mean away from all these people!"

"It is nearly over," said Huntly, by way of encouragement.
"Two or three hours more, at most. . . ."

But his brother-in-law was not listening to him. "I always
have the hardest things to do," he muttered, as though to himself.

Huntly laughed so that the pale, baggy skin of his narrow
face was puckered in a thousand wrinkles. "Well, you are
paid in proportion," he said.

A herald smote with his staff on a shield suspended from a
pillar at one side of the hall, as a signal for the resumption of
the session. Every one returned to his place. The jurors' benches
filled up again. The judges sat behind their table. When quiet
was restored, the Earl of Caithness, as Chancellor of the Court
of Nobles, addressed them. Slowly, he perched a large and
roughly made pair of spectacles upon his nose, then, taking up
a paper, he began, in the dead, business-like voice employed by
every one with the exception of the Earl of Lennox's messenger,
reading out the judgment of the court. It ran as follows:

"In view of the fact that the Earl of Lennox in the letters he
has addressed to Her Majesty the Queen repeatedly and in so
many words demanded a swift and decisive action in his cause,
and that in that demand he agrees with the advocates here
appearing for the Earl of Bothwell, present in his own person,

who make it on account of the serious position of their client, therefore, the court here in session on a Scottish noble, has, after long deliberation, decided that the said process is to be concluded on this day, in accordance with the laws of the land, and despite the protest of Robert Cunningham on behalf of his lord, the Earl Matthew of Lennox, such protest further, not having been sustained, as is prescribed by the laws of the land, by any helpers.

"So far as touches the Earl of Bothwell," the dull voice droned on, into the chilly silence, "who has appeared here in person before the court of his peers to learn of what crime he is accused in the charge of the Earl of Lennox, and who, in reply, denies all guilt, the Court of Nobles after long deliberation has decided unanimously, both in general and on each specific count in the indictment, that the Earl of Bothwell is clear and to be acquitted of every charge of having taken part in the murder of the King made against him in the accusation that has been read to him.

"Further," the voice droned on, "and in view of the fact that this whole process has been appointed to be held on so early a date simply and solely on the express request of the Earl of Lennox himself, and that such appointment was carried out in strictest conformity with the laws of the land, the court cannot accept as valid a protest which cancels that express and personal request of the Earl of Lennox, on which ground alone any question of malicious error is excluded.

"The said judgment, unanimously arrived at by the entire court together with the whole body of jurors, lords and barons, is to be published, in order that it may be known to all the world as the confirmation of the proceedings of this day of law on a Scottish noble, carried through with all due formality."

The voice fell still.

The day of law on the Earl of Bothwell, on the charge of Earl Matthew of Lennox, was at an end.

★

At night, the whole town was agog with the remarkable events of the day.

Every one knew what had taken place in the Town Hall.

"They heard no witnesses," said one.

"They needed none," replied others. "When a case comes before the nobles' court, it is for the accuser to bring witnesses."

"He had no time, poor Earl Matthew!"

"That is his own fault: why was he in such a hurry at first."

"A nobles' job," said another. "One against the rest, and our Queen at the head against him."

They all shook their heads, sucked their wine-glasses, shook their heads again, and told each other dreadful stories of their ruler. At last the best joke of all occurred to somebody, and leaning back, he laughed aloud, shrilly: "They acquitted him of the ninth of February, but at two o'clock, when the crash came, it was the tenth!"

"They may know that it happened on the ninth!"

"Likely! The Queen was still with him then. I saw her riding home myself; it was not yet midnight."

"Well, they can call it acquitted or not acquitted, just as it pleases themselves."

This night, Holyrood lay as though dead: sentries walked round, endlessly, spears on shoulders.

In the town, there was no quiet, the whole night through.

In the morning, there were placards affixed at the street corners. They said:

> Farewell, good King Henry!
> Vengeance on Mary!

On one, there were verses:

> I say, this is a splendid law,
> See how the bloody murderers draw
> The plans up for their evil act,
> And bind together in a pact

With all the other stupid fellows
Who fear to see themselves on gallows!
God is not glad though ye acquit,
His vengeance waits, and shall yet fit
Ye who the hapless lamb thus slew
Who trembling to your springes flew.
Let him go free, I do not care,
The dusky light shall yet be fair.
The further in the mire ye press,
The harsher is your way's distress.
And you, the captain of the crew,
Who Christ betrayed resembles you.
An sum ego, Jesu Christi?
He answers, Juda tu dixisti!
Enough that this is said to ye,
The evil doer ye set free,
Whether ye spake in fear or favour,
Malicious error stinks for ever.

On the day of his acquittal, the Earl of Bothwell caused it to be proclaimed by heralds and notices that he was ready to meet in single combat any one of honour who dared to charge him with complicity in the murder of the King.

Further, he sent intimation to the French and English Courts that inasmuch as the King of France and the Queen of England had sent urgent letters to his own Government demanding his arrest and punishment, he, now freed by the judgment of the court of Scottish nobles from every suggestion of guilt, had no more passionate desire than to have the charges that were being made on all sides behind his back, repeated to his face by no matter whom. In order that time and place might be found congruent, no matter in what country it might be, and that he could publicly fight the matter out, provided only that the Sovereigns of the respective countries would ensure him free passage to and fro.

★

Immediately after the day of law on the Earl of Bothwell, Parliament assembled, to give legislative sanction to the decrees issued in the course of the past year by the Queen and her Privy Council. Parliament had not met since the abortive assembly of the previous year, which had been prevented by the death of David Rizzio and the abduction of the Queen. This time the direction of business was in the hands of the Earls of Morton, Argyle and Bothwell, as the leading dignitaries of the realm, the chosen chancellors and caretakers of the kingdom. They had to propose the enactments that required sanction.

Above all, the acquittal of the Earl of Bothwell came before Parliament for ratification and entry as a legal act in the archives. The assembly then passed to transactions between the Crown and the nobles. The proscription of the Earl of Huntly and his family was rescinded, and he restored to all his family estates. Lord Lethington, who had long since been compensated by the Queen on account of the Abbey of Haddington, transferred from him to the Earl of Bothwell, was confirmed in his new possessions.

The same was done in the cases of the Earls of Murray and Morton, and of Lords Robert and John Stuart, and many other nobles were either confirmed in the restoration to old, or the acquisition of new, estates.

On its first day, too, Parliament issued a drastic law against the affixing of defamatory placards on to walls, etc. Inasmuch as these slanders touched the nobility of Scotland and even the person of the Queen herself, their authors were adjudged guilty of high treason, of which the penalty was death. Those who wrote or circulated, or even read and left undefaced, such placards were, if not executed, to be punished with imprisonment, loss of property, or banishment.

On the remaining days of its session, Parliament dealt with the concerns of the Protestant Church in Scotland, whose long and earnest appeal for the grant of a yearly income sufficient to maintain its ministers and institutions was at last acceded to.

★

The session of this Parliament lasted from the 14th to the 19th of April. On the evening after its conclusion, the lords assembled in the first inn of the town, Ainslie's Tavern, for a banquet given by the Earl of Bothwell to his friends and nearer acquaintance, constituting, at the moment, the entire nobility of Scotland then assembled in Edinburgh.

From afternoon on, they sat in the vaulted chambers of the inn. The table glittered with the costly silver from the Earl of Bothwell's town mansion. They sat, eating of the best that could be procured in Edinburgh. Without intermission they drank the strongest wines of Edinburgh's cellars—and, from of old, the country had had the most lively trading relations with France in the matter of wines. After they had eaten their fill, they sat on, singing, roystering and shouting, telling broad stories and passing vulgar jokes, making lewd, half-drunk and quite senseless speeches, and drinking every one's health, above all that of the Earls of Bothwell and Huntly, first individually, then together: then those of Argyle, Lethington, and even Morton: of every one who had been banished, every one who had received new estates or got his old back. Between each toast, they shouted, "Hurrah for the Queen! Long live Queen Mary!" It was a sort of victory feast of the Scottish nobility, who celebrated the fact that they had kept their word and fulfilled the bond they had taken to destroy utterly that cheeky, tyrannical young ass, Henry Darnley, for his insolence to the Scottish nobles and his intolerable conduct to the Queen, his wife. They were quite among themselves. By themselves, they had carried through this campaign to triumph; none dared call them to account; the matter was entirely their affair. They had sought to show their power, prove what they could do if they stood solid against a world. Some one mentioned England. Another retorted: "What are these monkeys to us? Spawn of the devil! That crew of hucksters cannot touch us. Anyhow, who holds the Prince? They can come begging!"

There was talk, also, of the prize of victory. "In no case is she to marry any one else but the man we elect! And this time it shall be a man who will cure her of her Mass!" No one knew who started this topic, but all at once they were all on to it. "We must marry her at once, or else the whole thing is pointless! . . . And she is ready, only too ready!"

They stood about in groups, moving awkwardly, standing propped against chairs and table, wine-cups and glasses in their hands. Earl Bothwell talked with the Earls of Argyle, Morton and Sutherland. Some one approached one of the younger lords, not one of the intimates of the group, and touched him on the shoulder: he had been sitting by himself, busy with his wine, singing, and now turned round to find Sir James Balfour behind him. As the young lord stared at his puffy, pallid face, with the skin stretched so tight and smooth over its fat cheeks that it looked as though water were running over them, he repressed a shudder. Something like a will to evil for its own sake looked out between the slits of those little glittering eyes of his, and this although the man was certainly quite sober. What it was that terrified him, the young lord could not have said. In the next room, said Sir James, taking him confidentially by the arm, there lay a little paper—or, if his lordship preferred, a large one—of which, in any event, the contents were interesting, very, very interesting.

"It concerns us all, you and me and every one here. When are we likely to find another opportunity as charming, as snug, as this, of being just by ourselves, all together and cosy? I fear never, never again: life is not so merciful. . . . It is a question of the Queen," he said, pressing his companion's arm warmly against his soft side, which felt as though it were upholstered. "Yes, yes, of the Queen. Is she to elude us with another marriage? That was a shocking trick, the other time. And this time she will think of marrying a foreigner, some great Prince . . . she has plenty of choice . . . one on whose might she could rely . . . supposing we happened to get across her one time or other. . . . Oh, she is a clever, clever woman! And then we shall have had all the trouble and work . . . for what? As for me," he tapped his breast with his free hand,

"I am out of this anyhow. It is the Earl of Bothwell she is to marry, every one knows that. That is really the whole point."

The young lord's head whirled. Was it all so simple, really? Was there not some obstacle, something . . . whatever it was, he could not lay hold of it . . . but it wound round and round in his head like a rabbit in a cage . . . at last, suddenly, a door out of his dark cellar seemed to open before him, and he cried, "But the Earl of Bothwell has got a wife already!"

Sir James smiled so pityingly that the other was ashamed. "True," he said, "it is of course well known that the Earl of Bothwell has already got a wife. A noble lady, a Gordon, no less, the Earl of Huntly's sister, no less. Of course we all know that. But come, look here. Who are those standing there, talking together in the greatest possible intimacy? It seems to me as though it were the Earl of Bothwell and him of Huntly. And how do they strike you, eh? As good, true friends? I tell you they are even better friends than they seem. In these days you have doubtless often seen them standing by each other. Do you imagine that the Earl of Huntly does not know what is at stake in this whole matter? And if you see that the attachment between the two is in no wise diminished . . . what do you think? . . . must it not be all right for the Gordons in the upshot?"

The young lord's cellar-door had long since slammed to behind him. But there was something inside it that hurt him, hurt him badly.

"Such matters can be disentangled with the greatest ease," laughed Sir James, "so soon as the parties concerned approach them with a modicum of good-will and mutual understanding. And I can assure you, that is there, on all sides." His tone suddenly changed, became dead serious. "Her Majesty desires it," he said sharply and brusquely, shutting his mouth like a trap.

The young man went with him into the next room, to sign. Sir James Balfour glided away among the groups.

Soon the paper was no longer signed in the next room. A knight mounted on a table, to read it out aloud. It was too long: no one could understand him; they did not even listen. He contented himself, therefore, with roaring out the principal points to the hot, thick, red faces before him. Amid gales of laughter, they shouted out their agreement.

The Earl of Bothwell sat, smiling still. His face was pale, save for two scarlet patches that burned high up above his cheek-bones under his eyes. His eyes flickered: he sat, far back in his chair, with the Earls of Morton and Argyle beside him, listening to the reading of the plan of confederation. The knight on the table waved the paper about until Sir James Balfour at last took it from him, while they all yelled: "Scotland! Hurrah! Long live Earl Bothwell! Long live Queen Mary! Hail! Hail!" They roared: "Down with the accursed foreigners! Down with the Mass! To hell with the damned Papists!"

The paper, pen and ink, went the round: every one signed. Sir James fussed about. When, at last, he got his paper back, he said: "What writing! Half of them write like pigs!" Eight earls had set their names to the bond, twenty peers, and many other lairds. And each of the gentlemen answered for his whole family. The entire nobility of Scotland was in this.

The document ran as follows:

"We, the undersigned, understand that the noble and mighty Earl James of Bothwell, Lord of Hails, Crichton and Liddesdale, High Admiral of Scotland and commander for our Queen Mary on the Borders, is not merely injured and slandered through placards which have been found fixed to the doors of the Cathedral and Town Hall of Edinburgh, but that he is being pursued by his rivals and secret enemies with the allegation that he has by thought and deed brought about the hideous murder of the King, the Queen's late husband. Yet after the Earl of Lennox, as kin to the deceased, has, in letters to the Queen, earnestly pleaded to have the aforesaid Earl of Bothwell charged with the aforesaid murder, the Earl of Bothwell has, according to the proper forms, been tried before a public court of the peers and other barons of this realm and found by them to be of untainted honour, innocent and free of the horrible crime laid against him, and has been acquitted according to the laws of this land. And inasmuch as the Earl has further declared his readiness to prove and demonstrate his innocence with weapons in his hand, in accordance with the rules of knightly honour, he has omitted nothing in the rebuttal of these charges that a nobleman can do in accordance with his honour and the law. Therefore, and in view of the ancient greatness and distinction of his house, the honourable and loyal service of his forbears, and, especially, his own service to his Sovereign, whom with her realm he has defended against her enemies, and, further, in view of the bonds of kinship and of friendship which unite each one of us to him, and in the light of our own experience, which is that every nobleman who enjoys the deserved favour of his Sovereign is, on that account, daily exposed to the vilest slanders and attacks: on all these grounds we bind ourselves, each one of us, by our faith and our honour, by every drop of truth that is in us, as true as we are noblemen of this land and shall one day stand for it before God, that, should it ever appear that the slanderous charge against the Earl of Bothwell, completely refuted by the decision of the court of nobles, is again raising its head, we will, each one of us, with the whole of our friends and sib, all our lieges and dependants, every man that belongs to us, stand behind him openly and loyally, defending his quarrel as our own, pursuing it with life, estate and all that we possess, and not permitting either by word or deed, anywhere on the earth, anything to be done to his reproach or dishonour. Moreover, however, and in view of the fact that our Queen's Majesty has no husband and should, for the realm's sake, not continue in that lonely state, we venture, in view of the loyal devotion and proved services of the Earl of Bothwell towards her, and in view of his other distinguished qualities, humbly to lay before Her Majesty that— should she be inclined in entering upon a new marriage so far to demean herself as to contemplate preferring one of her own native subjects to any foreign prince, her choice should then fall upon the Earl of Bothwell. We, on our part, each one of

372

the undersigned, pledge ourselves solemnly to support and promote this marriage with our voices, our power, and our counsel, by word and deed, at whatsoever time it may please Her Majesty to conclude the same, and so soon as the law may permit of its celebration. And in the event that any one, overtly or covertly, openly or under any pretext whatsoever, shall seek to prevent or hinder this marriage, we will treat such preventers and hinderers as our common enemies and detractors and support the Earl of Bothwell, in so far as the Queen's highness shall permit, as we are answerable to God and our consciences. And should we be found remiss in carrying out this bond, may we be reckoned for all time to have forfeited our honour, and looked upon as faithless and unworthy traitors. In sign of which we set our hands as follows."

★

A shock followed for every one.

The Earl of Lennox had fled to England. Queen Elizabeth had released his wife from imprisonment.

★

Lord Herries, a laird of some thirty years of age, whose property lay in the south-west, came to the town and to the court, in order to fall upon his knees before the Queen and say: "Your Majesty sees me here at your feet. I have come down from my mountains, because I could bear it no longer, to have every one throughout the country saying . . ."—imploringly, he raised his two hands—"that Your Majesty intends giving your hand to the Earl of Bothwell, a man who, let him be acquitted a thousand times, is still gravely tainted with suspicion of the King's death!"

Queen Mary's face had gone hard as iron. But all she said was, "First of all, stand up, my Lord!"

"Not before Your Majesty has told me that I may be at ease! Let Your Grace only reflect," he appealed more pressingly. "Do not abandon your son: do not compromise him! Him and Your Majesty's gloriously flawless honour!"

"Stand up, my Lord," repeated Queen Mary, her face now as red as it had before been pale. "It beseems me not even to listen to such words."

The man rose up, and stood before his Sovereign; he was tall, with a handsome, open countenance.

"I am not thinking of what you would put into my mind," she said, cutting off any further speech of his. "I know absolutely nothing about all that you have been saying."

He stood, hesitant. "Your Majesty will then forgive me my too great frankness," he said, after a pause, since the Queen seemed unwilling to add a syllable to the words she had uttered. Mary inclined her head coldly as a sign that the laird was dismissed. He went, without so much as being permitted to touch the hand of his Sovereign. An hour later, he was on the way back to his mountains. For his friends had said to him, "Are you really anxious to feel a blade between your ribs? The Earl of Bothwell is no joker."

Sir James Melville received a letter from a trusty friend, an Englishman, always counted a loyal adherent of the Queen of Scots. Her party in England was, he wrote, in the utmost anxiety and upheaval of mind. There could be no truth in the stories that were going the round, with new circumstances added to them daily. It could not be that the Queen of Scots had any idea of marrying a man whom all the world considered mainly responsible for the murder of her husband. He begged Sir James to inform his mistress of the anxiety that possessed him and his friends. Could he perhaps show her this letter? He wrote:

"It is impossible that Her Majesty can take an action that would destroy, at a stroke, the fruits of so much painful effort, and represent ruin to her noble aims! Would she not then draw down God's extremest wrath upon her head and cause the hearts of men in England, Scotland and Ireland to turn

from her utterly? Are we to contemplate the Earl of Bothwell
as some day King of Scotland, Ireland and England? Or, at
best, to have it supposed that we do? Has not the Earl of Bothwell been the head and front of the plan of murdering the King?
Is there a crime on earth which is not already attributed to
him? And, by God, is he not a married man?"

On the previous evening, Sir James had been permitted to
look at another letter, despatched from London by Mr. Thomas
Randolph, to his good friends in Scotland. He stated that a few
days ago, Queen Elizabeth had allowed him the honour of
walking with her, and he had seized the opportunity of showing
her a letter from the Laird Kirkaldy of Grange, one of the
bravest men in Scotland, which contained the following:

"What is to happen here Heaven alone knows! The Queen's
marriage with the Earl of Bothwell is imminent. She is so shamelessly in love with the man that when a certain person—I name
no names—endeavoured to make representations to her, she
merely replied with a scornful laugh that she would rather lose
England and France and her own country all together and go
with the Earl of Bothwell to the ends of the earth with nothing
but a shift to her back, than give him up."

But, so wrote Mr. Randolph, Queen Elizabeth had heard this
letter very unwillingly. No one could, as she said, regard the
behaviour of her cousin with greater aversion, nor had she
shrunk from making the most earnest representations to her,
as she felt to be her duty. But that was quite another matter,
and all in order. For subjects to venture to write of their God-
ordained ruler in such a tone as that of this letter—that she
could not understand. Even more incomprehensible was it that
any one should bring such an impropriety to her notice.

Sir James Melville rose and dressed. He determined to adventure on the course of action suggested to him in the letter.

He found the Queen at work with Lethington in her writing-room. He explained briefly that he had received a letter, from the circle of Her Majesty's devoted adherents in England, with a request to him to lay it before her; and, with that, he handed it over to Mary, who took it from him to read it. After perusing the first few lines, she turned in her chair away from the two men, and towards the window in whose deep embrasure her seat and little working-table were both placed, so that her back was almost turned to them. After a time, still reading, she turned away still more. Long stayed she so, holding the sheet, which she must long ago have read through, still in her hands, without moving or speaking. Sir James stood respectfully at a little distance by her side. The State Secretary sat silent, looking at the Queen. Gradually, Sir James felt a tide of pity rising in his heart as he thought of the young woman he had known in the glowing happiness of her perfect gifts, when, in joyous pride, she had felt that heaven and earth must open to her smile: and saw her now, the toy of incomprehensible forces, unable to look her servants in the face.

At last Queen Mary turned round to them, with a cold smile on her lips, and, passing over Sir James, handed the letter to the State Secretary—"Truly, a somewhat singular epistle! Read it!" In reply to Lord Lethington's interrogative glance, "It is a pretty invention, all made up to injure the Earl of Bothwell and myself!"

Lord Lethington took the letter; the Queen, as though Sir James were not present, bent over some great documents before her on the writing-table. Lord Lethington signed to the other to step out of the room with him. "Man, what devil made you conceive the notion of showing the Queen this letter?" He laughed. "On one point you may be quite at ease—before noon today the Earl of Bothwell will know sentence for sentence what is in the letter. Are you tired of life?" He went on: "No one can do anything."

"It is pitiable," ventured Sir James, "that every one here can see our Queen only a hair's breadth from certain ruin and no one lifts a finger to stop her."

"Well, you have raised a whole hand, so you can be at rest," replied Lethington. "But show enough sense to take my advice and clear out, to safety."

Sir James actually stayed away from his dwelling in the palace for some days, living instead with friends domiciled in the neighbourhood. He was informed by confidential friends at court that the Queen had actually communicated the entire affair immediately to the Earl of Bothwell, but only on condition that he pledged his word to her to attempt nothing against Sir James Melville, who was her really loyal servant. In spite of this, the Earl, in a towering rage, had gone about everywhere denouncing Sir James: if he came into his hands, he would crack his skull for him, as a double-dyed liar and slanderer. Whereupon, so it was reported, the Queen reproached him. If he went on like that, she would soon have nobody, and this at a time when they both stood in need of attaching every faithful servant to them. Whereupon the Earl promised to keep quiet, and danger was now presumably over.

Sir James therefore ventured to return to court. Indeed, he could not rest until he had again spoken to the Queen of the letter. Nothing in his whole life, he said, had ever caused him so much pain as the fact that it was possible for Her Majesty to have read a letter from so genuinely devoted and deeply concerned a friend of hers as an invention designed to injure her. The letter, contrary as it was to his own feelings, was genuine. But he would say no more upon the matter, since he saw that any such discussion was unpleasant to Her Majesty.

Queen Mary said nothing in reply to this.

Afterwards, however, she frequently summoned Sir James Melville to attend her when she rode out for exercise in the neighbourhood. Almost invariably the Earl of Bothwell was at her side, but his manner showed no enmity to Sir James, only a cold remoteness. When the Queen rode through the town, a body of trained soldiers surrounded her, as a guard, after the fashion of some foreign rulers, but one that, hitherto, had never been adopted by the Kings of Scotland, despite experiences that might well have made it seem necessary.

★

Queen Mary rode towards Stirling, accompanied by troops and by a suite including the Earls of Sutherland and Huntly, State Secretary Lethington and his wife, and Sir James Melville. The Queen desired to visit her son in Stirling. Before the gate of the castle, the Earl and Countess of Mar, the guardians of the Prince, received them with great courtesy. Indicating the Queen's soldiers, however, the Earl of Mar said that it was unfortunately impossible for him to admit so great a crowd into the interior of the castle, for want of space and other reasons. Would Her Majesty not please to take up her residence in the castle with her ladies only? Her troops could be quartered in the town or elsewhere. It seemed at first as though Queen Mary were going to take offence at these words. But she only said, with a bitter laugh, "It seems to me, Lord Mar, as though it were for me to decide whom I will see about my son, over whom your watch is set by me alone. Am I always to ask permission to have the Prince with me? Or to take him with me? I could hardly save him seeing my men, nor do I think it would hurt him to grow accustomed to them." The Earl could only turn red, bite his lips, and swallow his Sovereign's reproof. But he insisted that there were no quarters for the troops in the castle. "Place them where you can and will," said the Queen.

She rustled past him, to her son's room, which she entered with Mary Lethington and the Countess of Mar. The child, now ten months old, was crawling about the floor in a short frock; he had a ball in his hand, which he threw down to stare at his mother, as she came in. She dropped down on the ground beside him. "My treasure, don't you know your mother any more?" She picked up the child, which seemed at least to remember her sufficiently to stay quiet with her. "I have brought a dolly for my princeling," said Mary. "Such a pretty tumbler! Look, we pull the cord and the silly fellow has got to jump! And he likes doing it, and laughs, as loud as ever he can. And we laugh too, don't we?" She went on, "Our little lord is getting a great big boy. Soon he will be able to run and be ever so clever, and be glad when his mother comes to see him." Dandling the child in her arms, she went up and down the room. Once she murmured, "How like your father you are!" Still studying the child's face, she said, "But there is a good deal of your mother in you too, and of all her kinsfolk, grand-parents, and great-grand-parents, and they were all grand, fine, splendid people." She sat down, the child on her knee, in the window-seat with Mary Lethington and the Countess of Mar, to ask how the Prince was and how he was getting on. The little one wanted to get off her lap: she let him go. Lost in thought she watched him crawling and sprawling after his ball.

Queen Mary stayed in Stirling for three days. Although she had contracted a very severe cold on the day after her arrival, she rose to ride back to Edinburgh. On the first day she got as far as Linlithgow, where she spent the night. On the following morning, the twenty-fifth of April, her troop started off very early. Following their Sovereign's example, they all rode at ease. The day was unusually warm for spring; overhead the sky arched deep blue; the air was impregnated with the sweetness of coming summer. Queen Mary, who had hardly spoken a word the whole way, at last rode quite by herself, a little ahead of the others. Her ladies and gentlemen, and her troops, followed in close formation. They rode through woods, and the Queen seemed quite without apprehension, for she still rode alone. Then the woods divided and, at the crossing of the road from Linlithgow to Edinburgh with that running eastwards, they saw a mass of horsemen halted, almost an army, fully armed, standing by the bridge that spanned the stream at that point—a forest of spears. At the sight of the royal train, all these troops immediately set in motion, and came on quickly, at a trot, more quickly; the earth groaned under the horses' feet and such a cloud of dust rose up that it hid them and their riders completely. The Queen fell back among her companions, who crowded round her. But the others came on; they did not halt; they knew their goal; these were foes and their number was far, far greater than that of the Queen's men; as they rode they filled the whole breadth of the road and they were in deep formation—there must have been at least a thousand men.

"Your Majesty! At least we know how to die for our Queen!" cried the young Earl of Sutherland, passionately.

Queen Mary was pale as death. "No bloodshed, for God's sake!" she cried, holding her hand up commandingly to Sutherland. "I shall deal with them, I, I alone; for God's sake, no bloodshed!"

The horsemen were right upon them; their leader was the Earl of Bothwell. In a flash he had broken through the ranks round the Queen, and seized the bridle of her horse. "Your Majesty will . . . with me . . ." Whatever he might have intended to say, his voice was so thick that nothing intelligible came through. He dragged Mary's horse to him, without more ado. She turned, again, in the saddle, to cry, anxiously, again, "No bloodshed! Nothing will happen to me, nothing!" The Earl dashed off with her. His troops, which had quickly opened ranks and held a way for him, closed, at once, behind him. A portion rode off; no one knew whither. Meantime the blade with which the young Earl of Sutherland was striking about him was smitten out of his hand by the captain of the troop. The Earl felt for his pistol at his belt; that, too, was taken from him, with the calm of superior strength, by the man, a fellow of gigantic proportions. When he came to Sir James Melville, to do the same, he said, with a half laugh: "You do not wish to vex Her Majesty's heart by open disobedience?" The gentlemen— the Earls of Huntly and Sutherland, Lethington and Sir James Melville—were taken by the soldiers and put in their midst; Lady Lethington likewise. The men were disarmed and then let go.

People in the towns, Aberdeen, Edinburgh, and elsewhere, came shouting—"The Queen has been abducted by the Earl of Bothwell! The Queen has been taken to Dunbar!"

Messengers ran speeding to all the quarters of the heavens. In Edinburgh, the alarum bells rang. The folk of Aberdeen sent to the great lords for help and began preparing a campaign against Dunbar, with intent to release their Sovereign from a shameful imprisonment. They sent messengers to Dunbar: somehow or other, whether by force, guile, or other means, they must get through to the Queen and tell her that her faithful burghers of Aberdeen were ready to do everything in their power to free her from and revenge her upon the accursed robbers and shamers of her honour.

The messenger found no difficulty in carrying out his commission: he was led straight to the Queen, whom he found in the finest apartment in the castle. Lady Lethington was with her and she looked beautiful and proud and unbroken in spirit, entirely unaffected by what had happened, whatever it might be, and, indeed, as though she had never found herself in more perfect harmony of mood. Sitting in her chair, she listened to the messenger from Aberdeen, reflected for an instant, and then said, in a clear ringing tone, "We thank our faithful servants from our heart for their readiness to serve us. Assuredly something has passed which has surprised us, and which we must characterize as singular and even as wrong. But now we are so well placed that we have nothing whatever to complain of. And therefore, no greater service can be rendered us than a quiet demeanour on the part of our faithful subjects."

The Aberdeen messenger received a letter from her to his city, saying what the Queen had said to him by word of mouth. On its receipt, the burghers indignantly laid aside their spears for the time being.

★

But Queen Mary was not always so calm and collected, in Dunbar as the messenger found her. She occupied the same rooms as she had done when she had escaped thither with her husband after the murder of David. But of those times she hardly thought at all. For the new brought more than enough of new to occupy her.

Baron Lethington came to her, in a state of genuine excitement, to offer every help. It would be easy for Her Majesty to make her escape from the fortress. He, the State Secretary, had already talked over plans with many gentlemen. Queen Mary looked at her minister, at first without saying anything. There was no embarrassment in her look; it suggested rather that she found something so singular that she could not, at once, overcome her astonishment at it. At last she said, slowly:

"I thought, my lord, that you were the sworn friend of the Earl of Bothwell?"

"Your Majesty, everything has its limits!" he exclaimed, with passionate emphasis. He moved hastily up and down, while Queen Mary sat quietly on her little round stool. He smote his brow. "So it is really, really true! And, double and triple fool that I am, I have always refused to believe it! I told them all, You are wrong. That is impossible. Allow her a great deal. She has a right to it. But in the last resort she knows herself and her limitations, and what she can allow herself to do and what she cannot." He paused in front of Mary. "Your Majesty, I must say to you—a marriage with the Earl of Bothwell is simply inadmissible." He reminded Mary of her English plans. She could not want to give them up . . . because . . . because of an infatuation! That was what it amounted to, a complete abandonment of everything she had lived for hitherto, if she were really, as he now felt that he had got to believe, to try to put through this impossible marriage. "In the first place, you cannot do it; you will see, you cannot do it! Then the Earl is England's sworn enemy . . . Oh . . ." The Queen tried to interrupt, but Lethington drove on, "And if he is not, every Englishman thinks him so. And that is what matters. For an Englishman, his name is that of the Evil One. There is no altering that. And whatever the English may put up with, they will never put up with having the Earl of Bothwell crowned as King of England—never."

Mary's face expressed utter contempt: she seemed to say—
The whole of England, in that case, is a matter of complete indifference to me. Her minister went on, quickly:

"Madame, it cannot be done. This marriage—never. We have
never grudged you the right," he went on, "to take any
pleasures that seemed good to you. God knows, that is your
right. Without that, your position would be intolerable.
Further, we have let you give, freely, although that is a very
different matter. On that, no more need be said. But this is impossible. This can never be. This is too much."

"Do you dare . . . ?" cried Queen Mary, roused at last.
But she did not stop him.

"I must," he said. "It is my duty. Does the Queen of England
marry the man whom she wants?"

"You dare to compare me with her!" Mary flamed up.

"Yes. For she is right. A thousand times right. There is the
greatness of that narrow woman, that she does not do it. That
she knows that a Queen, God knows, has something else to do
than give way openly to her own feelings!"

"How can you think of the Earl of Bothwell and that man
in the same breath!"

He was not listening. "You are ready to destroy the State
for the sake of your feelings. But your feelings are nothing to
the State. The State is interested in you only so long as you are
of service to it, so long as you are a centre, a hope of union."
He begged: "Use your good sense, Your Majesty!" He implored: "Your Majesty knows not what you do!" He threatened: "It is a question, now, of your very existence!"

"I demand, then, to be allowed to decide it for myself!" She
raised her head, forced him to meet her eyes. "Who has pressed
the Earl upon me as a husband? A certain paper has lain before
me, there, on the table!"

"Do not think of such things, Your Majesty!"

"Why not?" she asked, at once astonished and indignant.

"I did not sign it," said Lord Lethington, in despair.

"Well, I shall manage without your agreement!"

He turned round at her words. "Your Majesty, it is no longer a question of that. All that is words, words, words. Big words, for my part. But we cannot use them here. What is the sense of them here? There is no one here whom they fit. . . . Come, Your Grace. Nothing is lost, yet. Come with me out of this. Let the Earl go free. Afterwards, you can proceed against him. Time will put everything right. Time puts the most impossible things right."

"I think you are mad," was all that Queen Mary replied. She would say no more; she was tired of it, wanted to hear no more of it. He turned to other matters.

They were still talking when the Earls of Huntly and Bothwell came quickly in. The Earl of Bothwell was in a state of great excitement. He came to charge the State Secretary with having tried to get at his, the Earl's, own people; he had proof of this. Lethington replied. . . . The Earl called him a perjured traitor, in the pay of England. The reason for the deadly enmity of the State Secretary and all his group to the new tendency was simply and solely that it aimed at making an end of this policy of surrender, and having Scotland, at long last, stand on itself and its own dignity.

"One and all, you have sold yourselves for pelf, from the beginning," he shouted. He threw one insult after another in Lethington's teeth. The latter felt for his dagger. The two Earls drew theirs. They rushed on one another. The Queen threw herself between them. She held Bothwell firmly by the arm: "Touch a hair of his head, and your lives and lands shall pay for it, both of you." The men glared at each other, like mastiffs which have just tasted blood.

Queen Mary signed to the State Secretary, "Be gone!"

Thereupon the Earl's wrath was turned against the Queen herself. This was the result of her unworthy fawning on England, he said. What had Scotsmen ever had to hope from them?

At last, collecting herself, Queen Mary replied: "The two countries are bound together, naturally. Think what the endless horrible wars between them have cost both. To have peace is a simple necessity."

"All that is quite true," he said. "But how do humbleness and appeals, and this endless giving way, help? Either one has might, and consequently, right, or one has neither. Why should these English be so insolent? We have encouraged them in it."

"Is there a single other person who thinks as you do?" asked Queen Mary.

"We shall teach them, and they will soon learn."

"So long as the Scottish nobles are poor, they will always run after English money."

"Not all of them. We shall collect those who do not. And train the others to do differently."

But Queen Mary parted with her friend in a bad humour. It was late; she retired to rest. Contrary to her custom, she stood like a pillar, while her women—girls whom she had sent for to Holyrood: no one of rank among them—undressed her, although as a rule she was inclined to talk freely with her intimate circle. They took her garments from her, one by one, and combed out her hair, to arrange it more loosely for the night. Queen Mary seemed numbed; she thought, incessantly: thought that her friend had not, like her, had to try for five years to rule over the country. Gradually, however, as one thought slid into another, it seemed to her that only he could be right.

Then her thoughts broke loose again, and right in front of them there stood that fact she knew, the fact that Lethington had put into harsh words this very day, when he played his last trump against her.

She moaned.

One of her maids said gently, "Madame!" Mary saw that the girls were waiting to be dismissed, their tasks completed. She told them to go, and looked darkly after them, for she thought she had detected from their bearing, and from one or two words they had let fall, that, in their hearts, they were not as devoted as they ought to have been to the Earl of Bothwell.

In her bedroom, Mary knelt before her prie-Dieu, to say her prayers, at first to herself, and then, since her thoughts wandered, aloud. She rose, went to her bed, lay down: she drew the quilt over her. Then she sat up again. She heard the even tread of the guard in the passage, heavy, slow. Then it was so quiet that she felt as though she could hear the blood singing behind her temples. And still her thoughts went round and round the same single track. She sat, motionless. The burning of the light on the little table by her bed was audible. It seemed to her as though the panelling were moaning. The shadows lay dark in the corners of the room, and moved, as the light flickered. Mary thought of all the enemies who had ever wished her evil. But she would not call her women. Nor would she put out the light. In the dark it would be even worse.

She sat and thought of that other night, not a year ago, hardly eight months. And yet it seemed as though a lifetime lay between that and this. She thought of how she had come from Alloa, and shrinking from Holyrood, had taken up her abode in Edinburgh in the Checquer House. Vividly as at the time she felt how the murmuring sweetness of the late summer night had drawn her out of bed. The moon had poured into the room; she had opened the window, and sitting on the window-seat, gazed down into the garden, far below, full of smiling magic, with the wind rustling among its trees. And she had thought—perhaps everything was really over for her, and had wept bitterly.

And then the man was standing in the middle of the room, the man who was now her beloved, though she had not thought of him so then.

Mary sobbed bitterly, as all this came back to her. She jumped up, seized her cloak, to creep through the deserted rooms to her beloved, and press close to him, so close. With him, she felt at once as though all her fear and trouble, all opposition, all enmity, were mere imagining; as though this alone were her real life, and it was utterly impossible that she should not realize it and have it, in the end, quite obvious to every one else too that so it was. To him, with whom she did not need to be clever, did not want to be clever, she talked, softly.

"I have been so afraid."

He replied darkly, "You did not want me to come to you."

She sighed, and said, after a while, "I thought you would come."

Then, after a pause: "I am always thinking of her."

He was silent.

She went on: "But she does not love you!" And asked: "Has she written to you?"

"No."

"But she will write, tomorrow, and you will be upset, and I shall feel as though I wanted to die." Bursting into tears, she pressed her face into his shoulder.

After a difficult pause he said, in a constricted voice, "She has done nothing to me."

Mary roused herself. "Yes, yes." She wanted to talk.

Pressing her to him, he begged her, "You must give me time. I did not know it was so hard. Can you not understand? She has done nothing to me!"

But she complained: "It is so hard, because you do not love me."

"Ah, but I do, very much," he murmured: and again, "Can you not understand?"

"Yes," she sighed. "Often. Really, always. But every now and then, I cannot. I mean, I always understand you. But that you can love me, that I can never realize. And when you are away, I cannot help thinking of her. And then I do not believe that you love me, and think you cannot do it." She laughed, softly. "And yet I know what it is like to have some one terribly in love with me. When Chastelard stood behind my chair, he used to tremble so that the whole chair shook."

After a while he asked her, "Will you have me beheaded, too, if I ever become a nuisance to you?"

She put her soft bare arm about his neck as though he were already threatened. "You! Oh, how can you even say such a thing! I cannot understand it. It is dreadful, dreadful! I hardly cared for Chastelard," she went on. "It was entirely his doing. I could not help it. I stood enough, on his account, out of pity for him. But I had to do it. Why did he do it?"

"And John Gordon?"

It seemed as though she had to think, to recall it. "Ah, that is so long ago!"

"Four years."

"Yes, but he was to blame, too."

"You looked very sweetly at Chastelard, and John Gordon too. I know that. I have seen it myself, a hundred times. That is why I did not like you at that time."

She broke into tears. "How you torture me! How can you say such things? How can you speak of yourself in the same breath with the others?" She pressed close to him. "You are not to talk any more. I wish I need never rise again, but could die, in your arms, and you die too, and we lay together in one coffin, and in Heaven should be together always."

★

Queen Mary remained in the fortress until the third of May, receiving visitors and even holding meetings of her Privy Council. Then, amid solemn salvoes of greeting from the cannon of Edinburgh Castle, she re-entered her capital. The Earl of Huntly and Lord Lethington rode by her side. The Earl of Bothwell, on foot, humbly led her horse by the bridle.

Two days later, on the fifth of May, the dissolution of the marriage of the Earl of Bothwell and his wife was pronounced both by the Catholic and the Protestant Church. The Catholic Spiritual Court, which had been restored by the Queen only a few weeks previously, declared that the marriage of the Earl of Bothwell and Lady Jean Gordon was invalid because their relationship brought them within the prohibited degrees of kinship. At the time of the marriage, the bride had had in her possession a dispensation from the spiritual officers issued in view of his kinship. She did not now present it. The Protestant

JAMES HEPBURN
9TH EARL OF BOTHWELL

Church granted a divorce on the ground of the wife's complaint that her husband had, on several occasions in May and June of the past year, broken his vows with one of the maids on his Haddington estate. This complaint was sustained by witnesses. Five days elapsed between the first bringing of this complaint and the completion of the divorce. A considerable property was assigned to the Countess, now in her twenty-second year, as guarantee of her claim for support against her divorced husband.

Chapter 12

THE CASKET LETTERS

QUEEN MARY STUART'S LETTERS AND POEMS TO THE EARL OF
BOTHWELL

GLASGOW, 22 AND 23 JANUARY, 1567.

BEING gone from the place, where I had left my heart, it may
be easily judged what my countenance was, considering what
the body without heart, which was the cause that till dinner I
had used little talk, neither would anybody venture himself
thereunto thinking that it was not good so to do.

Four miles from thence a gentleman of the Earl of Lennox
came and made his commendations and excuses unto me, that he
came not to meet me, because he durst not enterprise so to do,
considering the sharp words that I had spoken to Cunningham,
and that he desired that I would come to the inquisition of the
facts which I did suspect him of. This last was of his own
head, without commission, and I told him that he had no receipt
against fear, and that he had no fear if he did not feel himself
faulty, and that I had also sharply answered to the doubts that
he made in his letters as though there had been a meaning to
pursue him. To be short I have made him hold his peace; for
the rest it were too long to tell you. Sir James Hamilton came
to meet me, who told me that another time he went his way
when he heard of my coming, and that he sent unto him
Houston, to tell him that he would not have thought that he
would have followed and accompanied himself with the Hamiltons. He answered that he was not come but to see me; and that
he would not follow Stuart nor Hamilton, but by my commandment. He prayed him to go speak to him; he refuses it.

The Laird of Luss, Houston and the son of Caldwell and

about forty horse came and met me. The Laird of Luss said he
was charged to a day of law by the king's father, which should
be this day against the signing of his own hand, and that knowing of my coming he has delayed it, and hath prayed him to go
see him, which he hath refused and swears that he will endure
nothing at his hands. Not one of the town is come to speak with
me, which makes me to think that they are his, and yet he speaks
well of them, or at least his son does. I see no gentlemen but
those of my own company.

The King sent for Joachim, and asked him Why did I not
lodge nigh to him. And that he would rise the sooner if that
were so; and why had I come, and was it for a good appointment? and why I had not brought Paris and Gilbert with me to
write. And that I would send Joseph away. I wonder who has
told him so much: even about the marriage of Bastian. I inquired of him about his letters, in which he had complained
of the cruelty of some; he answered, that he was astonished,
and that he was so glad to see me that he believed he would die
of gladness. He found great fault that I was pensive.

I departed to supper. The bearer will tell you of my arriving.
He prayed me to return, which I did. He declared unto me his
sickness, and that he would make no testament, but only leave
all things to me; and that I was the cause of his malady, because of the regret that he had that I was so strange unto him.
And thus he said: You ask me what I mean by the cruelty contained in my letter? It is of your cruelty I speak, for you alone
will not accept my offers and repentance. I confess that I have
failed, but not into that which I ever denied; and such like has
failed to sundry of your subjects, whom you have forgiven. I
am young. You will say, that you have forgiven me ofttimes,
and yet that I return to my faults. May not any man of my age,
for lack of counsel, fail twice or thrice, or in lack of his promise,
and at last repent himself, and be chastised by experience? If
I may obtain pardon, I protest that I shall never make fault
again.

And I crave no other thing, but that we may be at bed and

board together as husband and wife; and if you will not consent hereunto, I shall never rise out of this bed. I pray you now, tell me your resolution. God knows how I am punished for making my God of you, and for having no other thought but on you; and if at any time I offend now, you are the cause, because, when any offends me, if, for my refuge, I might make plaint unto you, I would speak it to no other body; but when I hear anything, not being familiar with you, necessity constrains me to keep it in my breast, and that causes me to tire my wit for very anger. I did still answer him, but that would be over-long to write at length. I asked why he would pass away in the *English* ship. He denies it, and swears thereunto; but he grants that he spake with the men. After this, I enquired him of the inquisition of Hiegate. He denied the same, till I showed him the very words spoken. At which time he said that Minto had advertised him that it was said that some of the Council had brought a letter to me to be subscribed to put him in prison, and to slay him if he made resistance. And he asked the same of Minto himself, who answered that he believed the same to be true. In the morning I will speak with him upon the point. As to the rest of Willie Hiegate's, he confessed it, but it was on the morning after my coming that he did it.

He was very fain that I should lodge at his lodging. I refused it, and said to him that he ought to be purged, and that could not be done here. He said to me, I hear said that you have brought a litter with you; but I had rather have gone with you. I trow he believed that I would have sent him away a prisoner. I answered that I would take him to Craigmillar, where the mediciner and I might help him, and not be far away from my son. He answered that he was ready when I pleased, so as I would assure him of his request.

He desires nobody to see him. He is angry when I speak to him of Valcar, and says that he will pluck the ears out of his head, and that he lies; for I enquired of him upon that, and that he was angry with some of the Lords and would threaten them. He denies that and says he loves them all and prays me to give trust to nothing against him. As to me, he would rather give his life than do any displeasure to me. And, after this, he did show me so many little flatteries, so coldly and so wisely, that you would be astonished. I had almost forgotten that he said he could not doubt of me, in this purpose of Hiegate's, for he would never believe that I, who was of his own flesh, would do him any evil; further it was shown that I refused to subscribe to the same. But as for any others that would pursue him, at least he would sell his life dear enough, but he suspected nobody, nor would not, but would love all that I loved.

He would not let me depart from him, but desired that I should watch with him. I made it seem that I believed that all that is true, and take heed thereat, and excuse myself for this night that I could not watch. He says that he sleeps not well. You never saw him better, nor speak more humbly. And if I had not proof of his heart of wax, and if mine were not as a diamond, which no stroke can break but that coming from your hand, I would almost have had pity of him. But fear not, the place shall hold unto the death. Remember, in recompense thereof, that you suffer not yours to be won by that false race that will work no less with you for the same.

I believe they have been at school together. He has ever the tear in his eye; he salutes everybody, yea unto the least, and makes piteous caressing unto them, to make them have pity on him. This day his father bled at the mouth and nose: guess what a presage that is. I have not yet seen him: he keeps his chamber. The King desires that I should give him meat with my own hands; but do you give no more trust where you are than I do here.

This is my first despatch: I shall end the same tomorrow. I write all things, howbeit they may be of little worth, to the end that you may take the best of all to judge upon. I am in the doing of a work here that I hate greatly. Have you not a desire to laugh, to see me lie so well, at least to dissemble so well, and to tell him the truth between hands? He told me almost all there is in the name of the Bishop and of Sunderland, and yet I have never touched one word of all that you showed me, but only by force, flattering, and to pray him to assure himself of me, and by complaining of the Bishop, I have drawn the worms out of his nose. You have heard the rest.

We are joined with two false races; the devil seeks to sunder us, but God knit us together for ever, for the most faithful couple that ever was united. That is my faith: I will die in it.

Excuse that I write ill; you may guess the half of it; but I cannot mend it because I am not well at ease; and yet very glad to write to you when the rest are sleeping, since I cannot sleep as they do, and as I would desire, that is in your arms, my dear love, whom I pray God to preserve from all evil, and send you repose. I am going to seek mine till the morn when I shall end my Bible; but I am grieved that it should stop me from writing news of myself unto you, because it is so long.

Advise me what you have determined in the matter you know upon this point, to the end that we may understand each other well, and nothing may be spoiled.

I am weary, and going to sleep, and yet I cease not to scribble all this paper so long as any of it remains. Curses on this pocky fellow that causes me so much pain, for without him I should have a far pleasanter subject to discourse upon. He is not very badly marked, but he has greatly fallen off. He has almost slain me with his breath; it is worse than your uncle's, and yet I came no nearer to him than a chair by his bedside, he being at the other end thereof.

I had almost forgotten that M. de Livingstone said in Lady Reres' ear at supper that he would drink to the folk that I wist of, if I would pledge them. And after supper he said to me, when I was leaning upon him, and warming myself at the fire, You may well go and see sick folk, yet you cannot be as welcome to them as you left somebody this day in regret, that will never be blithe till he see you again. I asked him who that was. He pressed my arm and said, Some of his folk that left you this day. Guess you the rest.

THE CASKET LETTERS

I worked this day till it was two of the clock upon this bracelet, to put the key of it within the lock of it, which is tied underneath with two cords. I have had so little time that it is badly made, but I shall make a fairer one in the meantime. Take heed that no one here see it, for the world will know it, because, owing to haste, it was made in their presence.

I am now going to my tedious purpose. You make me dissemble so far that I have horror at it: and you cause me to do almost the office of a traitor. Remember how, if it were not to obey you, I had rather be dead than do it; my heart bleeds at it. In sum, he will not come with me, except upon condition that I will promise him, that I shall be at bed and board to him as heretofore, and that I shall leave him no more; and on my word to this, he will do all things that I please, and come with me. But he hath prayed me to remain with him until the day after tomorrow.

He spoke very bravely at the beginning, as the bearer shall tell you, upon the purpose of the Englishman, and of his departure; but in the end, he returneth again to his humility.

He showed, among other purposes, that he knew well enough that my brother had shown me the thing which he had spoken in Stirling of which he denieth one-half, and, above all, that he ever was in his chamber. To make him trust me, it behoves me to fence with him in some things: therefore, when he requested me to promise him that when he was hale we should both have one bed, I said to him, fencingly, and making as though to believe his promises, that, if he did not change purpose between this time and that, I would be content therewith; but in the meantime, I bade him heed that he let nobody know of it, because, to speak among ourselves, the Lords could not be offended nor wish him ill on that account; but they would fear because of the boasting he made of them, that, if ever we agreed together, he would make them feel the small account they make of him, and counsel me not to side with them, at his expense: they for this cause would be in jealousy if, suddenly, without their knowledge, I should break the play set up to the contrary in their presence.

He said, very joyously, Think you they will esteem you the more for that? But I am very glad that you speak to me of the Lords, for I believe at this time that they desire that we should live together in quietness, for, if it were otherwise, greater inconvenience might come to us both than we are aware of; but now I will do whatever you will and will love all that you love, and desire you to make them love me in like manner, for, so they seek not my life, I will love them all equally. Upon this point, the bearer will show you many small things. Because I have ever much to write, and it is late, and I give trust unto him upon your word. Summa—he will go upon my word to all places.

Alas! I never deceived anybody; but I remit me altogether to your will. Send me advisement what I shall do, and whatever thing shall come thereof, I shall obey you. Advise too with yourself, if you cannot find out any more secret invention by medicine, for he should take medicine and the bath at Craigmillar. He may not come forth of the house this long time.

Summa, by all that I can learn, he is in great suspicion, and yet notwithstanding he gives credit to my word, but yet not so far that he will show anything to me: but nevertheless, I shall draw it out of him, if you will that I avow all until him. But I shall never rejoice to deceive anybody that trusts in me—yet notwithstanding, you may command me in all things. Have no evil opinion of me for that cause, for the reason that you are the occasion of it yourself; because, for my own particular revenge, I would not do it to him.

He has made some charges against me which touched me to the quick with fear—saying that his faults were made public, while there are those that commit faults and believe that they will never be spoken of: and that there is speech of great and small. As touching the Lady Reres, he said, I pray God that she may serve you for your honour; and said it is thought, and he believes it to be true, that I have not power over myself unto myself, and that because of the refusal I made of his offers. Summa, for a certainty he suspects the thing you know, and for his life. But, as to the last, so soon as I spoke two or three good words to him, he rejoices and is out of doubt.

I saw him not this evening, for ending of your bracelet, for which I can get no clasps. It is ready for them, and yet I fear that it will bring some ill-chance, and may be seen if you chance to be hurt. Advise me if you will have it, and if you will have more silver, and when I shall return, and how far I may speak. He is enraged when he hears of Lethington, or of you, or of my brother. Of your brother he says nothing. He speaks of the Earl of Argyle. I am in fear when I hear him speak, for he assures himself that he has not an evil opinion of him. He says nothing of those that are out, neither good or evil, but flies from the point. His father keeps his chamber, I have not seen him.

All the Hamiltons are here, and accompany me very honourably. All the friends of the others convoy me when I go to see him. He desires me to come and see him rise tomorrow betimes. To make short, the bearer will tell you the rest. And if I learn anything here, I make you a memorial of it at night. He will tell you the occasion of my remaining. Burn this letter, for it is over-dangerous, and nothing is well said in it, for I am thinking upon nothing but troubles. If you are in Edinburgh on the receipt of it, send me word soon.

Now seeing that to obey you, my dear love, I spare neither honour, conscience, hazard, nor greatness whatsoever, take it, I pray you, in good part, and not after the interpretation of your false brother-in-law, to whom, I pray you, give no credit against the most faithful lover that ever you had, or ever shall have.

See not her also whose feigned tears ought not so much to be praised nor esteemed as the true and faithful travails which I sustain for to merit her place. For to obtain which against my nature, I betray them that may impeach me. God forgive me, and give you, my only love, the hap and prosperity which your humble and faithful love desires unto you, who hopes shortly to be another thing unto you, for the reward of my irksome travails.

It is late; I desire never to cease writing unto you: yet now, after the kissing of your hands, I will end my letter. Excuse my evil writing, and read it twice over. Excuse the part that is scribbled, for I had no paper yesterday when I wrote my memorial. Remember your love, and write unto her and that very often. Love me as I shall do you.

Remember now of the purpose of the Lady Reres.

Of the Englishman.

Of his mother.

Of the Earl of Argyle.

Of the Earl of Bothwell.

Of the lodging in Edinburgh.

★

GLASGOW, JANUARY 25, 1567

It seemeth that with your absence forgetfulness is joined considering that at your departure you promised to send me news from you. Nevertheless I can learn none. And yet did I yesterday look for that that shall make me merrier than I shall be. I think you do the like for your return, prolonging it more than you have promised.

As for me, if I hear no other matter of you, according to my commission, I bring the man Monday to Craigmillar, where he shall be upon Wednesday, and I shall go to Edinburgh to be bled, if in the meantime I get no news to the contrary from you.

He is more gay than ever you saw him; he puts me in remembrance of all things that may make me believe he loves me. Summa: you will say that he makes love to me, in which I take so much pleasure that I have never come in where he is but incontinent I take the sickness of my side sorely, I am so troubled with it. If Paris brings me that for which I have sent him, I trust it shall amend me.

I pray you, advertise me of your news at length, and what I

shall do in case you be not returned when I am come there, for in case you work not wisely, I see that the whole burden of this will come upon my shoulders. Provide for all things, and discourse upon it first with yourself. I give this to Beaton, who goes to a day of law of the laird of Balfour. I will say no further, saving that I pray you to send me good news of your voyage. From Glasgow this Saturday in the morning.

★

GLASGOW, MONDAY, JANUARY 26, 1567.

Sir, if regret for your absence, the pain caused by your forgetfulness, and by fear of the danger which every one predicts to your beloved person, can console me, I leave you to judge; considering the ill fortune which my cruel fate and constant trouble have promised me, in the sequel of sorrows and terrors recent and long passed; all of which you well know. But, in spite of all, I will not accuse you either of your scant remembrance or scant care, and still less of your broken promise, or of the coldness of your letters, I being so much your own that what pleases you pleases me. And my thoughts are so eagerly subject to yours that I am fain to suppose that whatsoever comes from you arises not from any of the aforesaid causes, but from such as are just and reasonable and desired by myself. Which is the final order that you have promised me to take for the safety and honourable service of the sole support of my life, for whom alone I wish to preserve it, and without which I desire only instant death. And to show you how humbly I submit me to your commands, I send you, by Paris, in sign of homage, the ornament of the head, the guide of the other members, thereby signifying that, in investing you with the spoil of that which is principal, the rest must be subject to you with the heart's consent. In place of which heart, since I have already abandoned it to you, I send you a sepulchre, of hard stone, painted black, *semé* with tears and bones, I compare it to my heart, which, like it, is graven into a secure tomb or receptacle of your demands, and especially of your name and memory, which are therein enclosed, like my hair in the ring. Never shall they issue forth till death lets you make a trophy of my bones, even as the ring is full of them, in proof that you have made entire conquest of me, and of my heart, to such a point that I leave you my bones in memory of your victory, and my happy and willing defeat, to be better employed than I deserve. The enamel round the ring is black, to symbolize the constancy of her who sends it. The tears are numberless, as are my fears of your displeasure, my tears for your absence, and for my regret not to be yours, to outward view, as I am, without weakness of heart or soul.

And reasonably so, were my merits greater than those of the most perfect of women, and such as I desire to be. And I shall take pains to imitate such merits, to be worthily employed under your dominion. Receive this then, my only good, in as kind part as with extreme joy I have received your marriage, which shall not leave my bosom till our bodies are publicly wedded, as a token of all that I hope or desire of happiness in this world. Now fearing, my heart, to weary you as much in the reading as I take pleasure in the writing, I shall end, after kissing your hands, with as great love as I pray God (oh, thou, the only prop of my life!) to make your life long and happy, and to give me your good grace, the only good thing which I desire, and to which I tend. I have shown what I have learned to this bearer, to whom I remit myself, knowing the credit that you give him, as does she who wishes to be ever your humble and obedient loyal wife, and only lover, who dedicates to you for ever her heart and body, with no change to come, as to him whom I make possessor of my heart, so that you may hold it always in the assurance that, unto death, it shall in no wise be changed, and nor good nor evil shall ever estrange it.

HOLYROOD, WEDNESDAY, JANUARY 28, 1567.

I watched later up there than I would have done, had it not

been to draw out what this bearer will tell you; that I find
the best matter to excuse your affair that could be offered.
I have promised him to bring him to him tomorrow; if you find
it good, put order to it. Now, sir, I have broken my promise,
for you have commanded me not to send or write. Yet I do
it not to offend you, and if you knew my dread of giving offence,
you would not have so many suspicions against me, which, none
the less, I cherish, as coming from the thing in the world which
I most desire and seek, namely your good grace. Of that my
conduct shall assure me, nor shall I ever despair thereof, so
long as, according to your promise, you lay bare your heart
to me. Otherwise I shall think that my misfortune, and the fair
attitude of those who have not a third part of the loyalty and
willing obedience that I bear to you, have gained over me the
advantage won by the second love of Jason. Not that I compare
you *à un si malheureuse* nor myself to one so pitiless, however
much you make me a little like you in what concerns you; or
to preserve and guard you for her to whom alone you belong,
if one can appropriate what one gains by honourably, and
loyally, and absolutely loving, as I do and shall do, all my life,
come what pain and misery there may. In memory whereof, and
of all the ills that you have caused me, be mindful of the place
near here. I do not ask you to keep promise with me tomorrow,
but that we meet and that you do not listen to any suspicion
that you may hear without letting me know. And I ask no more
of God than that you may know what is in my heart, which is
yours, and that He preserve you at least during my life, which
will be dear to me only while my life and I are dear to you. I
am going to bed, and wish you Good-night. Let me know early
tomorrow how you fare, for I shall be anxious. And keep good
watch if the bird leave his cage, or without his mate. Like the
turtle, I shall abide alone, to lament the absence, however short
it may be. What I cannot do, my letter would do heartily, if it
were not that I fear you are asleep. For I did not dare to write
before Joseph and Bastian and Joachim, who only went away
when I began.

HOLYROOD—MIDDLE OF APRIL.

My heart, alas! must the folly of one woman, whose ingratitude towards me you sufficiently know, be the cause of giving
you displeasure, seeing that I could not have remedied it without knowing it? And since I perceived it, I could not tell it
you, without knowing how I was to govern myself in that
matter, for neither in that nor in anything else do I wish to
undertake anything without knowing your will in the matter,
which I entreat you to inform me of, for, all my life, I shall
follow it even more gladly than you can state it to me. And if
you do not tell me this night what you desire that I should do,
I shall take my chance of putting it through, although that
might do harm to that which we both desire. And when she is
married, I beg you to give me your opinion of another who may
not be hurtful in your mind to my constancy.

Mistrust me as you may, but when I seek to put you out of
all doubt and to clear myself with you, refuse it not, my dear
love, and suffer that I make you proof, by my obedience and my
fidelity and my constancy and my voluntary subjection, which
to me is the greatest good provided that you will accept it; and
make no ceremony about it, for you could do no greater outrage to me nor give more mortal grief.

STIRLING, APRIL 20, 1567.

My lord, Alas! why do you trust so unworthy a person, to
suspect her who is entirely yours? I am enraged! You promised
me to consider everything and tell me every day what I was to
do. You have done nothing of the sort. I warn you, be on your
guard against your false brother-in-law. He has come here to
me, without bringing me anything from you, and says that you
have ordered him to write to you what I should say, and where,
and when you were to meet me and what to do concerning him:
and thereupon has preached me a sermon on the folly of the
enterprise, and how I could never marry you with honour, seeing that, you being married, you did carry me away, and that

402

his people would not tolerate it and the Lords would oppose. In sum, he is all contrariety.

I said to him, that having come so far, if you did not of yourself draw back, no persuasion, not even death itself, could make me fail of my promise. As to the place, you were so neglectful (pardon me) that you left that entirely to me. Choose yourself, and let me know. In the meantime, I am sick, and must postpone, and for our proposal it is too late. It has not been my fault that you did not take thought in time. And if you had not changed your opinion since my absence, and more than I have done, you would not now be asking such resolutions of me. For there is nothing lacking on my part, and since your negligence puts us both in danger through a false brother—if it does not succeed, I shall never recover. I send this bearer unto you, for I venture to trust your brother neither with letters nor for diligence. He will tell you in what state I am, and you can judge what improvement these uncertain news have caused me! I would fain be dead. You promised me far other things, from your providence. But absence has power over you, who have two strings to your bow. Hasten with your reply, that I may not fail and do not trust your brother-in-law. For he talks as though he were against it all.

God give you a good night.

STIRLING, APRIL 21.

Of the place and the time, I remit myself to your brother and to you. I will follow him, and will fail in nothing of my part. He finds many difficulties. I think he does advertise you thereof, and what he desires for the handling of himself. As for handling of myself, I find it well devised.

I think that your services, and the long friendship, with the good will of the Lords, so far as you have it, do well deserve you a pardon if you advance beyond the duty of a subject not to constrain me but to assure yourself of a place near unto me, so that other admonitions or foreign persuasions may not prevent me from consenting to all that you hope your service shall make you one day to attain. And to be short, to make yourself sure of the Lords and free to marry and that you are constrained, for your safety, and to be able to serve me faithfully, to use a humble request joined to an importunate action.

And to be short, excuse yourself and persuade them as far as you can, that you are constrained to make pursuit against your enemies. You will say enough, if the matter and the ground are to your liking; many fair words to Lethington. If you like not the deed, send me word, and leave not the blame of all unto me.

STIRLING.

My lord, since my letter was written, your brother-in-law that was came to me, very sad, and asked my counsel, as to what he should do the day after tomorrow, because there are many folk here, and among them the Earl of Sutherland, who would rather die, considering the good they have so lately received of me, than to suffer me to be carried away when they are in charge of me; and he feared lest there should some trouble come of it. Or, on the other side, that he had been ungrateful to have betrayed me. I told him that he should have resolved with you upon all that, and that he should avoid, if he could, those that were most to be mistrusted.

He has resolved to write to you, by my advice, for it abashed me to see him so unresolved at the time of need. I assure myself that he will play the part of an honest man, but I have thought it good to advise you of the fear he has that he should be charged with and accused of treason to you, so that, without mistrusting him, you may be more circumspect, and that you may have more forces with you. For we had yesterday more than three hundred horse of his and Livingstone's. For the honour of God, be accompanied rather with more than less, for that is the principal of my care.

I go to write my despatch, and pray God to grant us a happy interview shortly. I write in haste, to the end that you may be advised in time.

THE CASKET LETTERS

THE FRENCH "SONNETS"

O Dieu ayez de moi compassion,
Et m'enseignez quelle preuve certain
Je puis donner qui ne lui semble vain
De mon amour et ferme affection.
Las n'est il pas ia en possession
Du corps, du cœur qui ne refuse peine
Ni deshonneur, en la vie incertaine,
Offense de parents, ni pire affliction?
Pour lui tous mes amis j'estime moins que rien,
Et de mes ennemis je veux espérer bien.
J'ai hasardé pour lui et nom et conscience:
Je veux pour lui au monde renoncer:
Je veux mourir pour lui avancer.
Que reste il plus pour prouver ma constance?

Entre ses mains at en son plein pouvoir
Je mets mon fils, mon honneur, et ma vie,
Mon pays, mes sujets, mon âme assujetie
Est toute a lui, et n'ai autre vouloir
Pour mon objet que sans le deçevoir
Suivre je veux malgré tout l'ennui
Qu'issir en peut, car j'ai n'autre envie
Que de ma foi, lui faire aperçevoir
Que pour temêpte ou bonnace qui face
Jamais ne veut changer demeure ou place.
Bref, je ferai de ma foi telle preuve,
Qu'il connaitra sans feinte ma constance,
Non par mes pleurs ou fainte obeissance,
Comme autres ont fait, mais par divers épreuves.

Elle pour son honneur vous doit obeissance
Moi vous obeissant j'en puis recevoir blâme
Nétant, à mon regret, comme elle, votre femme.
Et si n'aura pourtant en ce point préeminence

Pour son profit elle use de constance,
Car ce n'est peu d'honneur d'etre de vos biens dame
Et moi pour vous aimer j'en puis recevoir blâme
Et ne lui veut céder en toute l'observance
Elle de votre mal n'a l'apprehension
Moi je n'ai nul répos tant je crains l'apparence
Par l'advis des parents, elle eut votre accointance
Moi malgré tous les miens vous porte affection
Et de sa loyauté prenez ferme assurance.

Par vous mon cœur et par votre alliance
Elle a remis sa maison en honneur,
Elle a joui par vous la grandeur
De tous les siens n'ayant nul assurance
De vous mon bien elle a eu la constance,
Et a gagné pour un temps votre cœur,
Par vous elle a eu plaisir et bonne heure,
Et pour vous a recu honneur et reverence,
Et n'a perdu sinon la jouissance
D'un facheux sot qu'elle aimait chèrement.
Je ne la plains d'aimer donc ardemment
Celui qui n'a en sens, ni en vaillance,
En beauté, en bonté, ni en constance
Point de second. Je vive en cette foi.

Quand vous l'aimiez, elle usait de froideur,
Si vous souffriez, pour s'amour passion
Qui vient d'aimer de trop d'affection,
Son doigt monstrait, la tristesse de cœur
N'ayant plaisir de votre grand ardeur
En ses habits, mon étroit sans fiction
Qu'elle n'avait peur qu'imperfection
Peut effacer hors de ce loyal cœur.
De votre mort je ne vis la peur
Que meritait tel mari et seigneur.
Somme, de vous elle a eu tout son bien

Et n'a prise, ni jamais estimé
Un si grand heure sinon puisqu'il n'est sien
Et maintenant dit l'avoir tant aimé.

Et maintenant elle commence a voir
Qu'elle était bien de mauvais jugement
De n'éstimer l'amour d'un tel amant
Et voudrait bien mon ami deçevoir,
Par les écrits tout fardes de savoir
Qui pourtant n'est en son esprit croissant
Ainsi emprunté de quelqu'auteur luisant.
A feint tres bien un ennui sans l'avoir,
Et toutes fois ses paroles fardes,
Ses pleurs, ses plaintes remplies de fictions,
Et ses hauts cris et lamentations
Ont tant gagné que par vous sont gardes.
Ses lettres écrits auxquelles vous donnez foi,
Et si l'aimiez et croyiez plus que moi.

Vous la croyez las trop, je l'apercois,
Et vous doubtez de ma ferme constance,
O, mon seul bien et mon seul ésperance!
Et je ne vous puis assurer de ma foi:
Vous m'estimez léger ouie la vois,
Et si n'avez en moi nul assurance
Et soupconnez mon cœur sans apparence,
Vous defiant à trop grand tort de moi.
Vous ignorez l'amour que je vous porte,
Vous soupçonnex qu'autre amour me transporte,
Vous estimez mes paroles du vent,
Vous depeignez de cire mon las cœur,
Vous me pensez femme sans jugement,
Et tout cela augmente mon ardeur.

Mon amour croit et plus en plus croitra,
Tant que je vivrai, et tiendra à grandeur.
Tant seulement d'avoir part en ce cœur,

Vers qui, en fin, mon amour paraitra
Si très à clair, que jamais n'endoutra.
Pour lui je veux réchércher la grandeur,
Et faira tant qu'en vrai connoitra
Que je n'ai bien, heure, ni contentement,
Qu'a obéir et servir loyamment.
Pour lui j'attends toute bonne fortune;
Pour lui je veux garder santé et vie;
Pour lui toute vertu de suivre j'ai envie,
Et sans changer me trouvera toute vie.

Pour lui aussi, je jete mainte larme,
Premier quant il se fit de ce corps possesseur,
Du quel, alors, il n'avait pas le cœur.
Puis me donna un autre dure alarme,
Quant il versa de son sang mainte drasme.
Donc de grief il me vint laisser doleur,
Qui me pensa ôter la vie, et la frayeur
De perdre là la seule rampart qui m'arme.
Pour lui depuis j'ai mesprisé l'honneur,
Ce qui nous peut seul provoir le bonheur.
Pour lui j'ai hasardé grandeur et conscience,
Pour lui tous mes parents j'ai quitté et amis,
Et tous autres respects sont apart mis.
Bref, de vous seul, je cherche alliance.

De vous je dis seul soutien de ma vie
Tant seulement je cherche m'assurer,
Et si j'ose de moi tant presumer
De vous gagner malgré toute l'ennui.
Car c'est le seul désir de votre chère ami
De vous servir et loyamment aimer,
Et tous malheurs moins que rien éstimer
Et votre volonté de la mien suivre.
Vous connaitrez avec quel obéissance
De mon loyal désir n'omettant la science

THE CASKET LETTERS

A quoi j'étudierais pour toujours vous complaire,
Sans aimer rien que vous, sous la subjection.
De qui je veux sans nulle fiction
Vivre et nourir et à ce j'obtempere.

Mon cœur, mon sang, mon âme et mon souci,
Las, vous avez promis qu'aurons ce plaisir
De déviser avec vous à loisir
Toute la nuit, ou je languis ici
Ayant le cœur d'extrême peur transi,
Pour voir absent le but de mon désir
Criant d'oubli un coup me vient a saisir:
Et l'autre fois je crains que redurci
Soit contre moi votre aimable cœur
Par quelque dit d'un mérchant reporteur.
Un autre fois je crains quelque aventure
Qui par chemin detourne mon amant,
Par un fâcheux et nouveau accident,
Dieu détourne toute malheureux augure.

Ne vous voyant selon qu'avez promis,
J'ai mis la main au papier pour écrire
D'un différent que je voulus transcrire,
Je ne sais pas quel sera votre advis,
Mais je sais bien qui mieux aimer saura
Vous diria bien que plus y gagnera.

Chapter 13

CARBERRY HILL

THE good burghers of Aberdeen were not alone in offering their services to Mary, while she was in Dunbar. On the news of their Queen's abduction, the leaders of the Scottish nobility gathered in Stirling Castle, on the summons of the Earls of Morton, Argyle, Mar and Atholl. These lords, too, sent a letter to their Sovereign, which, like the other, was transmitted to her without let or hindrance. It stated that the faithful lieges of Her Majesty, assembled in Stirling Castle, felt themselves injured in their own honour through the abduction of their ruler. They were entirely at Her Majesty's service, to set her free and take bloody vengeance on her abductor.

But Queen Mary rejected this offer too. Indeed, she replied to her lords in a tone of barely concealed displeasure, advising them that their dispersal would be their best sign of good will towards their ruler.

In apparent obedience to this command, the lords separated.

★

On the day of her return from the fortress, Queen Mary appeared at the solemn session of her full Crown Council, to make an announcement: "True, we have been seized and taken against our will by the Earl of Bothwell to the fortress of which we gave him command. But in view of his admirable behaviour thereafter, and in remembrance of the loyal and unwearied service of the past as well as in anticipation of still more notable loyalty and devotion in the future, we are yet willing to pardon the Earl of Bothwell and all those with him at the time." Queen Mary continued to the effect that her appearance here before her assembled Council might be taken, in particular,

410

as indicative of the fact that she now felt herself to be perfectly free to determine and to do what might seem good to her.

This declaration gave the Earl of Bothwell her public pardon for his offence. Outside of herself, the injured Sovereign, no one could raise any complaint on this head. Further, according to Scottish law, the very gravity of the offence, committed as it was against the reigning head of the State, and consequently the most serious that could be committed, meant that, so long as there was no change in the ruling authority, the Earl of Bothwell could not be accused of any past crime. The annulment of the greater offence excluded all lesser ones.

At this session of the Crown Council the Queen was solemnly informed of the document in which the nobles, under the most solemn guarantees, committed themselves to the cause of the Earl of Bothwell as their own, and recommended him to their ruler as her most suitable husband.

★

In Edinburgh people stood about in groups, talking of all the amazing events that had recently occurred, declaring that the way things were going was a disgrace to Scotland, and always coming to one conclusion—she is bewitched.

Meantime the lords came, individually and in groups, to the French Ambassador, M. du Croc, to confide their fears and troubles to him. They said to him: "Scotland is visibly on the edge of an abyss. The whole people is seething with indignation at the idea of the Queen's marrying the murderer of her husband. Up and down the country they are saying that Bothwell killed the King in order to marry the Queen. But she egged him on, and promised him to make him King of Scotland, if he killed the King, which she wanted in revenge for David's murder." The Lords said all that did not concern them. They were prepared to say nothing about it rather than commit the crime of rebellion against their hereditary, God-ordained Sovereign. But there was something far more important at stake, no less than the whole future of Scotland. Their Prince's life was in danger! For the Queen would certainly have children by Bothwell, probably many of them, and she would love these children more than her first-born, who would always remind her of his murdered father. And the Earl of Bothwell would have to make away with the Prince, since otherwise he would grow up to be the avenger of his father, bound in duty to exact retribution for his father's blood. "They have begun with the father: they will have to go on to the son. Or else all their work is vain."

The Lords said: "She is in bondage. The fact that she perpetually asserts the contrary, is the sign of the completeness of her subjection. . . . There is nothing for it but for us to take and depose her. She is really mad. She will not rest till she has destroyed the whole realm . . . If the French King will not help us, we shall have to go to England."

During his time as Ambassador in Scotland, M. du Croc had seen enough to enable him to form an opinion of Scotland and the Scottish nobles. The men who sat before him, were, if rumour could be trusted, no less guilty of the King's murder than the Earl of Bothwell. There were several there to whom the main part in the crime was attributed. This man was said to have been the soul of the business; that to have laid the powder mine; a third, there, to have strangled the King with his own hands, after a desperate struggle. Before the Frenchman sat the Earl of Argyle, in all the splendour of his superb ugliness; beside him, Earl Morton, short, heavy, compact of build. They sat there, talking openly, looking sincere, full of honourable indignation. M. du Croc thought of the day when the Earl of Argyle had presided over the court that acquitted the Earl of Bothwell of any guilt and declared that his honour was without a stain. Earl Morton was said to have sworn friendship to the Earl of Bothwell over the Queen's hands. In any event he had punctually received the price of this vow. The names of both these lords stood at the head of the list of signatures to the paper which they had themselves presented to their Sovereign in Crown Council, where they declared with most solemn oaths that the cause of the Earl of Bothwell was their own and recommended him to her as husband. They at least must have known what they were doing in all this. The Frenchman's thoughts travelled to the lovely and charming young woman, down there in her palace under the shadow of the Crags, who, whatever she had done, had shown these men nothing but an inexhaustible kindness. It was only too probable that in a state of inconceivable ignorance as to what was known, said, all too readily believed of her, she had herself planned this silly abduction business, with the idea of softening the scandal of such a second marriage by presenting it as carried through under compulsion. If so, she was hideously deceived. For precisely through that action she put her betrothed at the mercy of men who could pose as patriots in the very act of breaking their solemn word of honour to him.

At the same time M. du Croc thought it no part of his function to argue with these gentlemen about such strictly domestic matters. Earl Morton said: "We must do it for Scotland's sake." The Earl of Argyle confirmed this view, and M. du Croc realized that these men could never tolerate having one of their own number made lord over them against their will. They had detested the Earl of Bothwell ever since he had made his way in the world on his own feet. They had let him feel the weight of their hatred. Then he had been a young, unimportant man, with nothing behind him but his own personal force. Now however he had the Queen's will at one with his.

When would such an opportunity come again?

With all this in his mind, M. du Croc replied that he had already done all he could with the Queen. As instructed by his Government, he had expressly informed her that if she married the Earl of Bothwell, she would smash the friendship with France. But, so he reported, the Queen had remained entirely inaccessible to all such representations. She had told him that she was perfectly well aware of what she was doing and, further, that she was acting in the best interests of her country. The French Government would certainly reconsider its attitude when it saw that it had absolutely nothing to lose by Scottish affairs being put into hands strong enough to create and maintain order. "Is the Earl of Bothwell an enemy of France?" she asked. "He is the enemy of no one who desires my welfare and that of my realm. And in that he stands alone! As for the others! They say Scotland, perhaps, even, Our Queen. But what they mean is always and only themselves."

The Lords sent one letter after another to their good friend in England, Mr. Thomas Randolph. As was his duty he disregarded all instruction to the contrary in the letters themselves, and took the missives straight to his Queen, only, on each occasion, to meet with an unexpectedly cool reception from her. Queen Elizabeth curled her upper lip contemptuously. "These gentlemen are above themselves! To think of deposition! To write in such strain about her! Is it credible? The Prince is to be crowned King! A likely story!" True, she repeated that she took the greatest possible objection to the conduct of her cousin. "I may say that I am positively ashamed of her. But, from me, that is a quite, quite different affair." After a while Queen Elizabeth returned to the notion of deposition. "There can be no talk of that. The Prince as King? Too tasteless." She said that her information was that there could be no question of a genuine imprisonment of the Queen by the Earl of Bothwell. Therefore, these matters should be left to her. Queen Elizabeth's sangfroid in regard to events so extraordinary seemed to her Ambassador more and more remarkable. But, on reflection, it occurred to him that her father's daughter must, in love and marriage, hardly be capable of astonishment. To murder a husband and then marry the murderer. . . . Anne Boleyn, the Queen's mother, had listened, in the prison cell in which she waited to be taken to the scaffold, to the gun-salutes celebrating her father's betrothal with her successor, who had been one of her ladies-in-waiting. For the love of this wife, the Queen's mother, King Henry had commanded his country to change its religion. He had tortured and burned the best of his subjects, when they failed to understand that their ruler

414

was not interested in the reform of religion but in getting a divorce when he entered the lists against a Pope whom he had once championed in the face of all Europe. And who had had one word to say? At the beck of my Lord the King, the English Parliament had put Queens up and put them down; had condemned them to death; had idolized their children as the future heirs to the Throne; had then declared them illegitimate, and invalidated their succession only, at the next turn of the wheel, to lift them up again as entirely legitimate and indubitably entitled to succeed. In Queen Elizabeth's childhood and youth such events had been her daily food.

At last Elizabeth said that if the Scottish lords were really anxious to do a providential piece of work and steer clear of disaster, they should, without any resort to violence, bring the Prince to England without delay, where he could be clear of all dangers that might hang over him in Scotland. Here he could be brought up better than anywhere else in the world.

★

When Queen Mary heard of the meetings of the nobles, she laughed contemptuously. "Atholl is a weakling," she said. "Argyle? I know well enough how to stop his mouth. Morton? He has only just pulled on his boots again; they are still full of mud. He must go back to his old quarters."

There had been times, she said, when things were more threatening for her. And yet she had mastered her enemies.

At the same time, she called for troops, and looked about for money. The golden bath which Queen Elizabeth had sent for the Prince's christening was melted down into coinage.

★

To her relatives in France, Queen Catherine, her Guise uncles, and all her friends throughout the country, Queen Mary had set out the reasons which had caused her to determine on her marriage with the Earl of Bothwell. A special Ambassador was sent to France with this communication. Queen Mary con-

415

fronted her relations with the fact that, by the time the message reached them, she would be married. She said that the mere recital of the circumstances would explain the haste of her marriage. She praised her husband to them, his loyalty and integrity; from his earliest youth up, his powers had always been placed at the service of his monarch or of her mother, the Queen Regent, in spite of every attempt to persuade him to join the rebels. A specially fine instance of his unwavering devotion had, so Mary wrote, been afforded at the time of the rising undertaken against their Sovereign by the Scottish lords in the name of religion when she, the Queen, was still living in France as the wife of François II. For the Earl had then preferred to see his whole property ruined to joining with the enemies of his Queen, nor could superior force, even strengthened by assistance from England, force him to yield. From that time on, he had shown unvarying loyalty and devotion to his ruler, and invariably had his actions and character distorted by enemies, whose machinations were the more effective that they were, for the most part, carried on in secret, while their authors showed him the utmost friendliness in public. So successful had these opponents of his been that they had actually induced his Sovereign, although she knew that the Earl was regarded with universal hatred merely because he had been almost alone in standing unflinchingly on her side, to consent to his banishment—a banishment that lasted until the malice of his enemies revealed itself as directed against her too, and so enabled her to recall her most faithful liegeman. Whereupon he had instantly come, scattered her enemies almost at once, and within a short time laid a subjugated land at her feet, a land, moreover, in which he was able to create such a peaceful order as the realm had hitherto hardly experienced. But his merits caused an equivalent growth in the envy and ill-will of his enemies, which culminated in the plan of destroying him by an attempt to involve him in the plot of murdering the King. His Queen, however, had never experienced anything at his hands but loyalty and devotion, up to the hour when he revealed to her his wish to be nearer to her, more to her, to be her husband. Then, deeply alienated, she rebuffed the Earl, only to have him renew his addresses and support them with passionate appeals. Finally, receiving steady refusal as sole response, he went so far as to seize his Sovereign and carry her to the fortress of Dunbar. Here he continued his siege most pressingly, begging and imploring her, and appealing to her pity by complaints of the hardness of a destiny that set enemies all round him while his mind held no other thought than that of perfect service to his Queen. He appealed to her to clothe him with her favour so that he might, at last, be in a position to show the devotion that had always been the one desire of his heart. Alone, in his power, which he did not shrink from using, cut off from all her friends, Queen Mary had, at last, been forced to accede to his wishes.

"We admit," she wrote, "that we have been used by him otherwise than we expected and wished at his hands. But since what happened has happened, we desire to make the best of it."

The Earl too had shown her a document, dating from the session of Parliament, and containing the names of all the Scottish nobility. May it please the Queen, so it was there written, to meet the wishes of her lieges, by raising, not a foreign stranger, but this the most faithful of her subjects to the position of her husband.

Queen Mary further added that the Earl had been separated from his first wife according to the rites of the Catholic Church.

To her uncle she said that now that she was in a position to hope for peace and freedom of action in her own country, she would soon call the Papal nuncio to Scotland, as she had not been able to do hitherto, owing to the disorders of the times.

★

On the day on which, in the morning, the court pronounced the decree of divorce of Jean Countess of Bothwell and her husband, a messenger from the Queen came, in the afternoon, to Master John Craig, who, since John Knox had been living in England, counted as the chief of the Protestant ministers in Edinburgh. The messenger demanded the publication of the banns for the marriage of the Queen and the Earl of Bothwell. But the preacher replied that he could not publish these banns. The Queen had been abducted and was still held prisoner. The messenger departed only to return straight away from the palace with a letter in the Sovereign's own hand. Queen Mary wrote she had neither been seduced nor was she now deprived of her freedom. Therefore she commanded her subject, Master John Craig, to obey her order without delay. He took counsel with the outstanding members of his congregation. Then he asked to be brought before the Privy Council. He desired to lay his views before them. His messenger returned with the intimation that his wishes were acceded to. Master Craig entered the Council room, where he found the State Secretary, Lethington, the Earl of Huntly, and Lords Livingstone and Seaton sitting in a row at the long table. Standing before them, he began explaining his ground for objecting to the posting of the banns in this case. Where a marriage was dissolved on the ground of one party's adultery, the Church forbade the re-marriage of the guilty party. Second, the law forbade a seducer's achieving possession of his victim by ultimate marriage. In this particular case, moreover, there was a third obstacle—the suspicion that the grounds on which the divorce had been granted in the given case had been arranged between the respondent and his wife, and represented a case of criminal deceit. The entire divorce had been accomplished with breathless haste within a period of four days. Furthermore, did not there hang over the whole plan of marriage, as the last and worst objection to it, the awful cloud of suspicion that, barely four months earlier, the King had been murdered, to enable it to take place?

In silence the gentlemen listened to the preacher's statements. Finally, Lord Lethington, stroking his beard with his right hand, as his habit was, replied, What was the use of Master Craig's making all these objections? He could not evade the duty of publishing the banns.

He was prepared to obey, replied John Craig, but not without making his position in the matter clear to his whole congregation.

On the following Sunday, after his sermon, he did so. From the altar, he read the banns for the Queen and the Earl of Bothwell. Thereupon he proceeded to give a detailed account of all the steps leading up to his doing so. Finally he raised his arms and called heaven and earth to witness that such an alliance filled him with nothing but repugnance and horror. And if, as the universal silence, the absence of any public resistance seemed to indicate, the leading portion of the people really approved such a marriage, he implored his faithful ones to follow him in praying with folded hands, in silence, that God would not visit on this land the results of plans that violated so frightfully both conscience and reason.

He was called before the Privy Council to answer for this protest. This time the Earl of Bothwell himself was at the table when John Craig appeared. To his face, the preacher declared that he could only repeat his words, and was ready to defend them against all and sundry. He was proceeding to speak at length, when the Earl of Bothwell, knitting his brows, raised his hand: "We know all that already. Anything more?"

"At any rate, my Lord, I will be no party before God to this atrocity!"

"You have demonstrated that already to your own satisfaction. Go now, and keep your mouth shut."

Master Craig consoled himself with the thought that his method of proclaiming the banns might have roused consciences.

★

On May the fourteenth, Queen Mary elevated her beloved to the rank of Duke of Orkney, with hereditary possession of the lands that went with that title, in particular the islands of

419

Orkney and Shetland. Magnificently attired, with the great
cloak of black velvet richly embroidered in gold, hanging from
her shoulders, she bent over her lover as he knelt before her in
front of the whole court. With her own hands, she set the ducal
crown on his head and draped the ducal mantle round his
shoulders.

Next morning, on May the fifteenth, a Thursday, the betrothal of the Queen and the Duke was celebrated, about four
o'clock. Outside of the officers of the royal court, there were
present only the Earls of Huntly, Sutherland, and Crawford,
and the Lords Oliphant, Boyd, Fleming, Seaton, and Livingstone, although the Queen had sent numerous invitations to her
nobility to be present at this elevation of one among their own
number. Three Catholic prelates, the Bishop of St. Andrews,
his brother the Abbot of Abberbrothock, and Bishop Lesley of
Ross, were associated with the betrothal. But it was actually
conducted according to the rites of the Protestant Church.
Master John Craig was present. The marriage ceremony itself
was conducted by the Protestant Bishop Adam of Bothwell,
a cousin of the bridegroom. He said, in his marriage address,
that the bridegroom repented of the follies of his wild previous
life, and was earnestly set to another course, in the hope of so
proving himself worthy of the great happiness that had fallen
to his lot.

On the day after the wedding there was written, in chalk, on
the gate of the palace Ovid's line:

"Marriage in May never yet brought fortune to any."

★

The Scottish nobility, as a body, had raised no objection to
the marriage of their Queen with the man on whom she had
set her heart. But, after it, practically no one came to court.
As the days passed they showed Mary that she had not a friend
left in the wide world.

She had sent an Ambassador to the Queen of England, to justify the marriage on lines similar to those of the Ambassador to France. Her husband also wrote to both courts. To Paris, where he knew all the leading personalities, he merely sent a few lines:

"Your Majesty! Since the Queen has sent the Bishop of Dunblane to Your Majesty with proposals which he will expound, I seize the opportunity, because of the affection and the zeal which I feel and shall feel all my life, to lay my devoted service before you and your crown: further to ask the Ambassador to make, on my behalf, certain explanations to Your Majesty, for which I would beg that same kind credit that Your Majesty would extend to myself. I pray that the Creator may keep Your Majesty in his holy and gracious keeping.

"J. D."

To Queen Elizabeth he wrote:

"Your Majesty will pardon me if I take the freedom of writing to Your Highness notwithstanding the fact that I know that, in consequence of the slanders of my enemies, Your Majesty has often been incensed against me, although in right and justice I have never deserved that. In the situation to which I am now called, I shall always make it my business to maintain and consolidate the good friendship and good understanding that has hitherto existed between Your Highnesses. The Queen has sent her servant to Your Majesty, to lay her mind before Your Highness. I have likewise opened mine to him, and asked him to give Your Majesty a faithful report of it, for which I would solicit Your Majesty's credit.

"May I be so bold as to add—Men of higher birth and rank may have been called to such a position. No one, however, who can be more solicitous for the maintenance of the friendship between your two Majesties in every just fashion; no one who can be more zealous in honouring and serving Your Highness.

"J. D."

At first, neither the French nor the English Court replied, although they did not withdraw their Ambassadors.

The King of Spain, on whose friendship the Queen had been able to count hitherto, and through whose interposition she had received important subsidies from the Pope, received the news of her marriage in silence.

The Pope had once called her his dearest daughter, had promised her every assistance, had sent her money and promised to send more, had declared, that, were it necessary, he would hasten in person to the aid of his oppressed daughter, this woman with the heart of a man. But now he wrote in vehement anger and let it be known that this Queen of Scotland was now nothing to him. Those who lived for carnal lusts only, must go the way of destruction. He did not know which was dearer to him—the Queen of England or her of Scots. And, to this Pope, the name of Queen Elizabeth had been that of a daughter of Satan.

★

M. du Croc, moving uncertainly to and fro between the court, on the one hand, and the alienated lords on the other, was called by Queen Mary to the palace. In the antechamber he was asked whether he would mind waiting a little, since the Queen was talking alone with her husband in her room. Du Croc sat, waiting, and, as he did so, he kept hearing talking in the next room, and sounds that suggested that some one was weeping; a masculine voice replied, its tone low, but the expression that of anger and impatience. Suddenly, the voice of the Queen raised itself, distinctly: "A knife! I should like to drive a knife into my heart! God, God, I shall throw myself out of the window!" Then, loud sobbing. Uncertain as to what he ought to do, the Frenchman had risen to his feet. But the pages looked so calm that he did not know whether they had heard nothing or took this sort of thing for granted. Suddenly, the door of the room within opened, and Queen Mary came hastily out. She started when she saw the Ambassador. Almost mechanically, an effort to appear calm, to compose herself, passed over her distorted features; she seemed, almost unconsciously, to assume the correct court smile.

"Ah, Mr. Ambassador! It is true . . . I had quite forgotten. . . . Please, come."

She led him back into the room, where the Duke of Orkney was leaning against the mantelpiece. M. du Croc greeted him with some embarrassment, since he did not know what attitude he ought to take to the husband of the Queen of Scots, and was sure that his Government did not know, either. The Duke, whose expression was entirely overclouded with the blackest displeasure, drew himself up and returned his greeting with dignified courtesy. Queen Mary sat down at the table. M. du Croc noted how, despite of her efforts at control, her glance perpetually returned, unhappily, to the man who stood over there motionless, lost in gloomy silence.

Tears rose in the Queen's eyes. "We have trouble, Mr. Ambassador," she said, simply. Her tears fell down over her cheeks. "I feel as though I should never be glad again. . . . I have had so much to go through already. I no longer believe in happiness, and only wish I were dead."

Painfully embarrassed, the Frenchman attempted to comfort her, saying that time would doubtless remove all difficulties. Dispirited, Queen Mary shook her head. "I do not believe in anything good coming." Her tears now fell so fast that, holding out her hand to the Ambassador, she said to him, kindly, "Forgive me. I have still important matters to speak of with the Duke. Be sure to come again. I have urgent matters for you."

Du Croc went to seek out Lord Lethington, with whom he found Lady Mary Lethington and Sir James Melville. When he described the scene he had just witnessed, Sir James said, with distress, "Unfortunately, what every one foresaw has happened. That sinister creature is so hopelessly bad at heart that he can do nothing but torture the Queen continually."

"Obviously it cannot last a month, this so-called happiness," said Lord Lethington, grimly.

His wife, however, contradicted him, quickly. "That is a complete mistake, as I shall always insist. I know her. They really fit extraordinarily well together. When they quarrel—it is only talk. They need that. They may separate ten times; but they come together ten times, just as surely. Any one who should try to separate them. . . ." She broke off to say, in an undertone, as though speaking to herself, "Amazing. Most amazing. Just to see, once, any one so dreadfully deep in love." She turned again to the others. "I will go and see if they should want me."

In a very short time she was back again. "They are sitting on one chair," she said, "on each other's knees. She is kissing his hands and he her forehead, and she, with tears pouring down her face, is begging him to forgive her for ever having loved him, for all that he has had to put up with for her sake. They did not so much as see me come in." Mary Lethington shook her head.

After a time, M. du Croc was summoned by a page to come again to the Queen, whom he found alone and comparatively cheerful again. Her face, however, was still red and hot as though she had shed many tears. She asked him whether he could not use his good offices with the nobles. "You can do much with them. Believe me, it is also to your interest. We are not so weak as they may perhaps think. The times are hard, but they must be endured. It has often been worse, far worse, and afterwards things went quite well. Now too everything will come right, and then one will simply not believe that it was ever so bad before." She tried to smile, but tears came again to her eyes. "God knows that I have no injustice in mind, truly. It is all for the good of my country; and therefore He will not refuse us His gracious aid." M. du Croc, deeply moved, attempted to comfort her. He promised to do his best: certainly, everything would come out all right. "I hope so," repeated

Queen Mary, "for I have always got to think that what mattered most to me I have been given. All the rest will come of itself."

That evening the Frenchman was again with the Queen, for she had invited him to be presented at a masque to be performed by the people of the court in the great hall of the palace. According to her custom she had bidden to it such of the citizens of the town as cared to come. The Queen wore a dress of wine-coloured silk, fastened from top to hem with a series of small, finely worked golden clasps; on her head was a purple beret, set to the side of her fair hair, and adorned with a diamond aigrette; her fan hung from her girdle on a chain set with precious stones. Lovely and glowing with happiness, she moved about at her husband's side, giving smiling greetings this way and that while never for one moment letting go of his arm. She was wholly the newly married young wife, who displays her hardly won acquisition to all the world with blissful pride, as though saying: There! Does his like exist on earth?

M. du Croc had his place at her side. She laughed gaily at the jests of the masques on the stage, turned to her husband to ask him had he noticed this or that: and he, too, laughed so heartily now and then that his dark face was lit to boyishness, all clear and glad: and then his wife looked at him, transfigured; and the Frenchman thought of all the talk that surrounded this pair. And how, outside, the dark hordes of conspirators were gathering, with one single aim—to destroy them for ever. Those outside were perhaps hardly less guilty than these, here—but these had asserted a right to pluck the prize and, now floating on the clouds of passion, looked down upon the world, as though saying, in their every gesture, "Are we not unique?"

M. du Croc was afraid. Suppose the world, which had given them birth and nourishment, were to rise up to demonstrate that it could not be forgotten?

After the play the Queen talked with this one and that. The

Duke stood beside her, his head bare. But she seized his hat, to put it on his head. "Please, my Lord. Do you want to catch cold?"

Every day Queen Mary rode out with her husband, always accompanied by her guards, but always with a high gaiety of mien.

★

Meantime, important decrees were issued by the Crown Council. A royal law took back all the privileges that had granted the free exercise of their religion to the non-Protestants.

Queen Mary no longer went to Mass; it was no longer celebrated. The Queen's almoners and confessors left Scotland.

★

A proclamation of the Queen was promulgated all over the country:

"Has Scotland ever flourished as it has done under the rule of Her Majesty the Queen, since she took the sceptre into her own hands? During this whole time, no single foreign mercenary has dared to set foot on its soil. Every rebellion, swiftly met, has failed. For the benefit of the oppressed the laws are applied and strengthened. But as envy is ever the enemy of virtue, so has rebellion ever raised its horrid head in order, at a time when Her Majesty is thinking of no revolution, but only of a strengthening of the old condition for the benefit and profit of her subjects, to whisper in the people's ear that Her Majesty intends to break the law and, in future, to reign without any Council, contrary to the customs prescribed by the law of the realm.

"But the worst injury and offence are done to Her Majesty the Queen by the rumours, spread everywhere by her rebellious and thankless subjects, that the health and even the life of her precious only son are being neglected. Therefore the Queen finds herself compelled to ask her faithful subjects to read the plain record of her heart's intentions to them in all the deeds of the past, which must make it clear as day that she and she alone holds a protecting hand over the law. What can such hideous accusations touching her dearly beloved son, on whose welfare and well-being all her happiness depends, reveal but the deceits of those malevolent, thankless subjects who do not hesitate even to use a child against his mother, because his tender age makes it possible for them to forge their abominable plans under the cover of his name! Confidently can Her Majesty leave it to time to prove that Scotland has never had a juster rule than hers. Even so will her natural love for her son unfold all its lovely blossoms at the right hour."

★

The Earl of Argyle sent a messenger to the Duke of Orkney to give him warning that nine-tenths of the nobles, assembled at Stirling, had entered into a solemn compact with the object of taking him, the Duke, prisoner, in order that a new and thorough process be laid against him as murderer of the King. They were now gathering their people together, to launch an attack so soon as they were ready.

The next day the Queen's call went out to all her lieges, to gather without delay at the established points. Under the leadership of Her Majesty the Queen and of her husband the Duke of Orkney, dangerous disorders were to be suppressed, which had, as so often before, broken out in the southern provinces.

Lord Lethington left the court, secretly, without any open breach with his Sovereign, although he thought it good to withdraw his support from her. Earl Huntly came to Mary and asked leave of absence. There were troubles with robber bands in his mountains that made his presence necessary on his own estates. Queen Mary looked at him straight. "Leave of absence? Now? Go, then," she said, pale with anger, "and be a traitor, like your father before you. But"—she raised her voice—"take care that you do not end like him!"

The Earl, offended, assured her that any idea of treachery

427

was far from him, as he thought that his behaviour had shown.

"Now is the testing time," said Mary.

Therefore, he remained, he said.

On the evening of June sixth, as the Queen sat at table with her husband, a messenger from the country arrived, who asked to be brought at once before the Duke of Orkney. When he was brought in, he announced himself as another messenger from the Earl of Argyle. He handed a letter from his master to the Duke: In it the Earl said that the Duke was by no means safe in the capital and should flee at once. A coup against the palace was planned by the conspirators for that same night.

The Duke handed the letter to his wife.

About midnight, when the Lords approached with a great force, the news met them that the Queen and the Duke had departed two hours earlier, for the south.

The Lords proceeded to invest Edinburgh. There was tumult at the Cowgate. Earl Huntly and the Archbishop of St. Andrews attempted to rouse the burghers to resistance; but they found no support, and finally could but do their best to secure themselves against the advancing Lords. They retreated to the Castle, where James Balfour was in command. Before leaving Holyrood, the Queen had sent for him and instructed him specifically to turn the Castle guns on the rebels so soon as they entered the city. The Lords arrived. James Balfour did nothing. He gave Earl Huntly and the Bishop of St. Andrews the chance to escape secretly out of the fortress. They went to gather troops for the Queen.

The Lords, on their part, defended their cause in an open proclamation. They called the people to the standard of the nobles, to free the Queen, who was held a prisoner, to defend the Prince, to avenge the murder of the King, and maintain order. Taking to themselves the title of the Council and Government of the country, they publicly outlawed the Earl of Bothwell, whose new rank they did not recognize, as the seducer and abductor of the Queen and despoiler of her sacred person. His marriage, carried through by illegal means, was null and void before all nations as before the people of this realm and before the laws of God; to achieve it, he had planned, with the aid of his abandoned and evil following, the hideous murder of the King of Scotland, Lord Henry Stuart, and then carried it out with his own hand, as was clear as day to all by the witness of his actions after that deed of shame. Now, after the success of these black stratagems of his, a new crowd of evil fellows had been called to arms by the Earl of Bothwell, which, since there was no enemy in the land save himself, could have been called for no other purpose save that he might use against the Prince, the only son of the murdered King, the same act of murder that he had employed upon his slaughtered father. Therefore, and for the sacred purpose of freeing the Queen, their Sovereign, from the bonds of shameful subjection, the Lords, having determined to spend the last drop of their blood rather than permit such ruthlessness to overspread the land, called all good citizens and subjects to arms.

The Lords supported this proclamation with the announcement that the Queen was now pregnant by the Earl of Bothwell, and that this new heir meant that the Prince's life was in imminent danger.

★

On the day after these proclamations had been issued, a detachment of the Lords' troops, under the command of the Earl of Morton, set out for Borthwick, the small fortress into which the Queen and her husband had thrown themselves.

They reached it towards evening, with a sufficient force of both infantry and horse. As they were consolidating their positions next morning, a rumour suddenly arose that the Duke had broken out, with twenty or thirty men only, right through the enemy's forces. There, there, that group galloping there, that was he! The whole camp was in an uproar. Some of the lords threw themselves on horseback. They signalled to the outposts. Now they had got him! Oh, what fun! But the fugitives divided. The greater portion rode off to the left: the rest, to the right.

Where was the Duke? There, there! With the smaller troop there was one man on a magnificent horse, with golden armour and a great waving plume. They all made for him. They captured the golden horseman, as the advance guards, further out, fell upon the fugitives from the side. But they took him only to realize that they had been duped. The man they wanted had made off meantime, on a poor horse and in simple clothes, indistinguishable among the others.

The Queen, however, must still be in the fortress. The Lords therefore sent a messenger to her, who, bearing a white cloth about his arm, was admitted. He went through empty passages, on which his tread and that of his companions rang out. The Queen's soldiers were standing to their guns. There were plenty of them. And the Duke was gone. Today or tomorrow, he would be back with reinforcements.

Queen Mary was sitting at the window of a small room, whence she got a long view far over the country and, in particular, over the encampments of her hostile subjects. She was quite alone. The envoy from the rebels came between five or six soldiers. His Sovereign regarded him, sternly. He delivered his commission. The Lords were come, so he said, to lay their subject obedience at the feet of Her Majesty, and offer their Sovereign all their forces against every foe. Queen Mary, however, looked at him only with contempt. The only proof of devotion she could recognize was obedience to her commands, she said. Let the Lords return quietly home. M. du Croc, who had come with the parley party, now stepped forward, and asked if he might speak for a moment alone with Her Majesty? The Queen drew herself up. "You can say whatever you have to say to me before them all. Anyhow, there can be no discussion if the Lords aim at the Duke's life and liberty."

The messenger came back to the Lords. They were all standing before the fortress, considering its walls. They would certainly hold out for a time. And how many soldiers would the Duke bring with him, if he returned this evening or early tomorrow morning? In the afternoon, the Lords sent again to their Sovereign. Their sole object was to apprehend the breaker of the royal and constitutional laws, so they declared. Never would they turn their arms against their princess. Queen Mary dismissed this message with a shrug of her shoulders.

The night was brief. At daybreak the Lords were greeted by shouts from the ramparts—Where was the Queen? A messenger from her husband had arrived during the night, breaking through all the sentries, and brought her a letter from him. Thereupon, the Queen had thrown on man's attire, drawn on riding boots, and put a squire's cap on her head; with a handful of men she had slid out of the fortress on foot, that way, by the southern gate. She had made her way through the soldiers' camp fires to where, just beyond them, the Duke lay in the thickets with horses.

Later the Lords learned that their Sovereign had thrown herself, with her husband, into the fortress of Dunbar, where they were perfectly safe.

The Lords returned from the empty nest to Edinburgh.

★

There they took counsel, sore perplexed. They were many, and some thought that if they were really to take the Duke of Orkney they would be in difficulties.

The Queen had replied to the proclamation of her nobility with a proclamation denouncing all the rebellious Lords as traitors and conspirators. Now, at last, they had exposed, in all its ruthlessness, the wickedness of their hearts against their ruler and her husband, the Duke of Orkney. They had attempted to capture the Queen and her husband in the fortress of Borthwick under the lying pretext of seeking vengeance for Her Majesty's dead husband and freeing Her Majesty herself from captivity, with the slanderous further suggestion that the Duke, Her Highness' husband, had dangerous designs against the Prince, Her Majesty's son.

"But it is easy to rebut all these accusations as black lies. These godless traitors know perfectly well that by every means in his power the Duke has cleared himself of all suspicion that could be cast up upon him by the base arts of slander and ill will, first by legal process and then by challenging any accuser to combat. As for our alleged captivity, we are in no such case but in the company of our very dear husband, whom we have married in sight of the entire world and with the express approval of our nobility. As for the dangers alleged to threaten our son, these insane inventions are but pretexts to cover treachery and rebellion against us, the natural ruler, and all our posterity. Therefore, to meet open rebellion, we have been compelled to resolve to issue a call to arms, in the hope that all our faithful subjects will gladly raise heart and hand in our defence. As reward for such faithfulness, they shall receive the lands and goods of these unnatural rebels."

The Lords watched the effect of this proclamation. For days their drums had sounded throughout the land. But no one had answered the call. They saw that they could not count on any support beyond that coming from their own people. They could do nothing before Dunbar. To besiege the Sovereign in her own land was impossible, apart from the fact that they had no siege engines. They held the Mint. But the money had already been cleared out of it by the others.

"I think we had best disperse tomorrow and await a more favourable opportunity," said the stout Earl of Atholl, when they met in council of war.

"They will give us time!" retorted Morton.

"It is not like her, to wait in the fortress," said another.

Yet another joined in—"The country people are gathering to her in hordes. She has trumpeted forth—Who kills an earl, gets forty pounds reward. For a lord, the price is thirty; a baron, twenty."

"The Hamiltons are on the way to her," said yet another.

The Lords' faces were very black. At last some one opined

that he had often thought theirs really was a stupid enterprise. Earl Glencairn pulled him up. "We have acted according to our consciences. If God decides against us at least we can feel that we have done our duty."

There were murmurs that there would be no great consolation in that if the Queen took from them all they had and harried them into poverty. "Probably, however, it would not go as far as that. She would have us all beheaded or hanged. For this time her blood is up."

"Anyhow, it is not she now but Bothwell who is King of Scotland."

They departed, in the first instance to their quarters. The question was to be reopened in the morning. The June night was almost as light as day. Some of the Lords suggested that this white light was the very best for marching. Would it not be a good idea to be making home at once? Among those of lesser rank there were a number who asked themselves, What were they taking all this trouble for? The Queen, after all, had never done them any harm, nor the Earl of Bothwell either. What was there so terrible to be expected of them in the future? The Earl had accomplished, at a stroke, the thing for which they had, all these years, been vainly struggling—Catholicism was as good as abolished. The Mass had fallen. The Queen's own acceptance of the Protestant faith seemed only a question of time, and not of long time either. If she had children by her present husband, he would never permit them to be Catholic. And there was no doubt that he did what he liked with his wife. What concern was it of the lesser nobles, after all, if the great ones disliked feeling the Earl of Bothwell's foot on their necks? There might now be some order and peace in the land. The King's murderer? What sort of king had he been, a laughing-stock for every one who did not regard him with actual loathing and disgust. No Scottish knight had ever recognized him as lord. And his wife—what had he not done to her?

Further, the Lords reflected that Morton, Lethington and Argyle, and many another among the cocks of the walk in a campaign whose watchword was vengeance for the King's murder, knew just as much as the Earl of Bothwell about how that murder had really come about.

The leaders had remained with the Earl of Morton. Earl Glencairn said, waggling his chin, with its long white beard, unhappily up and down, "Let come what may. When I think that this man, for whom there is no vice so vile that he does not boast of being a master in it—that this man is now to be King of Scotland and my son must kneel before him and swear him fealty and go with him wherever he leads—when I think of that I know that I cannot tolerate such shame, but would rather go out of the country taking all my property with me in a handkerchief than sit down under such an outrage."

Earl Morton, who sat, fully armed, by him at the table, replied, "If not today, it will be tomorrow."

"If she only gives us the chance!" said Argyle. "She is in Dunbar . . . the country is devoted to her, amazingly, you all see it . . . I am afraid. . . ."

They were all silent, no one daring to make any proposal, each one thinking that his neighbour was working out in his own mind whether it was not possible even now to make peace with the Queen, or whether he was already so deeply involved that there was no safety but in flight.

At last they decided that they would retire now, and review the situation in the morning, in the light of day.

★

Soon after midnight, very early on the morning of the fifteenth of June in the year 1567, the herald of the confederate Lords blared forth throughout Edinburgh the call to arms to all their men. The Lords rushed to headquarters. Earl Morton, in full panoply of war, received them. News had come that the Queen had left Dunbar with her husband and all her troops to march straight on Edinburgh. They had passed the night at Seaton, between the fortress and Edinburgh.

Some four thousand men, so it appeared, were with her. Her

opponents, now, had to choose between flight and counter-attack.

Among the Lords was the laird Kirkaldy of Grange, most loved and honoured of all the knights of Scotland, both for his experienced and fearless valour and, even more, for a deed of his youth. At the time when Queen Mary was a tiny child, and Cardinal Beaton ruled in Scotland as Regent, detested for his domineering and avaricious personality and the looseness of his private life, the laird of Grange, then barely in his twenties, and accompanied by but fifteen companions, had broken into the strong fortress of St. Andrews, the residence of the Cardinal Regent, surprising the guards by his bold daring, and taking possession of the whole place within the space of a few minutes. With three friends, he had then burst into the Cardinal's room and killed him with repeated dagger strokes, in revenge for his having burned the preacher Wycliff, the first reformer in Scotland. A fantastic siege followed this deed; the youths held the place against Government troops a hundredfold their number for so long that they were finally able to arrange a surrender on favourable terms. Ever since the Laird of Grange had been regarded in Scotland as the protagonist of the Reformation.

Advancing years, accompanied by many a heroic deed, had only increased the esteem in which he was held. He now took his place by the side of the Earl of Glencairn, as the latter again declared that Heaven had decided for them, and there was no choice save between victory and defeat. A warlike mood had come upon the others, too, through the unexpected news.

"March, then!"

Without delay, they set forth.

★

Soon after sunrise, they reached the little town of Mussel-burgh, through which, over a bridge, ran the road from Edinburgh to Dunbar. As they marched through the town, the white mists of the summer morning began to rise, and as they came out of the streets, the country stretched out clear and open before their eyes. The Lords perceived, at once, that the Queen's troops must have started even earlier than they had done. For they held the heights of Carberry Hill, under which the road to Dunbar passed. The only rise in an upland but rather flat district, Carberry Hill dominated the whole region. Here the English had lain in ambush at the battle of Pinkie, very successfully, since the Scots had not been able to dislodge them.

The Lords' army advanced slowly, then halted. If they turned, they could see, rising through the blue mist of the morning, the mighty rocks of Edinburgh, huge in the distance and incomparably impressive as they heaved up out of the green landscape, its softness was hardly broken by Carberry Hill.

Both parties had infantry and cavalry. The Lords had reliable, trained and well-tried men to meet the Queen's hastily gathered forces, but she and her husband had brought some field-pieces with them from the fortress, and these, admirably placed, threatened the valley with their gleaming cannon mouths. The Lords encamped out of their range. Their leaders, so numerous as to constitute a detachment in themselves, kept joining in groups and then disjoining to return to their men. They saw that they must make up their minds to storm the enemy's army out of its position, in the teeth of their guns.

The various lords gathered their people round their clan banners. The men all came from their lords' lands. From childhood up, they had accepted the idea that they owed food and shelter, and every comfort that came to them and theirs, to their clan head, their laird. He had schooled them from infancy to bear arms and often taken them with him as children in expeditions against his foes, perhaps a foe in his immediate neighbourhood. They now knew that their lord was in danger. If he did not win, an enraged Sovereign would descend upon him, take him prisoner, and cut off his head, if she did not have him hanged.

Before the army waved a great white banner, which the Lords had had prepared while they planned this campaign. On it Henry Darnley was represented, lying in a piteous attitude, clad in nothing but a shirt, slain beneath a tree. On his corpse stood a little child, out of whose mouth came a device with the words—Oh, Lord, judge and revenge my cause! Other banners showed the Queen and her present husband in hideous distortion. On one Queen Mary was depicted in the act of raising her arm to show the Duke to strike, there, with his axe. On another, Kirk-o'-Field was represented in the act of blowing up, with the murder being enacted in front as a shambles. There were pennons on which Queen Mary was shown as a mermaid, naked down to the hips, below them in the form of a fish.

The soldiers sang songs they had learned about the woman Jezebel, cast out of the window for the dogs to lick up her blood on account of her crimes. They sang about Good King Henry:

> She is not satisfied, though he is dead;
> His murderer has ta'en the empty bed.
> Not once but twice is broke the wedded name,
> And the poor land sinks down in evil shame.

★

From the heights one or two shots came. The Lords decided to advance slowly. They were still a good distance off when M. du Croc came hurrying on horseback from Edinburgh and made his way straight to Earl Morton. The main leaders followed after him, arriving just as du Croc was saying to the Earl that he desired to approach the Queen once again, and put proposals of mediation before her. He urged the Lords that, for God's sake, bloodshed between Scot and Scot must be avoided. The Queen, he stressed, was gentle; she could not possibly find it in her heart to desire the destruction of so many of her subjects. .

"And on your side," he urged, "only think—suppose the battle won—what then? Suppose they are beaten, and you have got the Queen and the Duke prisoner?"

"Oh, as to her," Lord Lindsay laughed, "there will be nothing doing, there."

Du Croc blinked. "But her husband? Suppose you take the Duke?"

"He will not be taken, you can rely on that," replied Lord Ruthven.

They all stood, looking darkly before them.

"You might go to the Queen," said Earl Atholl, at last, thoughtfully, "and offer her: If she is willing to separate herself from Bothwell, who holds her in captivity, we, on our part, are ready to meet her and, as humble, obedient and devoted subjects, to honour her on our knees as our hereditary and anointed Queen. That is one way."

"Yes," Earl Glencairn continued, "and here is another: Bothwell shall come forth into the space between the two armies, and call on any of us who dares to maintain to his face that he is the true murderer of the King, knowing full well that not one, but four, ten, a dozen will present themselves."

"Such a proposal I cannot take to the Queen!" said du Croc, excitedly. "Gentlemen! Think of her rage! It is quite impossible. After all, you are talking of her husband!"

"She has long been tired of him," replied Ruthven. "Lethington says so, too. Only, she is ashamed to confess it. We are doing her the greatest kindness, in compelling her to it."

The Frenchman did not know whether or no the Lords had intelligence on this point: certainly it had not seemed so to him, even in Borthwick; anyhow, he repeated, emphatically, that there should be no movement of the troops until he had tried once again what could be done with the other side.

Accompanied by some fifty horse, assigned him by the Lords, he rode across country to the royal positions, led his horse up the hill, and dismounted on the eminence, so that he might go forward on foot, leaving his escort behind.

His experienced eye noted at once that the troops were admirably organized. Use had been made of the old escarpments to make excellent cover. It would be very difficult to take these positions, with the cannon threatening above them. But du Croc, comparing one army with the other, saw that the Lords had a great advantage in the fact that they had an army composed of trained men. Here, apart from the four or five hundred men of the royal bodyguard, he saw only raw recruits, whose lack of effective training could be seen in every movement, even in the way in which they lay in ambush.

Directed by a soldier, du Croc, slowly making his way through the camp, reached the Queen's stance, above which there waved the royal banner, the red Stuart lion rampant on a white field. Under the shelter of the wall of a great trench a very tolerable halting-place had been made for the Queen, for a tent roof had been stretched there between the boughs of a nut-tree to shelter her from the heat of the sun, already blazing in a brilliant, entirely cloudless sky. When du Croc saw the Queen she was engaged in lively talk with a man-at-arms, presumably the captain of her Watch, as she stood under the nut tree. Her appearance startled him, for she wore a garb that, on her, was astonishing. No doubt for the purpose of her flight to Dunbar, she had put on the dress of the peasant girls of the district, a brightly coloured skirt of pleated wool, a short velvet jacket, with sleeves only to the elbow, a beret in black velvet, and little shoes with white stockings. As he drew nearer and looked at her sideways, she seemed to du Croc hot, tired, and over-strained, as if she had not slept for many nights. The common talk, that she had for some time known that she bore her new husband's child, occurred to him. As he looked at her, seeing her anxious and distraught, the days of his earliest acquaintance with her came back to his mind, when, though but a child, she was Queen of France, and a creature of such loveliness, gaiety, grace of bearing, that it seemed to all the world that, in her presence, the drab dreariness of reality vanished before the radiance of a unique perfection. He thought of the pictures down there, in the enemies' bivouac, the songs roared out by excited men throughout their camp, and of all the darkness, the violence and the vileness that he had lived through with her throughout these latter days.

He approached her, as she turned to look at him in keen

anticipation. Greeting her with the deepest respect, he explained that he had come to offer his services towards the establishment of unity. He begged the Queen to consider, he said, that the men against whom the mouths of her cannon were turned were, after all, her subjects, and subjects who merely asked to be allowed to offer affectionate and faithful service to their sovereign. Could Her Majesty not consider meeting their demands?

"My loving and faithful subjects!" retorted Queen Mary, at once. "Traitors to God and man, that is what they are!" Tears of rage sparkled in her eyes: she was trembling so that she was hardly able to speak. "Of myself, I will not speak; I am accustomed to have my loving and faithful subjects betray me, since they are not able to murder me. But to whom did they pledge themselves, for life and death, on their sacred honour and consciences? Those self-same honourable knights, they and no others, in solemn court acquitted him on whom they now claim that they have got to wreak vengeance! They wish to impose conditions? Really? How extraordinarily kind of them! But I know one only, and I present it—they shall come and beg my forgiveness. Let them appear before me—and I shall consider what I choose to do. . . . I am to submit to their conditions? I do not see the smallest reason why I should. Are they victorious? They dare not even venture to attack."

After a while, she added, in a calmer tone, that the idea of shooting down her own subjects was horrible to her. Certainly she desired peace, if only it were possible. Therefore, she was ready to open her arms to all who came to her repentant, and to extend her grace to every one who approached in a spirit of humble submission.

Such peaceful submission was not to be expected from the Lords, replied du Croc, in some embarrassment. The people were too excited. If Her Majesty would not consider the Lords' conditions, there was nothing for it but a decision by force of arms.

She replied: "I repeat—if they will respect the Duke's life and liberty, I make no terms for myself."

As she spoke, the Duke himself, who had been occupied giving orders in the camp, approached. He came up behind the Frenchman, but the latter observed how the Queen's tense features suddenly relaxed. His mere nearness acted upon her like a draught of fresh life, like water placed to her lips, relieving the thirst of the heat of the exhausting day. He saw that what was being said, down there, about her secret desire to be free of her husband, was all lies and error.

The Duke was fully armed, and clad in a suit of dark mail finely inlaid with silver, with a scarf of deep red silk over it, across his hips. Du Croc, who never saw the Queen of Scots' husband without wishing that he had never existed, had to admit, at this moment, that there was something heroic in his appearance, and that his dark countenance, his every movement, bore the unmistakable accent of indomitable strength: a will, composed and resolute, ready to meet whatever might come. They exchanged courteous greeting.

"Mr. Ambassador, I have heard part of what you had to communicate to the Queen," the Duke began. "Indeed I know what is at the bottom of all these discussions. They are only after me."

"The Lords certainly proclaim themselves devoted and obedient subjects of Her Majesty," replied the Ambassador, adding, in a lowered tone, "To your lordship, I am afraid, their hostility is implacable."

The Duke laughed. "It looks like it. I have carefully preserved," he added, "their solemn assurances of good will, on God and their consciences. M. du Croc, what harm have I done these gentlemen? None of them can reproach me with any injury or insult I have done him. Envy of my position is the sole ground of their attack." He threw back his head. "That fortune is open to whosoever dares to take it! Mr. Ambassador, there is not one of those gentlemen down there who does not long to be in my shoes! That they are not—that is the real reason for all their enmity."

He laid his hand on the other's shoulder. "A word, please." Drawing du Croc a little aside, he said in a low tone, "You see how things are, Mr. Ambassador, and you will believe me when I tell you, I see it too. So I make one urgent request to you—tell me the truth, for the sake of my honour and God's. The Queen is suffering inexpressibly from all these unhappy events. It tears my heart to see her so utterly unstrung. I could not induce her to stay in the fortress, where she would have been perfectly safe. . . . Finally, it is a bitter decision . . . if she will stand for it. . . ." He searched the Ambassador's face. "Tell me frankly—can she really expect obedience and submission from the Lords?"

The Ambassador hesitated, not quite clear what the other had in mind. It was a big thing, and he must know it, know that everything, for him, was over, if the Queen gave him up: everything, for ever, not here in Scotland only. He would be simply cast upon the world, with nothing. There was nothing but annihilation before him, if the Queen separated her cause from his.

At last, du Croc replied to his question: "I think so, at least . . . the Lords . . . I do believe . . ."

"How can one trust them?" said the Duke. He considered. "The Queen has raised me to her side. Nevertheless, if one of them will come forward—a man, that is to say of knightly birth—I will lay aside my rank and fight with him. God will be with me. For in this matter, right is with us."

Queen Mary approached. "I have heard," she said to her husband. "You want to give yourself to them. But I will not have that, in any case." She stood before the two men. "That can never be." She laughed, nervously. "What would become of me, if they killed you?" She addressed herself again to du Croc. "What are these lords thinking of? We are not weak. At every moment, we expect large reinforcements. We should not have left Dunbar, had we not been sure of the result."

"I think they are moving to attack at last," said the Duke, who had kept the plain at his feet steadily under observation. He turned to the Frenchman. "You have seen the two armies," he said, smiling calmly, though his face was pale, "like Hannibal's and Scipio's, face to face, ready to set their teeth in one another. And you have seen a peace effort fail with both. If, as an impartial observer, you secure a good place for the show, I can promise you the most interesting spectacle of your life, for I think I can promise you a good fight."

Du Croc replied politely that he would very gladly once watch so interesting a piece, but not between these two armies. As things were, he rather felt that the spectacle would be purely tragic.

He looked about him. Everything seemed to him so admirably organized that, if the troops here were reliable, it seemed to him that victory must fall to his side. His apprehension found voice. "My Lord, the Lords over there knew that this is a life-and-death matter for them. They have their own people with them. . . ."

"You mean, I cannot rely on my men? Well, we have four thousand men, and the cannon. They have no guns, and cannot be more than three thousand five hundred strong."

The Frenchman had noticed that there was hardly any one of knightly standing in the Duke's camp. But the many in the other might cause a multiplicity of wills. Unity of command might be of advantage here.

Du Croc took a hesitating farewell of the Queen. Tears fell down her cheeks, as he bent over her hand to kiss it. The Duke, who accompanied him a part of his way, repeated his offer of his person in single combat. Only, there must be reliable guarantees given for the Queen's safety, in the event of the result of the fight being as he hoped.

The Frenchman returned to the confederate camp to report the Queen's gracious temper, and the readiness of her husband to take part in single combat. They laughed softly at her offer of pardon. Earl Glencairn said, indignantly, "We have not

come to beg for pardon, but, on the contrary, to avenge out-
rages and sins."

"We want him, and nothing else," they said. "We must set
the Queen, his prisoner, free. Otherwise, Parliament would call
us to account."

They seized their spears, took up their field badges. Du Croc,
thinking that battle must now be joined at any moment, withdrew from the camp. He did not desire to take any part in a
fight whose upshot, whatever it might be, must be painful to
him—not even by being present as a spectator.

But the fight did not start, even now. The Lords moved
their troops a trifle nearer to the enemy position, only to halt
again, still out of the range of the guns. They intended, if not
actually forced to attack, to wait till the sun, which now dazzled
into their men's faces, had turned.

Their foes, on the other hand, were longing for them to
attack. The Duke had left the fortress of Dunbar on receipt
of a communication from his friend, Sir James Balfour, in
command in Edinburgh Castle. Sir James had sent him a message to the effect that he would train his guns on the Lords
from behind, as soon as they had marched out of the town, so
that, if the Duke met them with the Queen's troops in front,
their whole force might be annihilated at a stroke. The Duke
had acted on this message as he thought he must. Since early
morning, however, he had realized that his friend had betrayed
him. He was far too good a soldier not to know, better than
any one could tell him, that with his hastily assembled troops,
raw levies, bound together neither by habit nor by the keen
drive of a sense of existence at stake, there could be no question of throwing his forces on the opposing army. His former
brother-in-law, Huntly, had sent him word that he would
certainly come to his aid about noon with fresh troops from
the Pentlands. But, as the hours passed, without any sign of
approaching reinforcements to be seen in any quarter, the
Duke decided that this message, too, was a trick. And the enemy

down there did not seem inclined to make the mistake of coming out to meet them.

On the contrary, disaster to the Duke and his forces moved with dry feet over the sun-steeped plain. His army began to dissolve in the heat that poured down its melting beams on the hill-top. The men lay, half dead, on the ground; their collars open, their chests bare: helmets, bonnets and caps long ago discarded, their hair was matted on to their yellow-grey faces. Others crowded round the beer and bread. The danger of a hostile attack might, even now, have pulled them together. But the Lords, doubtless informed by their spies as to how things were, waited still. Queen Mary sat, in a state of collapse, at the foot of her nut tree. Her husband went up and down, without intermission, encouraging, commanding, threatening, promising. The force of his appeals would rouse the prostrate men for a moment, but, as soon as his head was turned, they were on the ground again, and soon slinking right away. Before a single shot had been fired, desertion was so general that men made off in groups, dozens, even hundreds.

The Lords sent messengers. They accepted the offer by their opponent of his person in single combat. Queen Mary wanted to interpose, but her husband signed to her to be silent. The knight who had communicated the Lords' acceptance of the Duke's proposal, made his way back into the valley. The Duke prepared himself for combat, by changing his light field armour for a heavier suit, more serviceable for single combat. His squire brought his horse, another prepared the spears he would take with him. A messenger came from below: the Laird of Tullibardine would await his lordship in the arena between the two armies.

Queen Mary protested: "Have they no one of higher rank for you?" She turned swiftly to the messenger. "In no case will my Lord the Duke meet a knight who is not even a baron. Go. Go at once, and report my command." The man departed.

Down in the valley, the Lords discussed whom it should be. Earl Glencairn said that he was willing. But he was too old for the responsibility of so momentous a decision against a foe of whom every one of them could cite ten, a dozen proofs of dauntless valour. At last Earl Morton said, If no one else presented himself, he would go himself. At this the others looked at each other, thunderstruck. Earl Morton? But it was to be a judgment by God: they had come out to seize the Earl of Bothwell for the murder of the King. And, now, to have Earl Morton as avenger, who must know at least as much about this murder as the Earl of Bothwell himself!

At last, Lord Lindsay, who had filled the office of assessor on the day of law for the King's murder, offered to act in this affair.

He looked to his armour, to see that all its bolts and fastenings were in perfect order. Then he fell on his knees, in the sight of the entire army, and raised his hands to Heaven, to pray God in His mercy to watch over the innocent and cause His justice to appear in vengeance for the innocent blood of the King.

On the hill-top, meantime, the Queen had roused herself to oppose this duel with impassioned energy. Her husband, and every one of any consideration in her camp, like Lord Seaton and the Laird of Borthwick, had gathered about her, to persuade her to accept this method of settlement. All she said was: "It cannot be. Never. I do not permit it. Do you imagine I don't know what I am saying?" She leaped to her feet. "We must fight! We have the cannon! We must win. Why don't we begin?" She turned to the captains of the individual detachments, talked herself to the soldiers. Every one who fought bravely today should receive a hundred acres of land in fee simple, and, if he fell, his children. She became more and more excited, went hither and thither. But what was there left in the camp? Hardly a couple of hundred men. With so few troops, even retreat was out of the question. While the negotiations were going on, the enemy had occupied the roads to Dunbar. Nevertheless Queen Mary still wanted battle. "We have the cannon! There they are! Fire them! Let them shoot at last!"

"They are out of range," said her husband, who stood regarding the enemy.

"Oh, the cowards, the traitors!" She talked to him, clinging to his arm. "Let us throw ourselves on them. Even if we have only a few dozen men. We shall beat them, all the same." He sat down under the nut tree, his forehead sunk in his hand, silent.

Her eyes blazed at him. She talked on, of attack, of battle, of victory. He let his hand drop.

"You cannot fall into their hands, beaten, my dear," he said.

She laughed. "Oh, no, I shall not do that."

He rose. "You know as well as I that I must go."

She wrung her hands. "Why, why did we not fight? Then, when they first approached—we should have crushed them." She ground her teeth. "It was his coming, that French Judas, that has ruined us! They sent him, to delay us and spy upon us, and he has betrayed us to them." She said to the Duke, "You want to go because you think to make an honourable end for yourself. You know as well as I that this combat is impossible, is madness. Single combat? Murder! They will fall on you in dozens. They, let you out alive? Never. They cannot. For their own sakes not. And you know that. But you are thinking only of yourself."

He implored her, "Dear, say no more. And let me go."

Rising, he went, as though blind, past her, to his horse. She stood, in despair, not daring to oppose him further. Swinging himself on to his horse, he rode slowly forth. His squire bore his great lance for the combat. He rode through the half-empty dug-outs, where the cannon stood, almost deserted, out into the open. In the face of the two camps, he halted. His herald advanced, to repeat his challenge solemnly. The Duke of Orkney summoned every knightly-born champion to single combat who dared to say to his face that he and he alone was the murderer of the noble and high-born prince, one-time husband of Her Majesty the Queen, Henry Darnley, King of Scotland.

Slowly Lord Lindsay approached, also in complete armour,

and also on horseback, accompanied by squires and knights. His squire was just about to accept the Duke's challenge in accordance with the set form, when a messenger from the Queen came running down from the heights: the Queen commanded that the combat be at once suspended, and all preparations therefor. Her Majesty desired to treat with the Lords.

The Duke, with an oath, set spurs to his steed. "Forward!"

But Lord Lindsay fell back. Such a command from the Queen could not be disobeyed.

When the Duke came back into the camp, the Queen came to meet him. "I shall treat with them! At bottom, they are afraid of us. They know that we are far stronger than they in the long run. This is only a momentary affair. We shall get over it. . . . Do you go to Dunbar and hold it. I shall see what can be done with them. They are easy to handle, for they are always at sixes and sevens. One has only got to promise them rewards. If things do not go as I hope, I shall follow you to Dunbar. I shall keep you *au courant*. I shall write to you two or three times a day. See, a duel is impossible—you must see that. They cannot leave you alive, and what will become of me then?" Already she had sent a man down into the valley to demand that State Secretary Lethington should speak with her. The man came back to report that the State Secretary was not with the troops. Meantime the Queen had been speaking again to her husband: "You understand, do you not? I am not leaving you— you understand that?" Still she insisted: "Anything, anything, but a single combat, never."

When the go-between brought news, she asked for the Laird Kirkaldy of Grange. She would treat with him. His word stood. Kirkaldy of Grange obeyed her command. The Queen said to him: "You shall secure the Duke free passage to Dunbar; I will then accept the submission you offer me as your Queen."

The laird replied that in the name of the confederate lords he was entrusted to lay all their affectionate devotion at her feet. But the Earl of Bothwell, as a married man and the murderer of the King, could not be her husband.

"Murderer of the King!" she exclaimed, breaking out in fury. "I believe, Laird of Grange, that you are the only man among all those down there who has no right to that title!"

The Duke, who stood by her, took her hand to stay her wrath. The message that the laird should take to the others, he said, was that he desired single combat and only that. Let God decide who stood for right in this matter.

"In all things will I obey you," cried Mary, "only not in this!" She looked at him, shuddering and laughing at the same time, as though she saw him stretched bloody before her. "Single combat!" She turned to Kirkaldy. "Yet I think that I command here! Do my commission, and that at once." The laird departed.

During his absence, the confederate lords had learned that from the South the Earl of Huntly, with a thousand fresh men, was coming to relieve the blockade of Carberry Hill. They therefore instructed their envoy, on his reappearance among them, to go back to the Queen straightway to assure her of the submission of her lords on the condition she had named. Earl Morton gave Kirkaldy a letter to the Duke. When the latter opened it Morton's seal-ring fell out of the letter, which ran:

"You must clear out of the way for a while. Until I and the others have brought matters into order here. For the moment, the people are so hot against you, that there is nothing to be done. In sign of our old alliance, I send you my ring.
"MORTON."

Kirkaldy pressed for haste. If the Queen desired not to have her camp stormed, she must come quickly. She could see how the other army was in movement, pressed for the attack.

Meantime, it was almost evening.

Mary turned to the Duke, and drew him a little aside to use her persuasions upon him once more. She implored him, once more, to go to Dunbar and hold the fortress for her. She said:

449

"The Hamiltons are on the way. Huntly will still come. But they are not here now. Why did we ever leave Dunbar!"

He looked at her, silent.

"Go quickly!" she breathed, clinging to him. "For my sake! . . . It is only for a little while. Do you think I would let you go if it were not for a little while only? You understand why I want it like this?"

He saw that she could hardly stand upright. All the hot, endless day, she had eaten practically nothing. He knew that she bore his child. What could he do? His army had melted away. He could not take her with him. He could not let himself be cut in pieces before her eyes.

She pressed him to go and at the same time held him fast. He too was pale as death. Leading her further aside, he gave her papers with which she must not part, since they contained proof of the guilt of all the others—Lethington, Argyle, Morton, Balfour—all of them. He begged her, "Will you be true to me? As you have promised?"

"True—far, far truer," she stammered.

He held her in his arms, kissed her again and again. Then, leading her back, he signed to Kirkaldy to look after her, and turned to go. She came after him.

"It is only for a short time," he said, his glance averted.

"Yes, only a short time," she repeated, drawing herself up.

"You shall see, I will be brave." She tried to smile, but it seemed as though she must break down. She clung to him, in anguish. "Take me with you, take me with you! All is over!"

He put her from him with trembling hands, icy against the burning heat of hers. "You were going to be brave, Marie."

She drew herself up. "Yes, and I am."

He did not embrace her again: he merely gave her his hand. "Farewell, Marie."

She stood erect. "Farewell, James."

He went away from her, with rapid steps, towards his horse. The handful of men who were to accompany him pushed between him and those whom they were leaving. Mary stood, gazing after him. As the little group, at first hidden by the intervening bushes from her sight, again became visible at a little distance, making for Dunbar at a gallop, she still stood, looking after them, before she at last turned to the laird. "Under the conditions you have assured me, I give myself up to you."

Kirkaldy kissed her hand, as she extended it to him. She signed for her horse to be brought, and mounted it. The laird, at her side, led it down the declivity to the other camp.

At once they came into a heaving sea of soldiers. They too had stood waiting all through the long hot day. Nothing had happened. In the end, nevertheless, the enemy had had to yield, shamefully. The men seethed with angry impatience. There was the Queen; left in the lurch by her paramour, without his even attempting to fight—there she was, what a sight! There was a rush of men shouting, pushing on, yelling coarse words; the laird had to draw his sword, to get passage for himself and the Queen's horse. Making their way with difficulty through the roaring, swaying throng, they reached the spot where the Lords had gathered in a circle. Earl Morton came forward to meet the Queen.

He bent his knee. "At last Your Majesty is in the place that alone belongs to you."

Queen Mary rode straight up to him: astonished at her apparently threatening air, he rose to his feet.

"Ah, Earl Morton," she said, very loud, "as I hear, the object of this undertaking is to avenge the King's death. But I am told that you were one of the principals in it."

The quick blood overspread the Earl's face, up to the bushy eyebrows. "Quiet!" he said rapidly, raising his hand, "Quiet! Is this the place for such things?"

Mary looked slowly round the circle. "There are you, too, my Lord Lindsay," she said. "Come hither."

Not knowing what she might have in mind, he obeyed.

"Give me your hand." He did so. "My Lord Lindsay," she said, "as certain as I now have your hand in mine, so certainly shall I have you beheaded for having dared to seek to measure

451

yourself against the Duke." Suddenly she dashed aside his hand, which she had held in a grip of iron while she spoke.

Roused to anger, the Lords pushed wildly up against her. She drew herself up high in the saddle, raising her fist. "I will have you all hanged," she shrieked at them. "Make way." She wished to speak to the captain of her bodyguard, she commanded. "I want to send a messenger to the Earl of Huntly." No one replied. Some one said: "Forward! Now for Edinburgh." Two knights seized the bridle of her horse. She moved back. "I will not go to Edinburgh." It seemed that she sought to force her way alone through the camp. But the iron ring closed round her, on every side. They seized hold of her horse. They led her right through the camp, right through the shouting mob of soldiers, who pressed right on to her, pushing each other, treading each other down, and, all the time, laughing and shouting, "Look at the whore."

When the wild mass at last became an army again, a troop of men in full armour rode close round Mary. Right in front of her, high above all their heads, waved the banner depicting Henry Darnley lying dead, in his shirt, with the child stretching out its arms to him, crying for revenge. Round Mary danced the pennons, with their caricatures of her own face, that of her husband, and of the burning, ruined house. But she seemed to be blind and deaf to everything outside herself. Incessantly she spoke to the crowds. "Ah," she cried to one knight, "you are the Laird of Dunblarick. Was it not you who swore to me, as you knelt before me on the field, after the first rebellion, that you would never follow any other than the Royal banner?" The laird at first began slinking back into the crowd; then however he seemed to feel a sort of necessity to clear himself. "Why has Your Majesty not done justice to my son?"

"Ah," she replied, "him? Oh, yes, I know—the one who killed his cousin for the sake of a thousand crowns, killed him in bed, in his wife's arms—and she went mad afterwards of it."

Any man who knew that he was personally known to her drew back, out of her neighbourhood. She talked on, till her voice broke. She seemed unconscious, swayed in the saddle. Her hair had come loose, and fell in plaits and strands all over her shoulders and her face. Her shoes, her stockings, her skirt, were almost black with dust.

When they reached the town of Edinburgh, about ten o'clock, it was still quite light, for this was June fifteenth, round about the time of the longest day, exactly a month after the Queen's marriage to the Earl of Bothwell. The train passed through the English Gate into the High Street, and so along to the Town Hall. People were at all the windows, as they passed, on all the roofs, on all the trees. They shouted: "Look at the whore!" "To the fire with the adulteress!" "Death to the murderess!" The soldiers were still waving their banners on high. The shouting of the crowd swelled to thunder. They whistled, they screeched, they yelled: like a swarm of huge vermin from the inmost caverns of hell, they began falling off the trees, sliding down the walls, dropping off the copings of the houses. The Lords had hastily to close Mary in with a wall of spears, to keep the horde from falling upon her and tearing her to pieces with howls of savage joy.

Pending further decisions, they brought her into the Provost's dwelling right under the Town Hall, and there set guards in all the entries, on the staircases, even in the Queen's room.

Mary threw herself on to the bed, and tore off her bodice. Then she ordered the guards standing at the door to leave the room on the instant. She wanted her women, and only them. The soldiers paid no attention. Food was brought her. She pushed the dish away. There was poison in it. Only subordinates came near her: no one from the Lords, although she ordered first the State Secretary, then Earl Morton, then the Laird of Grange, to be sent to her. She lay down on the bed: then, getting up again, gazed about her. She rushed to the window, threw it up. "Help, help! People of Edinburgh, save your Queen!" Two soldiers pulled her back, and closed the window, placing themselves before it. Mary lay on the bed, tearing the pillows, groaning, moaning, burying her head in them. She began to talk, as though she thought she was with her husband, begging him for forgiveness for all the misfortune that had come upon him through her. So she lay all through the brief, pale night. In the morning, she again rushed to the window—there they were, already, the dense throng of people: hundreds of pairs of eyes stared up at her, full of hatred. The banner of the confederate lords, with dead Henry Darnley and the child crying for revenge, floated high in the morning wind. Tearing at the neck of her shift, so that it fluttered open about her bare breast, Mary beat against the window-frame, crying: "Good people, take my life or release me from these inhuman tyrants!"

Gradually, the people's expressions changed. Sobbing, the Queen hung at the window. A voice below cried out: "At least take the banner away." A couple of lads began clambering up the doorway of the Town Hall, to tear down the banner. Thereupon there came forth from the house where the Queen was Lord Lindsay with soldiers, and cleared out the mob. Lindsay himself came to the Queen: told her that she would pay for it with her life, if she did not keep quiet. She looked at him, with eyes in which the light came and went. "My life? You would be merciful if you made an end of me." She threw herself on to the bed again, again called her husband's name into the pillows, talked again to him of the misfortune that followed her always, everywhere. Then she began shouting: "I shall have them all, all beheaded. I was too kind. That was my mistake. Now they shall all die. Then there can be no more envy, when there is no one there to feel it." Again she ordered the soldiers of the watch to leave the room. At all costs she must be alone. She would throw herself out of the window on to the street, if the men did not leave her. At a loss what to do, the soldiers fetched their captain, and, in view of her uncontrollable despair, he could not refuse to remove the guards from her own room. She promised to do nothing to annoy any one, if only they would leave her alone: if they would only take these dreadful men away, she would be quite quiet. She did actually seem more tranquil when she was alone: indeed those who came in to see after her almost thought that she was asleep. When she roused herself again, she asked the soldiers who came in answer to her call to have writing materials brought to her. There were urgent messages she must prepare. They brought what she asked. She sat down at the table to write to the Laird of Grange and say, Was this the submissive obedience for which he had answered? She desired a Parliament to meet, in which the King's death could be investigated openly, before all the world. In that process, however, she would appear as accuser. She sent a few lines to Lethington. He was to come to her: she must speak with him. When one of the soldiers brought her food, she handed him a letter: "Take that to Dunbar, to the Duke. He will give you such a reward that you will never need to work again in all your life."

The man took the letter, to hand it over to the Lords.

In the afternoon, since none of the Lords presented himself, and none of her women came, she suddenly rose up from the bed and dashed to the window. Leaning there, dissolved in tears, she saw the State Secretary pass as he came out of the Town Hall. Swiftly throwing up the window, she called out to him: "Come to me, for the love of God!" But he, pulling his high hat further down over his brows, made as though he did not hear. "If I have ever done you good, you must listen to me!" she cried. Although the place was closely barred, the people could not be altogether kept out at this narrow part of the High Street, and there was a considerable number of them surging all round the house. Among them, now, a murmuring began. "My God, the poor, poor woman!" Lethington stepped swiftly into the next house. Lindsay came again to Mary. Did she want to be shot at from outside, that she was for ever at the window? If she tried it once again, she would be removed into a room on the courtyard.

Of the food brought to her she at last ate a piece of bread and drank a glass of wine.

Meanwhile the Lords deliberated where to put the Queen.

decision. "This is anyhow the position. Your Majesty must give up this man. The nobility of Scotland can never tolerate this man. Is all this atrocious work to have been done in order to have things worse after than before? Not if we know it! He must be sacrificed, or the country will not have an hour's peace."

"Indeed?" she said.

"Yes," he replied, grinding his teeth, "that man has been the root of hatred from his youth up."

"I believe it!" she replied.

He let himself go on the Duke: becoming more and more excited, calling him a beggar, and the most violent man in all Scotland, England and France. He repeated that the Queen's will, though of iron, could not avail to control this man: the Scottish nobles would in no circumstances have him forced upon them. Passionate as was his speech, she interrupted him.

"That is all very fine! You know very well that he would drive you all in harness—he and I. I know what is in your mind —you utter it shamelessly. What you cannot allow is that, then, I should not be abandoned any longer to your ruthlessness and self-will. You have the impertinence to reproach me with ruining my State because I give way to my feeling, and say, What has my feeling to do with the State? Very well. Listen to me. In my whole life, I have never done anything so conducive to the welfare of my State as this marriage—conducive to its real welfare: not to what you understand by it, for what you understand by it is nothing more or less than freedom for yourselves to exercise every treachery and every deceit! But you are not the State, and you must be compelled to peace in order that, at last, there may be peace and at last the State may flourish. I was not able to do it, how could I have done? I was eighteen, when I came to you. I had never known anything like it. But with my husband I shall learn how to master you. And you know that, and that is the reason of your hatred, the only reason, that I can next year take everything away that I ever gave you in my too great kindness and that you think I should do it, for you have all made yourself detestable to the Duke.

But he has been far too generous-hearted towards you, utterly loyal, where his word was pledged, and never bearing a grudge: he has always forgiven everything and even forgotten, since nothing false dwells in him. And you have come to me, from the very beginning, and shrieked in my ears: Look at that man, the scum of the earth and of his race! And if I asked diligently —since I did not know him at first: my eyes were sealed, that I did not see him at once—if I asked, Tell me, what is wrong with him? what have you been able to produce? I probed, thoroughly, but it never came to anything, amounted to anything; it all melted away and nothing was ever left save your black envy and your poisonous slanders and your devilish hatred. Then you said to me, for ever, from early to late, at every opportunity: If only Your Majesty would become a Protestant! If only Your Majesty would banish the Papist Mass from the land! If only Your Majesty would, on grounds of State, declare the Protestant religion the only valid one! Just this one thing, only this, and everything in Scotland is wholly under Your Majesty's Government, and thereby the cause of such happiness and blessing as Scotland has never known. Well, I have done it. Or, rather, the Duke has converted me to doing it. That was the first proof of his intention of ruining the country. But you find it easy to disguise your black treachery, which is really ruining Scotland, with lies that cry to Heaven. You and you alone are bringing ruin. I did not name the Duke King, because I did not want to draw down any more of your wrath upon him, and he himself did not desire it. But he *is* King. I have probably seen more kings in my life-time, and known them better, than you. The one real King I have ever beheld is the Duke. And because that is dark to you, and because you know that he will really rule, because he *can* really rule, because he is born to be a King, that is why you pursue him with your raging treachery and have always pursued him."

"What is this man to Your Majesty?" asked Lethington, at last. "He does not even love Your Majesty. Oh, no," he con-

"Naturally I said No, I could never do such a thing. She became impatient, angry. Then she wept and implored me to do it. It was of no consequence to the State or to the lords whether I did so or not. She could not help her husband, nor he her. I ought not to refuse two such unhappy people this poor comfort. 'He is longing for me, just for news of me,' she said. 'He knows, of course, that I am a prisoner. He hardly knows whether I am still alive. I only want to say to him that I think of him always, always.' Passionately, she entreated me, with uplifted hands. Tears poured over her face. She was trembling all over. 'Your Majesty must absolutely tear this terrible passion out of your heart, with all your strength,' I replied. Then, laughing scornfully, she threw the letter into the fire burning beside her on the hearth, holding her hands over it so that no fragment of the letter remained, since the Earl was not to get it. She said she would find other messengers who were not so inhuman."

"I had it in mind," added Sir James, "to say to her that the Countess of Bothwell was with her former husband. But in the end I could not do it."

"Is that the case?" asked Sir Nicholas.

"So it is said. The Countess, on the other hand, has expressly stated that she has had nothing to do with her divorced husband, and never will have. She has said that almost publicly, here in the town. Yet I am sorry that I was not able to say it. It might have been useful. Or not. Probably she would not have believed it."

Sir Nicholas wrote again to Queen Mary to say that she ought to prefer the lesser evil of bringing into the world a child without a legal father, to the danger to her throne and life—her own life, and that of her child. By the same circuitous route by which this letter had come to her, Queen Mary replied that no power on earth could induce her to consent to anything whereby the Duke, her legitimate husband before God and man, suffered any hurt.

★

The Hamiltons came together to make a solemn pact in which they pledged themselves not to rest until their Queen had been restored to freedom and all her royal rights. With them joined the Earl of Huntly, so that almost the whole of the west and north of the kingdom was for Queen Mary. The Earl of Huntly joined them only after he had denounced his brother-in-law, Bothwell. He was glad, said the head of the Gordons, that his sister was free of so evil a man.

The Duke, meantime, after lying *perdu* for a week in Dunbar, had left the fortress. First he went to the Gordons to whom he made proposals. The Queen's liberation must be accomplished. If the Hamiltons and the Gordons would stand by him, he believed that this aim could be achieved within a few weeks. But they gave evasive answers. Finally he was warned by a trusty hand that if he remained longer in the neighbourhood, his life was in danger. On the same night he rode off with a handful of squires. He reached his own Dukedom, the Orkneys, where the inhabitants still looked upon him as their lord, and gathered to him in greater numbers every day when he called them out for the liberation of their Queen. He had acquired some ships and declared that he would take any one, even a pirate, who would only agree to spare no effort until the ill-used Queen had been set free and her wrongs avenged.

The confederate lords were at a loss to know how this desperate man was to be suppressed. For the persecution of this most dangerous enemy of human and divine order, Queen Elizabeth offered both money and ships. Her ambassador learned that relatives of the Duke's, who possessed property in the Orkneys, had undertaken the murder of their cousin.

★

Meantime the intentions of the lords in regard to their Queen became plain.

On July 25th, some five weeks after Mary's surrender, Lords Lindsay and Ruthven, with Sir James Melville and a body of soldiers, rode to Lochleven, and crossed the lake to the castle on

Mary's lot did not improve after her abdication and the coronation of her son. Lord Ruthven came to take over the command of the castle guards. As though more severe measures were being prepared, the Queen was brought out of the big tower into the little round one, where her dwelling consisted of a single, semi-dark room. There she could be more easily guarded, Lord Ruthven said. She had won the hearts of the inmates of the castle and made contacts with friends outside. Lord Ruthven was soon at odds with old Lady Douglas about the Queen's treatment. The old lady had intended to display the glory of God by striking at the pride of the whole of her wicked family in the person of the imprisoned ruler. But when Queen Mary was actually brought to Lochleven, wellnigh destroyed in mind and body, and, during the first weeks of her imprisonment did nothing but cry alternately for revenge and to be allowed to go to her husband, old Lady Douglas declared that what was being done to the poor creature was utterly inhuman. If, as was natural enough, she would not allow any one in the castle to touch her, even for the most necessary care in her sickness, the women to whom she was used must be allowed to come to her. On the old lady's request, Mary Seaton and Mary Semple were allowed access to their Queen. Later on, Mary threw herself into the old lady's arms without reserve, so soon as she became aware of the warm current of pity moving in that heart and simply overleaping every feeling of wrath that might have found lodgment in it. She poured out all her despair before her. She listened patiently to Lady Margaret's unsparing admonitions to her—the point of which invariably was that Mary must turn in the humility of a really contrite heart, to the mercy of God. Mary asked for a Catholic priest: she could recognize no other as intermediary between God and herself. After long discussions and many efforts at conversion, Lady Margaret at last agreed to support this wish of the Queen's before the Lords.

★

Shortly after the coronation of the little Prince as King James VI, Earl James of Murray returned from his travels abroad. He came through Paris, where he promised the Queen's relatives to intercede for his imprisoned sister. Queen Elizabeth of England made the same request to him, and received a similar promise.

On the news of her brother's return, Queen Mary at once wrote to him, to beg him to come to her as soon as possible. He talked with the confederate lords, with the English and French Ambassadors, visited the Prince in Stirling, and, at last, accompanied by the Earl of Morton and some other gentlemen, came to Lochleven, to his sister.

The arrival of this brother, who had, at least, been absent during her recent horrible experiences, was awaited by Queen Mary with eager longing. He would stand by her, give her kind advice, help her to create order where she could not. So said his mother, also.

The Lords arrived late in the afternoon and soon sat down to table in the Queen's company. During the meal, Queen Mary observed that her brother was addressed as Your Highness, Your Grace—titles hitherto reserved for the immediate family of the ruler alone. If he spoke to his sister, he did it in so loud a voice that every word seemed to be addressed not so much to her as to those sitting by. When the meal was at an end, he said that, if the others would permit it, he would like a few words with the Queen alone. He added, with an uncertain laugh, that the others could count upon his not betraying the confederate lords.

He returned to this, first, as he walked with his sister up and down the little terrace that ran round the castle, at the edge of the lake, and again, when he sat with her in her room.

They talked till long after midnight.

Earl Murray began by reproaching the Queen. He collected every fault, or what he regarded as such, out of her earlier life, and held it out with a punishing finger. She replied vehemently—Was it for him to speak against her, he who owed his entire wealth, his position, his power entirely to her kindness? "What did your father design you for, my Lord, and what did I raise you to? You owe everything, everything, to me. True," she laughed bitterly, "there is one exception—the money the Queen of England paid you." When he spoke of the King's murder, she reminded him of what had taken place in Craigmillar in her presence. He spoke in unmeasured terms of her boundless passion for that creature, that Bothwell. The way in which she had clung to that ruffian was an outrage to every sense of decency, quite apart from its utter folly. Mary opened her lips to reply. On a sudden thought, she closed them again: anything more he had to say to her in this connection passed over her, like water. Becoming more and more excited by her coolness, he spoke of death by fire for adultery and murder.

At last Mary replied: "My Lord, I see now that you have always aimed at one thing only. If you now desire to take the place of a king, let me remind you of one example you may learn from me—it is among the first of kingly duties to spare your enemies when they are down."

Murray told her that she must, above all, not count on her so-called adherents, the "Knights of the Queen," the Hamiltons. Here, he had brought proofs with him—he drew letters from his pocket—the Hamiltons had sent Bishop Hamilton of Ross and his brother, the Abbot of Aberbrothock, as intermediaries to the confederate lords. They came with the question—What did the confederate lords intend doing with the Queen? So long as she lived, the men of the house of Hamilton must stand by her for good or ill. For, sooner or later, she would get free and then descend like an angel of vengeance wreaking destruction on her foes. She would find helpers enough, so soon as, again at liberty, she was in a position to give. Thus, so long as she lived . . . but, if she were dead. . . .

"The Hamiltons have never loved you," said Murray. "Why should they? There was much enmity between you and them, overt and covert. They regard themselves as the next heirs to the throne after the King, your son. To cut off the way to the throne from any one else, they now come forward on your side. If you were no more, only the little child would stand in their way . . . and . . ."

Queen Mary sank into a long, long silence. "So I have only God," she said at last, in a low tone, as though speaking to herself. "He will judge, in accordance with justice . . . even if I do not comprehend His judgment. And I shall accept what He chooses to send me."

In the course of their conversation she asked her brother to see after her precious furniture, her clothes, her silver and her priceless jewels. These things were practically all presents from her French relations and therefore her personal property. Nevertheless they should be added to the royal treasury, to remain there for the Prince who, alone, had, after his mother, a right to them. Murray replied that he did not know what the Council would decide in this regard.

Finally, Queen Mary said: "Everything has been taken from me that can be taken from a human being, up to this wretched remnant of mere life, to which I do not cling any longer, and which they certainly do not leave me out of mercifulness. On every street, they have said the worst of me. They have all betrayed and abandoned me, although I never did them anything but good. God knows what my intentions were when I first set foot in this lost country. I can only trust that He, before whom I have never sought to present myself as other than I was, will yet show the truth of everything. And meantime, I rest in the conviction that God knows the sins of those who now presume to sit in judgment upon me as the last of evildoers."

Murray said, finally, to his sister that his main reason for taking on the Regentship was that he was the only man who could be of use to her in this upheaval of everything. He alone could watch over her honour and her life, and he regarded to do so as his most sacred duty. At these words, Queen Mary smiled.

"They have pursued me, their hereditary Sovereign, to whom

477

they have sworn fealty on their lives, with their treachery and rebellion to the point at which they have driven me into the depths of misery. Are you likely to find more mercy in them?"

The Earl ended the conversation with a renewal of his admonitions to his sister. He desired her to know what would inevitably bring her danger and death, and what would serve to mitigate her condition, her captivity. All that could be done for her from without she could rely upon his devotion to effect. "You will, however, work for your own destruction if you make any sort of attempt to disturb the peace of the realm and the government of your son: if you stir up his subjects to disobedience and rebellion: if you stir either the Queen of England or the ruler of France to enmity and war: if you make any attempt to gain your liberty by flight. And, above all, if you persist in your fatal passion for the Earl of Bothwell." He recommended her, on the other hand, to approach God in a spirit of true repentance, and humble admission of her sins, after a fashion that showed that she was turning from her former way of life, and, above all, from the murder of the King and her life with the Earl of Bothwell. "Necessary, above all, is that you should let it be known, in terms that impose credence, that you have never thought of any kind of revenge on the Lords who had nothing else in mind but the maintenance of your honour and life." Moreover, she might find comfort in the thought of her brother-in-law, the King of France, whose Protestant subjects, the Huguenots, would soon have reduced him to the same condition in which she now found herself.

At the beginning of their talk, Mary had asked her brother whether he could not stay a day or two in the castle, in order that she might speak with him in more detail about her own position as well as the state of things in the outer world, so far as that affected it. The Earl now reverted to this request of hers. It was impossible for him to stay. Moreover, he had said everything that it imported the Queen to know. He was, already, suspect with the confederate lords on account of his great affection for his sister.

Queen Mary begged him to care for her poor servants, especially the French ones, who must be exposed to the most dreadful distress. If it were at all possible would he supply them
with means of returning to France where they could be compensated from the revenues of her jointure.

Next morning, when the Lords, ready for departure, came
down into the courtyard, Queen Mary appeared once again.
Earl Morton, whom she had avoided hitherto, approached her
in order, in accordance with the custom of former times, to
bend his knee before her. Giving him her hand, Mary said to
him: "My Lord, you have once felt my wrath, but also seen its
end. Let me now learn that your wrath can end too."

The horses were brought up. In that of the Earl of Murray
Queen Mary recognized Stella, her favourite. The horse turned
its head to her. At that, her self-control gave way.

"I wish that you would break his treacherous neck for him!"
she cried to the horse, in flaming anger.

★

The months went by. Queen Mary lived in Lochleven, for
her urgent request to be allowed to go to her child in Stirling
had been rejected. In her captivity on the tiny island, where
there was practically no possibility of exercise, she busied herself with fine embroideries over which she sat with the ladies of
Lochleven and her friends, Mary Seaton, Mary Semple and
Mary Ogilvy, who alternated in their mistress's service. She
was also on friendly terms with the other inhabitants of the
fortress. Lord Ruthven had to be removed from his post, because one day, in the grey of morning, he had pushed his way
into the Queen's room and fallen on her bed—the way to freedom, power and greatness was open, if she would only consent
to love him. Horrified, Queen Mary called for help. Her women
slept near her, and Mary Seaton rushed in to her room. Not
long afterwards, George Douglas, the eighteen-year-old
younger brother of the master of the castle, was removed
thence. The Lord, his brother, reproached him with having no

other interest in life but to please the Queen. Did he wish to ruin his whole family? George replied that the Queen was an angel of heavenly goodness and grace, innocently sacrificed to hellish treachery. The Lord of Lochleven replied that they might all like her and sympathize with her troubles, and wonder why she was not restored to the throne, but, he added, warmly, "That is not the question. She has been entrusted to our keeping, and we are answerable for her. If she escapes, we are finished."

"If she is Queen again, and we have been good to her, not at all. Quite the contrary."

"If, if . . . who is counting on that? If she does not get her throne back, they will pull our house about our heads."

"By God's appointment, the whole land belongs to the Queen. He gave it to her, and to no other," insisted his brother, "and who ever stands by her right does what is pleasing in the sight of God. And whosoever does not do so, but rather vexes her, is in truth a traitor and rebel, whom God will surely punish, according to his deserts."

There was, finally, a bitter quarrel between the brothers, as the result of which George left the Castle, to his mother's grief and distress.

Meantime, the Hamiltons had recovered their loyalty to their Queen, principally because they discovered that, as things were, there was no advantage for them in dividing power with another party, instead of having it all in their own hands. They assembled the points on which they insisted. The Queen must be set free, restored to her rights and, after her divorce from the Earl of Bothwell, married to a Hamilton. Five or six young knights offered themselves as candidates for the execution of the programme.

Queen Mary learned of those events in the outer world that affected her. She knew that the Queen of England had definitely declared that, during his mother's lifetime, she would never recognize the Prince as King of Scotland. That her ambassador was more energetically than ever threatening war on behalf of the captive Sovereign, and that the outbreak of hostilities had so far only been prevented by the dislike of the Queen of England to the expenditure of money.

Queen Mary also learned that her husband had been forcibly driven out of Scotland, or, rather, that he had succeeded in breaking through the nets stretched for his capture. Kirkaldy of Grange, troubled in his mind by his Sovereign's word to him —Was this treatment the condition he had answered for to her at her surrender?—went to the Lords to represent to them that he at any rate had understood the terms of surrender quite differently. He received the answer that the Queen, on her side, had promised to give up the Earl of Bothwell. But she had not given him up: on the contrary, she had called down fire and sword on every one who had dared to tear him from her. The Knight replied that she had in truth let him go. She must be allowed time, to come to her senses about him. What did it matter, if she, at first, called a few tender words after him? He regarded it as the first duty of the Lords to make the Earl prisoner and put him on trial, both in the interest of justice, and because the Earl actually, in his desperate strength of will, threatened to be a most dangerous enemy of the State. The Lords consented to give Kirkaldy ships with which to pursue him. He swore either to bring him back, dead or alive, or perish in the attempt.

In the Orkneys he fell upon the Duke's forces. Four or five ships had actually been got together by him. Those of his enemy were, however, larger and better armed, and, in particular, had cannon. They also sailed more swiftly, and although the Duke's vessels crowded on all sail and flew with the wind, the others were close behind them. Their cannon fired. A shot smashed the mast of the second vessel, and sent it crashing down over the side, threatening to drag its crew down with it into the whirlpool it made. Kirkaldy shouted out that the shipwrecked men, whose lives were of value in so far as they were accessories to the Earl's crimes, should be captured: he himself would follow the flagship of the enemy, which must carry the Earl. They

flew with all speed in breakneck chase. The distance between
hound and quarry inevitably grew less and less. Now they could
distinguish voices on the ship ahead: now, words. Kirkaldy did
not want to use his cannon. He was consumed with ambition to
take the Earl alive. His ship made a mighty tack in shallow
water and passed right under the cliffs. Criss-cross it went,
between the rocks, still at tearing speed. The pursuer was hard
after it. At the very moment when the quarry shot out into the
open sea again, the *Unicorn,* as the heavy hunter was called,
after the Edinburgh arms, drove crashing on the rocks. High
and clear rang out the triumphant yells of the enemy, as the
whirlpool between the rocks seized, shattered and tore asunder
the timbers, and leaders and men could barely save themselves
alive. When they had picked themselves clear of the wreckage,
the enemy's shining sails were disappearing far away on the
horizon.

Kirkaldy only brought a few of the Earl's men back to Edinburgh. They were cross-examined by the Council of the confederate lords themselves, put to the rack to extort confession,
condemned straightway and, next day, hanged, quartered and
dismembered. Small boys took their arms and legs in baskets
through the country, crying everywhere on the market-places.
—Here, as a horrible example for every one, are the limbs of the
King's murderers, justly condemned.

★

Earl Bothwell reached Bergen in Norway, a fief of the Danish King. His ship was towed by a Danish war-galley which
brought it, since it bore no flag, to higher waters to search for
papers. If there were none, there was no alternative but to
treat the vessel as a pirate and bring it into the nearest harbour
for thorough scrutiny. When the Danes first came on deck,
they found no one who appeared to be in command: then from
among the horde of wild, determined-looking fellows there, a
man in the same torn and tattered clothing as the rest came

forward and said that he was the Duke of Orkney, High Admiral of Scotland, nay, more, the husband of the Scottish Queen. The Danes asked for papers to substantiate so extraordinary a claim. He replied that he had none; that a rebellion on the part of the Scottish nobles against him and his wife had compelled him to make a lightning flight, in the course of which he had lost the rest of his fleet, and, together with his ship, all his clothes and armour, papers and valuables. The Danish officials could not reconcile the dishevelled appearance of this commander and of his whole troop with a certain decisive, aristocratic pride in the captain or with his remarkable facility in the French language. Even this incredible tale might, after all, be true. Plainly, however, it was their duty to bring in a ship that had neither flag nor papers found in their waters. They therefore bade the man who had described himself to them as a Duke come with them: as High Admiral of Scotland, he would know that they could not act otherwise. He should not be treated as a prisoner, but might go to Bergen, the nearest largest harbour town, on his parole of honour. The Duke expressed his concurrence. He had, anyhow, met the King of Denmark before.

An examination of the ship showed that the Duke had some papers, after all. In a portfolio was the contract of marriage between him and the Scottish Queen, signed by herself, and also a letter from her, in which, with many expressions of most tender love, she assured her husband that she had not deserted him, and could never, by any power on earth, be induced to do so: in the depths of misery into which she had been cast by hideous treachery, the thing that most grieved her heart was the thought of the horrors that were prepared for him.

With these papers there was, however, another in which the Government of the country stigmatized the Earl as murderer of the King and abductor of the Queen, and put a price of two thousand pounds on his head.

The Earl remained for some time in Bergen, where he was

honourably treated. Then there came a message from Copen-hagen, from the Danish King, that the Scottish gentleman should be sent to him.

Meantime, he had, in singular circumstances, lost the ship to whose possession he had been able to demonstrate his in-controvertible right. A lady came from the south of the coun-try, named Anna Trontheim, and said that the news of the wondrous seafarer had caused her to travel to Bergen. For she had claims to make on this same Scottish gentleman, since she was his wife, married by him when he was here years ago. She was ready to give up any marital claims. But the dowry which the Earl had then taken from her he must now restore. She belonged to an influential family. The Earl therefore agreed to hand over to her the only property he now possessed, namely his ship. She had it sold, and went off with the proceeds, after she had offered her former husband, as she called the Earl, thirty thalers out of the price, which he declined.

He was now taken to Copenhagen, where he sought to an-swer, before King Christian, the violent accusations on whose basis his extradition was being repeatedly and urgently de-manded by the Scottish Crown Council and Queen Elizabeth of England. He said that the very same Lords who were demand-ing his death were in truth the actual murderers of the King. Their envy of him, their loathing of any kind of discipline, their rebellious spirit, displayed in a long course of violence against their too gracious and gentle Sovereign, were the sole causes of the fall of himself and of his wife.

The King of Denmark was related to Queen Mary Stuart. A Danish Princess had been the wife of King James III. After the Battle of Sauchieburn, in which he was defeated by his rebel barons, the King had been murdered by them—not quite a hundred years ago. King Christian replied to the demands of the Powers that until the affair had been entirely cleared up before a completely impartial and unexceptionable court, he could neither in law nor in conscience deliver over the Earl. There was of course not the slightest doubt of the fact that a rebellion had taken place against the legitimate, God-anointed ruler. Yet neither the Scottish nor the English Government remitted its pressure. The Danish King therefore consulted the opinion of other European Princes on the matter. They all agreed that the English Queen had no jurisdiction over the Earl, who was not her subject and had done nothing against her. Nor had an unconstitutional Government. His own Queen, who alone could charge him, had no thought of prosecution, but always insisted that he was her legitimate and beloved husband. The King of Denmark decided to keep his prisoner for the meantime. He offered Queen Elizabeth and the Scots the submission of the matter to a Danish court for a dispassionate judgment. Of that no one would hear. The Earl therefore stayed in Denmark, and was sent to the fortress of Malmoe, where his conditions were tolerably comfortable. Whither could he have gone, even had freedom been granted him?

★

These events took place in September and October of the year 1567. In December the Regent of Scotland, James Murray, called a Parliament in the name of the King. By it a new judgment on the Earl of Bothwell as author of the murder of the King was promulgated, and the endorsement of his acquittal, issued nine months earlier, was recalled. Queen Mary was publicly charged with complicity in the crime: the Lords declaring that her letters proved her guilt only too clearly, to the shame and grief of all decent people. Her abdication was read out, likewise the installation of her son as King and the establishment of the Regency and of the Crown Council. Lord Lindsay again swore that these decrees had been voluntarily signed.

In this Parliament, however, the confederate lords over-shot themselves. In Parliament itself Lord Herries stood up, to raise an objection in the name of his party, the Knights of the Queen. These decrees, signed in captivity by the Queen, under peril of her life, were, according to the express provision of Scottish law, entirely worthless. Equally invalid was the endorsement by the Queen's beadle. Lord Herries declared that he knew that the Queen had expressly demanded, in a written communication, to appear in person before her Estates, and conduct her case. Where was this communication of the Queen's to her Parliament, which her Estates were entitled to see? He cried out before the assembly that their proceedings were of a clamant injustice that would call down the wrath of God upon their heads; left his place and cast a gold piece down before the president, which rang loudly as it fell upon the table, following the Scottish custom, in accordance with which this was a sign that he and his whole house declared feud. Thereupon many others imitated his example, and refused to accept the signature among the resolutions of Parliament.

From this day on, moreover, sympathy for the captive Queen began to find expression among the people outside, until at last there were loud murmurs abroad. Even in spite of the raging propaganda of the preachers, people began to say—The Queen might be a Catholic, yes. But had she ever oppressed a Protestant on grounds of his faith? Were not all her advisors Protestants? Had she not finally married a Protestant? and in a Protestant church? There she sat a prisoner, in the dark tower on the island, she, so young, so gracious, so lovely that she symbolized good fortune for all her people and made Scotland famous throughout the world because it had the most wonderful woman in the world for its Queen. There she sat, the gracious one, who loved gaiety so, and wrung her white hands and wept incessantly. And she, so the people said, had really been a Queen by grace of God and because she was a queen at heart. Yet she had never shown any sort of pride, like so many others who were far beneath her and yet went about as though they, and only they, were the real lords, to whom those of common clay might not so much as speak. They told of Mary's charm, and of her loveliness on this and that occasion when she had appeared in public. They spoke of her superb clothes, of her jewels. No one in all the world had more priceless jewels than Mary had had. And she had been so generous; although she was rich, she gave so much away that, at the last, she had nothing, and that was her ruin.

The most doubtful step taken by the Lords proved to be the executions of the Earl of Bothwell's adherents. They were condemned by the Crown Council for complicity in the murder of the King. According to Scottish law, the executions took place in public, although the court sat in private. Again, according to Scottish law, the condemned men might speak to the people before their death. This they all did. Many declared that they died innocent; many admitted their guilt. Many a one, however, said that although his death was just, there were many among their judges who ought rather to have stood where he now did than such a poor fellow as he, who could but be the tool of great lords who had him entirely in their power. They named names—those of Earl Morton, the Earl of Argyle, the Earl of Huntly, of Lord Lethington, of Sir James Balfour, of Archibald Douglas, of the Archbishop of St. Andrews—so often and so loudly that the Lords had to transfer the place of execution to the inner court of the prison. But these lords had, by then, been sufficiently cited. And there they all sat in the seats of government, rich, free, prominent, while the Queen languished in a dungeon and her husband, whom she had so loved, lay in prison in Denmark. And these two, whose voices could not be heard, were now alone to count as murderers and traitors.

Early in the year 1568, the Queen of England began to take action in earnest in the interest of her imprisoned sister. She had, Elizabeth declared, been held back and imposed upon long enough by the rebel lords. What she could not do by kind representations she proposed now to compel by force.

Her first step was to propose to the King of France that the two Governments, French and English, should close all their harbours to Scottish ships. This would make an end of the rebellion in the shortest possible time. The French King was quite ready to entertain such an idea. Negotiations were under way —their initiation was communicated to the Lords.

★

At the end of March Queen Mary made her first attempt to escape.

Every week, a woman used to come from a village on the lake to fetch and bring back the Queen's washing. Thanks to Mary's friendliness, and her promises that if she ever got back to power she would more than reward every good deed done to her, the woman had long ago been won over to acting as a carrier of letters and packets for her. Now, one morning, the Queen changed clothes with her; took the laundry basket on her back and tied a kerchief far over her forehead and so as to conceal both chin and throat. Thus disguised, she got past the guards out of the castle and into the boat that lay awaiting the washerwoman on the shore of the lake, rowed by two squires of the Laird of Lochleven's. Why should such a pretty girl have wrapped herself up so, asked one of them, stretching out his coarse hand to pull off her kerchief. Mary screamed and drew away. The churl felt the touch of a small soft hand against his rough palm, saw that it lay snow white against his brown one, and cried in terror, "By God, here is no washermaid!" He and his comrade held up their oars. For a moment, the boat drifted on the surface of the water. Then the man resolutely changed the course. "I am the Queen," said Mary. "Good people, you must save me!" But the churls merely replied, No, no, they could never do that. It was far too dangerous. They rowed back, without slackening speed. Queen Mary appealed to them: "I will make you rich. I will make knights of you. I will have you hanged, if you will not do it."

But their lord's authority was in the squires' bones. "He would drive us out."

"But realize that that does not matter at all. I would take you with me. I am the Queen. The whole country belongs to me. The lord has no command over you. He dare not, if I will otherwise. I have friends. They are waiting for me, over there, a whole crowd."

The men sat dumb, made no reply, went on rowing back to shore. The boat drove, grinding, on to the sand. She must just go up again, they said to the sobbing Queen. And they said, too, that they would say nothing about it, so that the lord could do nothing to her. Mary stumbled up to the castle. She got back to her tower, unrecognized. But the men kept silence for the day only. After that, a sharper watch was kept upon the Queen.

★

On the second of May, 1568, the Lord of Lochleven was sitting with his family at supper. His wife was absent: she was not supping with the Queen, as she did every evening, for she was not until the following day expecting to rise from childbed, when she would again spend almost all her time in the Queen's company. On this evening the Lord ate and drank with excellent appetite, and was well under way when Willy Douglas came in. This was a fifteen-year-old lad, who had come to the castle as a foundling and, educated there as a page, been given the name of his lord. He was a special friend of George Douglas. A sharp-looking slip of a lad, he came into the dining-room this evening with a cat under his arm, which immediately left him, with a giant spring and tail erect, on seeing the lord's dogs lying before the fireplace. The dogs leaped up and rushed after the cat. She, seeking a place of safety, leaped first upon the table, and then on to a high press. There was a rattling and scrabbling all about her. "Curse you, Willy, catch the creature for me," shouted the Lord. All the young folk, however, were on their feet, egging the cat against the dogs, and them against her. The animal fled from the press to the chimney-piece, where it stood, spitting, its eyes glowing green, its back arched high. The young people shouted, laughed, danced; the whole place was a confusion of noise and movement. At last the dogs were brought under control. The cat slid out of the door like an arrow. Willy Douglas had long since left the room. Laughing and still excited, the others were all at table again. Suddenly, the solitary soldier on guard burst into the room, his hair standing erect round a face as pale as ashes: "The Queen has escaped! She is in the middle of the lake by now! All the gates have been closed from outside!" The Lord looked at the place where, at mealtimes, all the keys of the castle were wont to lie in front of him. An overturned plate lay there; he lifted it; there was nothing beneath it. They rushed to the walls. There was the boat, already a long way off. There were three persons in it. A white veil fluttered. A soldier raised his weapon, to shoot. The Lord seized his gun: "Blood of Jesus! It is the Queen!" The shot spent itself in the air.

Dressed as a country girl, Queen Mary, with Mary Seaton, likewise attired, had come out of her tower so soon as Willy Douglas signed to her that it was time for them to come now, quickly. They went quietly through the yard, past the guards and through the gate, which Willy opened for them, passing through after them and barring it behind him. The keys he cast into the lake. They came to the lake edge, where, on this mild summer evening, two maids were rinsing washing. One looked up and, with a shock, evidently recognized the Queen. Boldly, Willy cried, "Be quiet, Rosy." She blushed, laughed, looked at the Queen, and bent over her washing. A boat lay ready on the beach: the others had been drawn up and there were great holes driven in their bottoms, of Willy's making. Mary Seaton and Willy seized the oars. When they were well out on the lake, the Queen loosed the veil about her neck, with the royal colours, white with red fringes, and waved it as a pennon, a signal to friends over there on the shore that the escape was successful.

They reached the further side. They ran in at a lonely spot under a coppice. Some horsemen, waiting there, pushed into the water, to surround the boat. "Your Majesty!" Mary, tears running down her face, but smiling at the same time, signed to them with her right hand. The keel drove softly into the sand. Disregarding the hands stretched out to her, the Queen sprang ashore. George Douglas, who came to meet her ahead of all the others, took her, almost fainting, into his arms. In a moment, she had recovered. "I thank you all, all!" she cried, laughing and weeping at once. She looked about her. "Where are the horses? where can I change my clothes?" Garments for her and Mary Seaton were ready in a little fisher-hut. Within a very short space, Queen Mary reappeared, in a dark green cloth riding-habit, with a beret on her head. In her left hand she held the train of her skirt and her riding-whip; the right she held out to the gentlemen. They all pressed round her, falling on their knees to greet their Sovereign, kiss her hand. Mary's eyes burned, her lips trembled. To all of them it seemed that during the long captivity, when all those who loved her had had to feed merely on her legend, she had grown even more lovely than before, the loveliest thing in all the world.

She was the first to collect herself. "Quick now! They can hardly be after us yet, can they, Willy? All the same, I want to feel safe, on other soil." Her horse was led up. Joyously she struck her hands together. "To ride again! What I have endured!"

They pressed on through the May evening, without making any halt. They passed through villages; here men and women sat chatting at the doors, and turned round as the troop went by them. The people said: "It is the Queen!" and some lads ran after them shouting, "Hurrah! Hurrah!" No one made so much as an attempt to stay them. They sped past the castle of an uncle of the Lord of Lochleven, who came out when he heard the noise of horsemen approaching. He greeted them now, reverentially. They rode on, and the spring evening passed into the white night. They rode across valleys and over hills, passed through woods. There it was at last. There was the Castle of Niddry, the castle of the Seatons. All the windows were brilliantly lit up. The troop approached. "The Queen is free! We are bringing the Queen!" shouted the knights in front, beside themselves. On the instant the place was alive. The gates flew open wide. As Queen Mary rode into the courtyard, torches were burning in every corner. The yard was full of knights, squires, armed men of all sorts. Queen Mary slid down from her horse. All those about her sank upon their knees. She alone stood upright in the midst of them, tall and slender. She stretched out her two hands first to this one, then to that, and wept aloud. The sobs of the others mingled with her own. Some of the knights came close up, to kiss the hem of her garment. At last the lady of the house, Lady Emily Seaton, came close up to her; Her Majesty must need refreshment and rest. First of all, said Mary, she must write one or two letters. So, they all went into the house, where a meal was waiting for the Queen; hastily she ate a little and swallowed some wine. Before she withdrew to her room, she turned to say that John Beaton and Hepburn of Riccarton, both young men who had accompanied her hither from Lochleven, should come to her after a short while, to get some letters which, if it were possible, should go on as soon as day broke.

When John Beaton came, he was given a letter to the French Court. In this Queen Mary informed her relatives that her enemies had, above all, suggested that she had turned from the Catholic religion. Such a statement was the blackest slander. She would live and die a Catholic. The French Government should at once send her any monies outstanding from her jointure and, in addition, a regiment of a thousand archers, for which she would make ample compensation. John Beaton, who was to carry this document to Paris in person, was instructed to make halt in the way in London, and there convey greeting from the Scottish Queen to Queen Elizabeth and the Ambassador of Philip of Spain, together with a similar appeal for help.

Then Queen Mary was left alone with the knight of Hepburn. He was a near relative of the Earl of Bothwell. Queen Mary said to him that he should with all haste, taking this and that support—she named one or two knights who would certainly support him—advance on the fortress of Dunbar and demand its surrender in the name of the Queen. "They will not refuse you. For before then we shall have got further. Once you have invested it, you are without delay to take ship and sail to Denmark, and seek out my husband the Duke. I

send you, because I know that you have always been true to
your cousin, even when all the others abandoned and betrayed
him. Tell him fully of my sufferings and say to him that I
have always, always thought only of him, at every hour of the
day and night. Everything is in this letter, but only hastily set
down, since I had no time. You are to bring the Duke straight
back with you. The King of Denmark will make no difficulties,
and as soon as I can see things a little more clearly, I shall
send expressly to him. You are to bring the Duke to Dunbar.
I shall come to meet him. And this time we shall strike down
our enemies, as we did the first time we took the field together."
She pressed the letter to her lips, her cheeks, before she gave it
to the messenger. "You are to tell the Duke, further, that I
live only for the hour when my love and my obedience can make
him forget all the sorrow that he has had to endure through
hideous treachery." The knight knelt before the Queen to swear
to her that he would do her commission, or forfeit his life in
the attempt.

Queen Mary threw herself, still dressed, on to the bed. She
had entered Niddry after midnight. Soon after sunrise she appeared again among the knights, ready to ride on. It had
been arranged that she should make temporary quarters in
Hamilton Castle, the ancestral seat of that family, which was
large and strong enough to shelter her for a time.

★

The news flew through the realm and came to Edinburgh:
The fire is lit again! The Queen is free!

The governing lords would not believe it. Messengers from
Lochleven brought confirmation. There was wild confusion.
Earl Murray was advised to go to Stirling where the person
of the little king would make a rallying point. His court was
deserted, secretly, by crowds, by every one who was not in complete despair of mercy from the Sovereign. Most of them went
to Hamilton in person. Some, like the State Secretary, Lord
Lethington, and Sir James Melville, sent messengers to lay

their loyalty and service at the Queen's feet. Within a few days, ten thousand knights and armed men had gathered in Hamilton.

Queen Mary sent a message to her brother, ordering him to restore the reins of government to the hands alone entitled to hold them. She was prepared to think of mercy and forgiveness. James Murray replied: Inasmuch as his position had been given him by a united nobility and Parliament, he could only give it back to them. On May 5th Queen Mary issued a proclamation to her people, in which she recalled her abdication. It had been wrung from her under duress, in captivity, by threats to her life, contrary to her express repudiation, and was null and void. The proclamation cited Sir James Melville as witness.

On May 8th her adherents called all faithful subjects of the Queen to arms in her name, to protect their ruler against the treachery of faithless and disobedient rebels. Nine Earls signed this proclamation, among them Argyle, Huntly, Cassilis, Rothes and Sutherland: eighteen Lords, including Fleming, Livingstone, Herries, Seaton, Ogilvy: nine Bishops, twelve abbots, and many other greater and lesser nobles.

Queen Mary had no mind to remain under the sway of the Hamiltons, who daily suggested to her, openly and covertly, that, after her divorce from the Earl of Bothwell, which was a thing too obvious to be so much as questioned, she should elevate one of the younger members of the family to the place of her husband. Queen Mary saw that the nobility was flowing to her. She had only to wait, to have the whole country on her side. Those who knew she could not forgive them fled. And she was mistress, to do what seemed good to her. She must take the chances that offered. Once her husband had returned, she could put him at the head of a real power. His skill as a commander—provided it was not lamed by any such extraordinary bad luck as that of Carberry Hill—any such contingency was to be avoided—must, within a brief space, bring her enemies under her yoke. Already he had saved her twice before. He would succeed again. And then she would be safer on her throne than ever. No one would dare, then, to think of the King's murder or any of the horrors of the past, to say nothing of talking about them. Nay, they would all be glad to have the Queen silent on that.

Therefore Mary determined to leave Hamilton and betake herself to one of the stronger fortresses of the country. Thence she would summon Parliament, since its decisions could only be to her advantage.

So, she moved off. In the fortress of Dumbarton, to the north of Glasgow, she would be quite secure.

★

The whole army of her supporters accompanied her. She had over six thousand trained troops, of which the Earl of Argyle took the command.

Thereupon Earl James of Murray, acting on the advice of Sir William Cecil of England, resolved to force a decision. Although he could not gather more than four thousand men, he wanted to throw himself across the Queen's train. If he could cut her off from Dumbarton, her position would be serious. In open country it would be hard for her forces to hold against an enemy that possessed the strongholds and the artillery and for whom victory must spell internal ascendency. Murray believed that he could count on victory, since he calculated on the Queen's having, against such experienced commanders as himself, Morton and Mar and Kirkaldy of Grange, only Argyle, of whose competence in battle Murray had a poor opinion. Of course the Queen could avoid attacking. She had only to turn westwards on her way from Hamilton to Dumbarton to put the town of Glasgow between her and every danger.

But the Hamiltons knew why their Queen was pressing on to Dumbarton. Therefore they resolved, in face of the express decision of the War Council at which Queen Mary herself had presided, to offer battle to the enemy. They would be victorious, and, after that, the Queen would clearly owe her freedom, her crown and her kingdom to them and them alone. And then they could prescribe their own reward.

★

So, on the morning of May 13th, 1568, Mary's army moved slowly, in a great arc, on to the enemy. Overnight, the Earl of Murray had taken up a strong position on a height above a cleft which the Queen's troops must scale, near the hamlet of Langside. Here battle was joined.

Queen Mary took up her position, on horseback, on a little hill to the side, which overlooked the whole area of battle. She saw the enemy over there, in admirable order, saw the gleam of their cannon mouths, saw their cavalry drawn up, and their infantry. She saw her vanguard pushing into the narrow neck of land in which the decision must take place, saw how the enemy threw his infantry upon it, and how the fumes of battle rose up out of the hollow. She heard heavy shooting down below, marked the glitter of lances. Beyond that, what was really going on down there, she could not tell. But, now, there were soldiers rushing back, in wild haste, in flight. And they were not enemies, breaking through in flight, but her own people. And they must be beaten.

So it was. The fight did not last more than three quarters of an hour. Kirkaldy of Grange threw the foot, at their first essay into the pass, back with such weight that they became involved with their own cavalry in the bottle-neck. The leader proved an utter failure. What had his plan been? There was no deployment, no organization of reserves, no use of the forces in any intelligent order. Actually, their numbers proved their ruin. Some of the Hamiltons fell, fighting bravely. Thereupon, their people threw away standards and weapons, and fled, fled without ceasing, tying themselves up in knots in the valley, driven by the enemy like a flock of sheep before a storm, until, reaching the open, they scattered to all the four quarters. Of dead and wounded there were only some two hundred.

Within the twinkling of an eye, the field about the Queen was a mass of fleeing men and horses. Horrorstruck, Queen Mary looked about her. What now? George Douglas, Willy the page, and Lord Herries were at her side on the instant. "Away! Away! Your Majesty! The enemy is hard upon us!" Already the enemy's flags, bearing the colours of the King, were waving in the valley. From beyond, their cavalry, free, now, were rushing towards the place where the Queen stood. She turned her horse. "If we try going round the back, making a half circle, we can still get to Dumbarton."

"No, not now," cried Lord Herries, "they hold the ferries over the Clyde." He pointed to the south. "That is the way. There we shall be safe!" Queen Mary set her horse at a gallop. Once again they rode as though on wings.

First they rushed down a lane that led out on to a moor. There, in dry places, peasants were cutting grass, as though the fact that ten paces away from them Scotland was in flame with civil war had nothing on the earth to do with them. But they did not want to let Queen Mary, ahead of the others, overleap their outspread hay, and raised their scythes threateningly. Lord Herries, whose little troop had been joined by a young Hamilton, Claude by name, and one or two of his men, pointed his pistols at the men. That forced them to give way.

They rode over a small wooden bridge, which Mary's companions broke down after the Queen had passed over it. They pressed on, all morning, all day. Once the Queen halted in the hut of a charcoal-burner, an utterly lonely spot in the middle of the woods, and there she ate a little oatcake and some buttermilk, for which she gave the man all the gold her purse contained. Then they hurried on again, through morass and moss-hag. The Queen's skirt hung in rags, owing to the thorns that tore at its hems as she leaped the hedges; it was stiff with the mud that bespattered it all the way up, and caked in the sun. They rode over mountains and across moors, up and down. They rode ninety miles. At evening, the Queen paused in a remote barn belonging to Lord Herries. There she threw herself down on a sack of straw to rest a little. She asked the peasant woman to give her one of her shirts, leaving her one of her own, delicate and finely embroidered, in exchange. Long before daybreak they were in the saddle again. They had ridden across half of Mary's kingdom when they reached the little town of Dundrennan, in the extreme south of Scotland, the seat of a great cloister. Here, when the monks hesitated, a burgher took Mary into his house. In his lowbrowed living-room she and her companions held a council of war.

Lord Herries said that the Queen might stay here for a considerable time, in tolerable security. So far, nothing was irrevocably lost. He had brought the Queen hither, because his property was in this region, and he knew the way intimately. He would now answer for the Queen's staying here in safety for weeks or even months, until new forces could have been collected. From here, moreover, it was not impossible to make their way secretly to some fortress or other.

But Queen Mary disagreed. So far as fortresses were concerned, the enemy would immediately fortify them as strongly as possible. She could not long lie here undiscovered. Was she to bring death and desolation on these peaceful regions?

"Yes, if it must be so," replied Lord Herries.

Queen Mary inquired: how far was it from here to England? As far as she could tell, the border must be quite near. Lord Herries replied: "We are certainly quite near. In an hour one would be on the other side. But what has Your Majesty in mind?" She wanted to throw herself into England, to push to London with all speed and there ask help of Queen Elizabeth. The men stood dumb, pale as death. "Your Majesty can never do that," said Lord Herries, at length.

"Why not?"

"The Queen of England is Your Majesty's deadly enemy."

"She is not. When every one forsook me, she alone took my part. She sent me letters in my captivity, and comforted me. She promised me every help, explicitly. She sent me a ring, and if I were ever in extremity, I was to send it to her and she would at once come to my assistance." Mary raised her left hand on which she wore a ring with a diamond. Lord Herries was horrorstruck. "But she cannot help Your Majesty! What can Your Grace be to her?"

"I shall not be with her," replied Queen Mary impatiently, "I desire no favour. I do not ask favour of her. If I wanted that —in France I have my jointure, I can go there any day, and on my own rights. But I will not go there."

Clenching her fists and speaking through her teeth, she cried, "I shall enter Edinburgh again. I shall punish these traitors, even if I have to go to the Turk for money and men!" Her passion made the laird's heart lose a beat. "I am not going to eat a beggar's bread in England," repeated Queen Mary. "I should think not! I have something to offer. The Queen of England wants my son. If she will solemnly recognize him as heir to her throne, she shall have him. I was brought up in France, in very similar circumstances, and it was the one time of my life when things went well with me. He will not regret Scotland, truly not!"

"But Your Majesty has not got the prince."

"Indeed!" replied Mary, bitterly. "And do you believe that, were he a thousand times a king, he would not think twice before turning against his own mother? To whom he owes all he possesses, since his father was little better than a beggar!"

"The Queen of England will turn him against Your Majesty."

"There are means against that! Nevertheless, and if I promise him a hundred fold—I have learned something from the others. . . ."

Darkness swam before Lord Herries' eyes. "For God's sake, Your Majesty, what a world does Your Grace live in? The others do not live in the world where feeling and fantasy are real, Your Majesty's world." A deadly, agonized fear seemed almost to destroy him. He thought of all she had done—impossible things, things no other would so much as have thought of, which yet, to her, seemed utterly natural. So, she would do it, this appalling thing. She would go over there, of her own free will, under the compulsion of no necessity, to those who, after all, were her deadliest enemies. He said to Mary: "There you will be no longer on your own ground. They can do what they like: you must take what they give you. Here, on the other hand, you are always the Queen. In you, every Scot feels himself. Whether he rises for you or against you, the glory or the shame fall on his own head. And in spite of everything, we all feel that, here. But, over there, let the Queen say Your Majesty is the enemy, and every inhabitant's duty is to help to destroy you." He implored Mary: "Your Majesty is free! Still free! But only since barely two weeks. Your Majesty has learned what captivity means. And, here, you were a captive in your own country. Here, you must, sooner or later, be free again. You cannot possibly give up your freedom of your own free will. You cannot desire to take this appalling step."

"What are you afraid of?" asked Mary. "Why do you keep harping on imprisonment? Their making me prisoner is not to be thought of. I live in the deepest peace with her. I have never harmed her. I come quite freely. On her promise. On her urgent request. She cannot do me any harm. I am a free Queen, like her. What an example she would give! No, she will never do it. She simply cannot do it. There are many things, possible for others, which princes cannot do. This is certainly one of them. Perhaps she may refuse to help me; that may be, though she will think long before she does. For it is to her interest to help me. She knows that I must realize that she does nothing for nothing. So, afterwards, she would have an immense superiority. Is she to give that up? What have my rebels to offer, to set against it? If I am not there, so that she requires a counterpoise, she has a far more difficult Government to deal with than me. There are too many of them. She has the greatest interest in supporting me. And, even if she does not do it—even in the event of her doing what is most improbable and refusing me aid—I am still free to turn over quietly what I am going to do. Things in Scotland may, meantime, take a favourable turn. In the worst event . . . it is always open to me to go to France.

But I am not going to fall into my brother's hands again."

Nothing was clear to Herries, in his struggle with her, but that she must not go. Overwhelmed by her swift skill both in thought and speech, he hardly knew why he felt, with such overwhelming force, that, if she went, she went to her ruin, a ruin so complete that all the horror the unhappy soul had endured would be nothing in comparison with what now awaited her. So he continued his pleading. "Your Majesty's position is by no means desperate! What does one lost encounter signify? At most, it has freed Your Majesty from the Hamiltons' tyranny. How many men fell? Not three hundred."

"And yet the whole army fled," replied Mary.

"Yes, but they will gather again. At once. Round Your Majesty. What would be the result of your taking away, from us, your loyallest supporters, our living centre? If you leave the country, where is our rallying point? As for this battle, its loss was entirely due to the pride of the Hamiltons."

"Another time, I should lose through somebody else's pride," said Mary, "or somebody else's treachery. I depend no longer on Scots. And I will not go to France. I will conquer. Even if it has to be with English troops."

"The Queen of England has supported your rebels a hundred times!"

"I know. That was secretly, however. I come to her openly. Before the world she cannot act other than honourably, if I take from her every means of even attempting something crooked. She knows what rebellion is. She cannot openly support rebels against their prince. She cannot let me fall. I am the heir to the English throne. She knows that half her realm is on my side. I have rights there."

"But does not Your Majesty see that the danger lies precisely in that?" He did not dare to say: "And if the English Queen says you are tainted with suspicion of murdering your husband—and uses that to put herself right with the world, she can do what she likes." But in his utter despair, he grasped at his final weapon. He said: "Your Majesty still loves your husband, the Earl of Bothwell, very dearly. Your Highness, if you put a foot in England, if you give the Queen there the shadow of a right over you—then you abandon him irretrievably and for ever. For she will certainly part you from him, that will be her first condition. So all the nameless misery you have endured for him is vain, and he is given over to destruction."

Mary went pale as death. "We shall see. I am a free Queen. In this matter, no one has the right to speak to me."

"But you have nothing behind you, nothing, if you do this." He begged her, finally, "Wait, Your Majesty, at least until you have securities for being able to come and go as you please."

"There have been exiled Kings of England in Scotland, and they were only honourably treated. I shall write today to Queen Elizabeth and cross the Solway tomorrow."

"Oh, no!"

"Yes!"

He threw himself at Mary's feet. "Oh, God, merciful God! That I have not the power to save Your Majesty from this madness! What does right avail, what do reasons avail?—the Queen of England has the power, and Your Majesty is giving yourself defenceless into her hands!"

Mary trembled. "Stand up, Lord Herries," she said. "At any rate, whatever happens, you are not to blame. But I am not going to fall into my brother's hands again."

★

On the same day, Queen Mary sent a messenger into England, with the following letter:

"MY VERY DEAR SISTER,

"Without relating to you all my misfortunes, which must already be known to you, I shall only say that those of my subjects to whom I had shown the greatest goodness and who had the greatest obligations towards me, have finally, after rising in rebellion against me, holding me imprisoned, subject-

502

ing me to the last indignities, now finally driven me out of my kingdom and brought me to such a state that, after God, I have hope only in you. Permit me, I beg, my dear sister, soon to have the honour of seeing you, that I may lay my circumstances before you in detail. Meantime, I pray God shower His grace upon you and give me the patience and the comfort that I look for, from you, through His grace.

"MARIE R."

Lord Herries approached the commandant of Carlisle, the nearest stronghold on the English side. The Queen of Scotland, he wrote, pressed by her rebels, was on the English coast. Could she count on protection, if she decided on flight to England?

★

Before an answer could be received to this inquiry, Queen Mary had put her resolution into action. On the evening of Sunday, the 16th of May, a year and a day after her union with the Earl of Bothwell, she entered the fishing barque which was to carry her and her companions over the Solway—here almost a sea—to the English coast.

Queen Mary sat, without speaking, as the boat sped over the waters. She looked back to Scotland, growing more distant: her own country, but lying behind her so alien, so it seemed to her, as it had done when she came to it seven years ago: she shuddered at the thought of it although her one desire was to see it, at last, vanquished under her feet. She turned her gaze towards the English cliffs which the boat was rapidly approaching. There was a country a thousand times richer and mightier than Scotland, which would fall to her, so soon as its Queen closed her eyes.

Mary's eyes met those of Lord Herries, and she smiled with pale lips when she met nothing but dark sorrow in his face.

The boat passed under the rock into a sheltered bay. With a clang its chain was thrown round a post, and the fisherman drew it right up to the shore. Unhesitatingly, Queen Mary stepped over the edge on to the landing stage. She stumbled on the edge, and almost fell: her hand touched the ground. Lord Herries helped her up.

"The ancients regarded such a chance as of good omen," said Mary. Calmly, with head held high, almost as though she were a victor entering a land hers by right, she stepped on English soil.